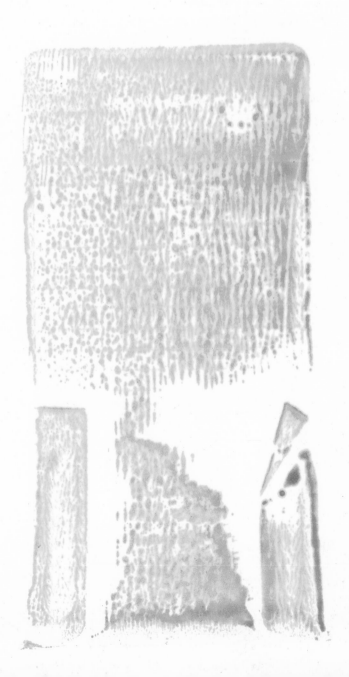

BØRGE FRISTRUP

THE GREENLAND ICE CAP

Rest on the ice cap during the Danish expedition to J. A. D. Jensens Nunatakker in 1878. Drawing by T. Groth.

UNIVERSITY OF WASHINGTON PRESS

THE GREENLAND ICE CAP

COLOUR PHOTOS BY THE AUTHOR

VIGNETTES WHICH INTRODUCE EACH CHAPTER AND
SHOW VARIOUS ICE AND SNOW CRYSTALS
WERE DRAWN BY STRIT PERONARD FROM PHOTOGRAPHS
BY W. A. BENTLEY

BLOCKS BY HAMMERSCHMIDTS KLICHEFABRIK,
COPENHAGEN

MADE AND PRINTED IN DENMARK
BY ROUNBORGS BOGTRYKKERI, HOLSTEBRO

LAYOUT BY MICHAEL MALLING

© RHODOS, COPENHAGEN 1966

AMERICAN RIGHTS:
UNIVERSITY OF WASHINGTON PRESS

SEATTLE, WASHINGTON 98105

Contents

Acknowledgements

Modern ice research depends on collaboration among many groups of people; not merely between engineers and scientists, for without tractor drivers, mechanics, pilots and radio operators the journeys across the ice sheet would be impossible, and the scientists themselves, of course, have to co-operate with one another. The exploration of the polar ice sheet is only possible if there is common cause among glaciologists, geologists, geographers, meteorologists, geodecists, seismologists and many other specialists.

A book about the Greenland ice sheet ought, therefore, to be written by a number of scientists and I still wish that such a book may yet appear one day. Meanwhile, I have ventured to publish this present book myself in the hope it may succeed in giving a wider circle of non-specialist readers an impression of the effort that has been and is being put into the study of this most extensive of Danish geographical regions.

Further it would not have been possible to write this book if I had not received support and help on my journeys in Greenland both from authorities and from private individuals, and I wish to thank The Royal Greenland Department; The Geographical Institute at the University of Copenhagen; the American research organizations, particularly US Army Corps of Engineers, Cold Region Research and Engineering Laboratory, the US Army Polar Research and Development Center; and my colleagues in Expédition Glaciologique Internationale au Groenland.

Research on the Greenland ice sheet is making such rapid progress that even within the short interval between the publication of the Danish original in the autumn of 1963 and the publication of this English edition new methods of investigation have been achieved, and I have felt it necessary to supplement the Danish text in a number of ways.

The colour photos and some of the black and white illustrations are my own photographs, but a part of the material has been placed at my disposal by the Danish Geodetic Institute or comes from the photographic collections of the various expeditions. I am pleased therefore to thank Pro-

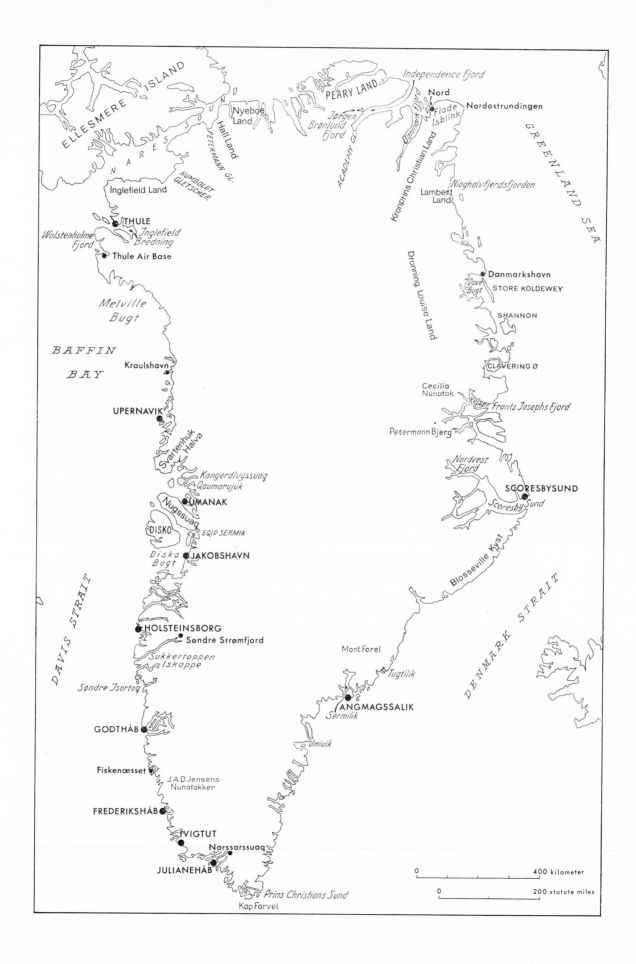

ELLESMERE ISLAND

NYEBOE Land

PEARY LAND

Independence Fjord

Nord

Jørgen Brønlund Fjord

Nordostrundingen

Flade Isblink

Hall Land

PETERMANN GL.

ACADEMY GL.

Danmark Fjord

Kronprins Christian Land

GREENLAND SEA

HUMBOLDT GLETSCHER

Inglefield Land

Nioghalvfjerdsfjorden

Lambert Land

THULE

Inglefield Brédning

Wolstenholme Fjord

Thule Air Base

Danmarkshavn

Dove Bugt

STORE KOLDEWEY

Melville Bugt

SHANNON

Dronning Louise Land

BAFFIN BAY

CLAVERING Ø

Kraulshavn

Cecilia Nunatak

Kejser Frantz Josephs Fjord

UPERNAVIK

Petermann Bjerg

Svartenhuk Halvø

Kangerdlugssuaq

Qaumarujuk

Nordvest Fjord

UMANAK

Nugssuaq

SCORESBYSUND

DISKO

EQIP SERMIA

Scoresby Sund

Disko Bugt

JAKOBSHAVN

Blosseville Kyst

DAVIS STRAIT

HOLSTEINSBORG

Søndre Strømfjord

Mont Forel

Sukkertoppen Iskappe

Tugtilik

DENMARK STRAIT

Søndre Isortoq

ANGMAGSSALIK

GODTHÅB

Sermilik

Umivik

Fiskenæsset

J.A.D.Jensens Nunatakker

FREDERIKSHÅB

ÍVIGTUT

Narssarssuaq

JULIANEHÅB

Prins Christians Sund

Kap Farvel

NARES SOUND

0   400 kilometer

0   200 statute miles

fessor Einar Andersen and Colonel J. V. Helk of the Danish Geodetic Institute; Dr. Paul Siple of the Directory of Army Research, US Army, Paul-Émile Victor, director of Expédition Polaires Françaises, as well as Dr. J. Georgi, Hamburg; and Dr. H. Lister of Kings College, Newcastle, for their willingness to help me on this occasion and on many others. For permission to reproduce figs. 1-3 I thank the Royal Danish Geographical Society.

The book has been translated by Mr. David Stoner, M. A., for whose patience and helpfulness with the technical problems I should like to express my gratitude, and my thanks are also due to Mr. Douglas Holmes, B. Sc. for proof reading and particularly for compiling the index.

Copenhagen, 1966. *B. Fristrup.*

TRANSLATOR'S NOTE

Place-names in this book are given in the language of the country concerned. Names of places in Greenland are in Danish.

In general descriptions, distances, weights, etc., have been expressed in British units, but the metric system has been used for all scientific measurements. For the benefit of readers not accustomed to this system, the equivalent in British units is frequently added, but the conversion is not always exact, but is rounded off to an appropriate figure. Similarly, temperatures are given in Centigrade (Celsius) and are followed by a conversion into Fahrenheit.

David Stoner.

Introduction

Now that the Arctic has entered the sphere of economic and military activity, the study of ice and snow has become more important than ever before. The great powers, in particular, have concentrated considerable resources on research in this field. The total world glacier area is 6.2 million square miles, or about 11 % of the total land area. There are, further, large areas over which the ground is frozen to varying depths throughout the whole year; this condition is known as permafrost, and this exists over a total of eight million square miles, or 14 % of the land surface of the earth. In lowland areas permafrost may extend to a depth of 2,100 ft, and in mountainous areas in the Arctic to as much as 2,900 ft.

During the winter 30—50 % of the surface of the earth is covered by snow for some length of time, and 20—30 % of the land surface of the earth is snow-covered for more than six months annually. Sea ice covers an average area of ten million square miles, or 7 % of the surface of the sea, and outside the area of sea ice proper, there are floating icebergs. But although these forms of ice cover a considerable area, they make up a very small fraction of the total mass of ice on earth; only glaciers are of any consequence, accounting for about 99 % of the volume of ice on earth.

The largest ice mass is the Antartic ice sheet, which has an area of about 5½ million square miles. The findings of research carried out during the International Geophysical Year seem to suggest that its thickness is between 6,500 and 8,500 ft, which gives a volume of about 6½ million cubic miles. The Greenland ice cap is the only really large ice sheet outside Antarctica; it has an area of 650,000 square miles and an average thickness of 4,800 ft. In comparison with the two great ice sheets, of Greenland and Antarctica, the other glaciers and ice fields are of little significance; they are found in Spitsbergen, Arctic Canada, Alaska, Novaya Zemlya, and Iceland as well as in Karakoram, in the Himalayas, the South American Cordilleras, and the Alps. Only small glaciers are found in the equatorial mountains of Africa, and there are no glaciers in Australia, but a few in New Zealand and New Guinea.

The total ice mass on earth may therefore be estimated at about seven million cubic miles; if it were shared equally among the three thousand million inhabitants of the earth, there would be about thirteen million cubic yards for each person; this would make an ice cube with 720-ft sides. At certain periods in its geological evolution the earth has contained much larger amounts of ice than it does at present: during the Pleistocene Ice Age, for instance, about one third of the land area of the earth was under ice, and it may be assumed that for long periods glaciers completely, or almost completely, disappeared. At the present time the ice masses on earth are of such a size that they have a very important influence on climate, and therefore on the conditions of life, over large parts of the globe.

Thus a study of these ice masses, their material budgets and their present state of balance, is of importance not only to the glaciologist, but in many geographical, biological, and climatological investigations too. Glaciology is the study of all aspects of naturally produced ice; it thus includes not only a study of the glaciers themselves, but also of such things as the snow cover, sea ice, and the permanently frozen ground. The glaciologist's interests range from a study of the formation of ice crystals in the atmosphere thousands of feet above the earth to determining the movement of the ice right at the bottom of the ice cap, or finding out the age of the permafrost which in places in the high Arctic regions is as thick as 2,900 ft.

In its pure form, glaciology is a part of geophysics, though closely connected with geography and geology. In its methods it draws upon a large number of sciences, such as geodesy, meteorology, climatology, seismology, gravimetry, atomic physics, etc. In return, research on the glaciers can also make contributions to the advancement of other sciences. If we know how to interpret them, the glaciers may be regarded as climatoscopes, preserving and recording the precipitation and temperature conditions of the past.

Thus drilling work in Greenland has brought up ice samples which fell as snow on the ice sheet when Eric the Red was at Brattahlid at the head of Julianehåbsfjord. In areas for which long-term records do not exist, the fluctuations of the glaciers can give us information about changes in climate. For instance, investigations of the dust content in drill cores from the ice sheets of Greenland and Antartica have yielded valuable information about the fall-out of atomic dust over the earth, and the American glaciologist J. Weertman, has modified the basic equations he had formulated to describe the flow of floating ice shelves in Antarctica. He showed how relatively small changes in the properties of different parts of the earth mantle could generate the forces necessary to cause continental drift, and in doing this he has made an important contribution to putting Wegener's theory of continental drift on a more realistic basis.

The Greenland ice sheet is the best known of the major glacier areas; it was the first ice sheet to

Traversing the crevasse system on the Danish expedition to J. A. D. Jensens Nunatakker in 1878. Drawing by A. Kornerup.

be studied, and although the first expeditions were a heroic battle for survival, they did succeed in gathering material which forms the basis of modern ice sheet research for which technical developments have completely changed the conditions of working. The Antarctic ice sheet was difficult to reach, completely barren, and far from inhabited areas, so that all supplies had to be brought from a distance.

It was, therefore, not until the International Geophysical Year of 1957—58 that this region was really opened up and studied, but the techniques employed in doing this were those that had been learned on the Greenland ice sheet. Nearly all the methods of investigation had in some form been tried out in Greenland before they were used in Antarctica. For this reason we today know more about the Greenland ice sheet than about any of the other major glaciers of the world.

The first attempts at exploring the ice sheet were made by Danes, but since then a large number of

Manhauled sledges were used on the first ice sheet expeditions. Drawing from J. A. D. Jensens expedition 1878 by A. Kornerup.

non-Danish expeditions, particularly American, German, French, Swiss, and most recently, international, expeditions have worked on the Greenland ice sheet. No other part of the kingdom of Denmark has been the object of international research as has the Greenland ice sheet, and there has been fruitful and mutually beneficial collaboration between Danish and foreign scientists.

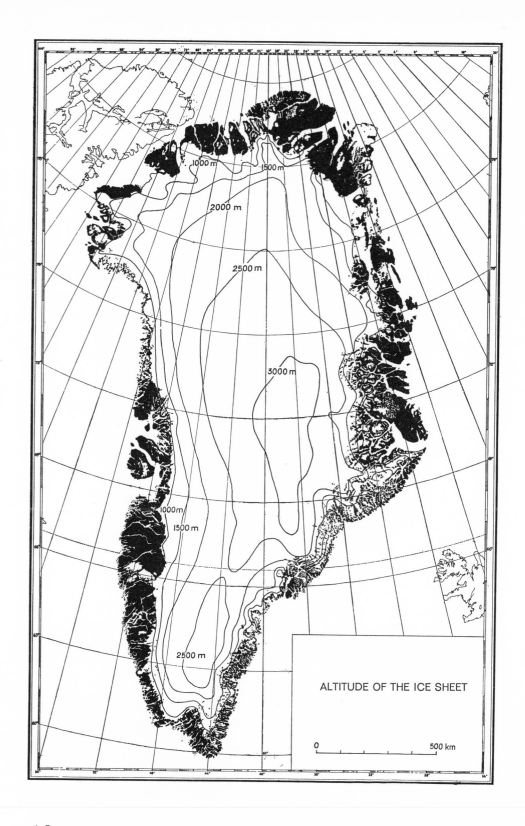

ALTITUDE OF THE ICE SHEET

0   500 km

The area and
distribution of the Greenland ice sheet

Distribution of Arctic Glaciers

It is natural that glaciers should be of considerable importance in Arctic and subarctic areas, for it is particularly characteristic of these regions that they are snow covered for varying lengths of the year. In many areas the summer season is so short that the snow does not have time to melt, so that permanent snow deposits or, if the area is by the coast, an ice-foot may be formed. In upland areas snow drifts and snow fields may become actual glaciers with outlets descending into the lowland areas.

If we look at a map of the Arctic, we soon observe that Greenland is in many ways geographically unique. With its 842,000 square miles, this country is not only the largest island in the world, but it is also the most heavily glacierized major land mass in the Arctic and the only country to contain a true ice sheet. Outside Greenland, the largest glacierized areas in the Arctic are found on Ellesmere Island, West Spitsbergen, Baffin Island, and Novaya Zemlya. Smaller glaciers are found in Nordaustlandet and Franz Josef Land, Severnaya Zemlya, and Alaska, but there are only few or no glaciers at all on the low islands of the central and western parts of Queen Elizabeth Archipelago. In the subarctic zone of the northern hemisphere glaciers are to be found only in Iceland, where the 3,350 square mile Vatnajökull is the most extensive glacier in Europe.

The other glaciers in the northern hemisphere are connected with the great mountain ranges, and even though they may be of considerable length, their total area is not very large. About 15 % of the total volume of land ice in the world is to be found in the Arctic, and the Greenland ice sheet alone accounts for 12 % of the total volume of ice on earth.

The Greenland ice sheet proper covers four fifths of the total area of Greenland. There are also large numbers of local glaciers outside the ice sheet. The largest of these is Sukkertoppen ice cap, which arches across the upland between Søndre Strømfjord and Evighedsfjord in west Greenland as a thin covering of ice. On many older maps and on small scale maps it can often appear as an outlet glacier from the ice sheet. It is, however, an independent ice cap, which at Mt. Atter rises

19

to a height of 7,200 ft. Glaciers descend from the central dome to all sides, to the north nearly reaching as far as the large lake Tasersiaq, and in the south and west reaching to Evighedsfjord and Søndre Strømfjord.

None of these glaciers, however, descends far enough to calve into the sea. At the north-eastern corner of Greenland is the second of Greenland's great upland glaciers: the very large, but little known, Flade Isblink, which borders the Arctic Ocean, and which, as its name suggests, covers the whole area in the form of a flat ice cap rising only imperceptibly inland. It is almost impossible, when one is travelling in the area, to determine when one is on sea ice and when one has reached the glacier ice. As a glacier, it is not particularly productive of icebergs, but possibly several of the floating ice islands to be seen off the northern and eastern coast of Greenland have originated from it. It is almost certain, too, that the floating island of ice that was observed on the first flight to Peary Land made in July 1947 by the Danish Peary Land Expedition is a broken-off portion of Flade Isblink. It is now aground off Prinsesse Thyra Ø.

In addition to these large ice caps outside the ice sheet, there are a large number of glaciers of varying sizes, so many that it would be impossible to give a definite number, and only the largest and most characteristic of them have geographical names of their own. The Greenlanders and others travelling in the country know them merely as "The Glacier" or "The Ice". Particularly in the nunatak zone of east Greenland and in the mountainous coastland of south and east Greenland, numerous glaciers have merged with the actual ice sheet, without being from a glaciological point of view integral parts of the ice sheet proper. It is therefore difficult to give a definite figure for the area of the ice sheet, but it is nevertheless necessary for many calculations and investigations of the ice sheet to know its area.

Total Area and Altitude of the Ice Sheet

In official Danish statistics the area of Greenland is given as 2,182,000 km² (844,000 sq. miles) and the glaciated area as 1,869,000 km² (721,000 sq. miles). These figures are based on old planimetrical determinations from the maps of the Danish Geodetic Institute, and new calculations based on up-to-date maps have not yet been completed. No figures are given for glaciers outside the ice sheet, and it is difficult, not to say impossible, to determine from aerial photographs and maps alone how much belongs morphologically to the ice sheet proper, and how much is made up of local glacial formations.

The area given for the ice sheet must therefore be accepted with a certain amount of reserve, and it is presumably too large. During and after the Second World War the American Army Map Service published a series of aeronautical charts of the whole world, including Greenland, to a scale of 1:1,000,000, and on the basis of these Albert Bauer, a French glaciologist, has made planimetrical determinations of the size of the ice sheet. Bauer calculates the total area of Greenland at 2,186,000 km² (845,500 sq. miles), of which the ice sheet covers 1,726,400 km² (665,000 sq. miles) and local glaciers outside the ice sheet cover 76,000 km² (29,500 sq. miles).

As the American maps are to a large scale and are fairly detailed and Bauer has taken pains to determine from the maps and aerial photographs how much belongs to the ice sheet proper, it may be assumed that this figure of 1,726,400 km² (665,000 sq. miles) which he gives for the area of the ice sheet is the best that can be obtained at present, and this figure will be used in calculations in this book.

If we take a look at the contour lines on a map of Greenland, we observe that the ice sheet does not form an evenly vaulted dome, but that it has a highly complicated and rather irregular form consisting of two domes: a larger dome to the north and a smaller dome to the south. These are divided by a depression which stretches from Disko Bugt and across the ice sheet to a point a little south of Angmagssalik. The highest part of the ice sheet is around Lat. 72—73° N, and the ice here is at an altitude of 3,200—3,300 m (10,450—10,800 ft) above sea level. The southerly dome is lower, reaching only to some 2,850 m (9,400 ft). The depression between the two domes is only slightly indicated on the surface, and its highest point is more than 2,000 m (6,600 ft) above sea level. The highest parts of the ice sheet are not found in the centre, but lie displaced to the east, so that the longitudinal axis is situated at approximately Long. 37° W. To judge from observations of the shape of the sastrugi, which reflect the dominant wind direction, the ice divide must in some places lie further to the east than is usually indicated on the maps. Only in the most northerly part of the ice sheet does the ice divide lie in the centre.

The Antarctic ice sheet descends directly into the sea over huge stretches, but the Greenland ice sheet is in most places separated from the sea by a belt of ice-free land of varying width, and it sends out only a number of more or less active glacier tongues. The largest ice-free areas in front of the ice are in north Greenland, where Peary Land covers 42,000 km² (16,200 sq. miles) or very nearly the area of Denmark, and in west Greenland, around Søndre Strømfjord. Only along Melville Bugt in north-west Greenland and along Jøkelbugten in north-east Greenland does the ice reach right to the sea for any distance. As there are such deeply indented fjords in Greenland there is no point of the ice front which is more than 55 miles from the sea, and it is therefore hardly surprising that the climate of the ice sheet, and of the marginal area in particular, is of a rather maritime character. The annual precipitation, for example, is more than three times that of Antarctica.

The ice sheet extends to southernmost Greenland; its most southerly point is at Lat. 60° 20' N and its northern edge extends to 82° 15'. The distance south to north is thus 1540 miles, or as far as from London to Malta. The width of the ice sheet varies considerably. It is widest in northern Greenland, where along the 79th parallel it extends 683 miles, or as far as from London to Venice. In central Greenland the ice sheet is 400—500 miles wide, while at the southern tip it is only a few miles wide.

In such a large area there are bound to be great geographical and climatological differences between the south and the north: the southern part has an almost subarctic climate with a large amount of precipitation, and the northern part has a high Arctic continental climate with very little precipitation. There are, in fact, just as great climatic and geophysical differences between the north and the south as there are between the climates of London and Malta. It is thus not possible to generalize about conditions over the whole of the ice sheet from measurements taken at one single place.

Seen from the coast, the ice sheet seems to rise very steeply, but this is only true of the marginal zone; further in, the rise is small and the surface is quite level and flat — so flat that often only by careful measurement is it possible to determine in which direction it is rising. It is therefore difficult to ascertain the highest point on the ice sheet, or to determine the exact course of the longitudinal axis of the ice. According to the World Aeronautical Chart (ICAO) 1964, the highest point on the ice sheet is at an altitude of 3240 m (10,630 ft), but measurements made on the expeditions of recent years indicate that the ice sheet rises to a height of at least 11,000 ft. On the basis of Bauer's planimetrical determinations already mentioned it is also possible to calculate the total area between the various contours and thus the distribution of elevation on the ice sheet. The average altitude of the ice sheet is 2,135 m (7,050 ft) and 65 % of it is more than 2,000 m (6,500 ft) above sea level. Antarctica has a corresponding proportion of highland and lowland, but elsewhere such a relative distribution of elevation is unknown for any major land area, and Greenland is thus one of the most extreme highland areas in the world.

On diagrams (and this also applies to those in this book) the sheet usually appears markedly domed, but this is solely due to the fact that such diagrams are always drawn with a considerable exaggeration of the vertical. If the same scale were employed for the vertical and horizontal axes, the ice would appear as a thin straight line of equal thickness throughout.

Crevasses

The much dreaded crevasses occur in the marginal zone. To all expeditions, from the first primitive wanderings over the ice to the highly mechanised expeditions of our own time, these have

22

presented a serious obstacle to further advance across the ice sheet. But if the crevasse zone is once passed, it is comparatively easy to advance across the unbroken white dome of the ice.

The crevasses occur where the tensile and shear strains of the ice are relieved by fracture; there is thus a connexion between the location of the crevasses and the substratum: where the land topography is uneven, or where mountain peaks force the ice to flow through narrow passes, many crevasses will occur. But in addition to the subglacial topography, crevasses are also determined by the differential movements of the ice, and there are so many factors here that it is impossible for even the most expert observer to always foresee where crevasses will be found. As a rule, crevasses occur as systems of parallel crevasses, fairly equidistant, or there may be two intersecting systems of parallel crevasses; this latter type are very frequent, for instance, in the lower parts of outlet glaciers descending into the sea and having floating fronts.

In the ablation zone, at least in summer, the crevasses will be open and therefore easy to discover. In the accumulation zone — and in the ablation zone during the winter — the crevasses will be covered by snow bridges formed of drift snow as it gradually accumulates like a cornice on the sides of the crevasse until it joins across like a bridge. These bridges can be of varying thickness but they are usually no thicker than that the slightest extra load on them will cause them to cave in, or a man may fall right through one and disappear into the crevasse beneath.

An experienced person is often able to keep a watch out for the crevasses by heeding the almost unnoticeable changes in the surface. These can often be seen only as faint shadows in the snow, and an inexperienced person has no chance of discovering them. If one once gets into a system of intersecting crevasses, it can be a nightmare to find one's way out again.

The crevasses are an obstacle to the polar Eskimo with his dog team, but not, perhaps, such a dangerous obstacle for him as for modern expeditions with their heavy motor-sledges and other vehicles. For one thing, the dog sledges are seldom so heavily loaded, and for another, experience shows that if the dogs can cross a snow bridge, then the sledge can also be pulled across, and it is possible for a man to cling to the upright of the sledge and be dragged across even though he may feel the snow giving way under his feet. In fact, the Eskimoes themselves very rarely come to grief in crevasses, though they frequently lose dogs in them. The dogs fall into the crevasses, and trying to save themselves, they slip out of their harness and fall right down into the crevasse. The motorised expeditions, on the other hand, have to rely on careful reconnaissance and modern electro-technical instruments.

Another obstacle is white-out, a peculiar meteorological state in which the light from the sky and the light reflected from the surface of the snow are of the same degree of brightness, so that all contours are blotted out. It is thus almost impossible to get one's bearing even though the visibility may be quite good. This is a serious obstacle for air pilots, and more than one has lost his way. Feeling certain that his instruments were not functioning properly, he has brought the plane down on the ice sheet while imagining that he was, in fact, climbing.

The Ice Margin

Unlike Antarctica, where the ice front over long stretches stands as a vertical wall out in the sea to gradually break off and float away as tabular icebergs, the Greenland ice margin is very varied in its structure. There are valley glaciers of varying sizes descending from the ice sheet into the ice-free land in front of the ice sheet. There are huge ice-streams which flow into the sea, or the ice front may be in the form of almost vertical walls of ice — or ice cliffs as these are called — or of ramps of ice of more or less even gradient may form the edge of the ice sheet. Such ramps have, of course, been the most usual routes by which modern expeditions have ascended on to the ice sheet. From a morphological point of the view the marginal zone of the Greenland ice sheet presents a much more varied and interesting picture than the monotonous central ice sheet, but for that reason it is a difficult in a book of the present limited scope to give a detailed description of the edge of the ice.

If we look at a map of Greenland we will see that nearly everywhere along the approximately 250 mile long coastline of Melville Bugt and as far as Kap York, the ice sheet extends northwards right to the sea, and in the southern part it forms an ice front 110 ft high which almost completely covers the coast of the mainland and leaves only the archipelago ice-free. Further to the north the ice front is lower, and the mountainous forms of the subsurface protrude through the ice in the form of nunataks or rounded ice-clad peaks.

The ice sheet seems to be so thin here as to be a thin covering of ice over the land rather than a collected glacier mass. There are numerous glaciers, but few of them are really productive; among the most active is Steenstrup Gletscher and Kong Oscar's Gletscher. The peninsula of Kap York is covered with local glaciers, and even the beautiful Pitugfik Gletscher, which flows out from the ice sheet down to the sea, is only in part an outlet glacier from the ice sheet, for it is mainly fed by the local upland glaciers.

In north-east Greenland, too, from Nioghalvfjerdsfjorden to Jøkel Bugten, the ice sheet extends right to the sea, but here it is quite low, so that it is often almost impossible to determine whether one is travelling on sea ice or glacier ice. South of here is the huge nunatak area of Dronning Louise Land, bordered on the seaward side by Storstrømmen which descends into Dove Bugt, where there is a considerable production of icebergs. These have difficulty in finding their way out through the narrow channel between the island of Store Koldevey and the mainland.

24

The ice front of Marie Sophie Gletscher is continually advancing: the sea-ice below it is forced upward and crushed.

To the south of Dove Bugt the ice margin is protected by the up-to-125-mile-wide east Greenland fjord region, where it is impossible to see the ice sheet from the coast. The mountains here are over 6,500 ft high, and there are very few large glaciers reaching the sea — the most important of them are Wordie Gletscher and Waltershausen Gletscher, which flows into Nordfjord. There are a number of very narrow glaciers entering the many ramifications of Kejser Franz Josephs Fjord, but most of these are not nearly as productive as might be expected of glaciers originating from the ice sheet. The seismic investigations of the French and international expeditions show also that the Alpine mountain formations of the coastland continue under the ice, and that there are no valleys of sufficient width or depth for any significant drainage of the ice sheet to take place by this route. The various glacier tongues must therefore be regarded in fact as purely local glaciers with a very small catchment area.

25

A number of glaciers discharge into Scoresby Sund, and of these the glacier to Nordvestfjord in particular is very productive. It is in fact so productive that it may have a similar production as Jakobshavn Isbræ, which is usually given as the most active glacier in the northern hemisphere. To the south of Scoresby Sund the ice margin curves to the east out onto a peninsula which terminates in Kap Brewster. Inland of Blosseville Kyst, which is heavily glacierized, there are numerous nunataks, and the whole peninsula is really to be regarded as a local glaciation only superficially connected to the rest of the ice sheet proper.

Not until Nansen Fjord does the ice sheet once more return to the coast with Christian IV's Gletscher, and to the west and south of Kangerdlugssuaq in particular the margin of the ice extends right down to the sea, but the production of icebergs here is small.

In south-east Greenland there is a small stretch of mountainous country which reaches its highest point in Mont Forel, which is more than 11,500 ft high and is the second highest peak in Greenland. The whole area is heavily glacierized and is snow-covered even in summer. Topographically, the area is part of the ice sheet, but glaciologically it must be regarded as an independent glacier area only superficially connected to the ice sheet and having its own balance sheet. It is also typical that, exept in the southern part, no outlet glaciers from the ice sheet reach the sea here, but a considerable amount of ice flows into Sermilik Fjord, which is filled with icebergs for most of the summer. To the south and west of here the ice margin again advances right to the sea, forming low glacier fronts which at Pikiutdleq and Umivik afford favourable access points for getting up onto the ice sheet. It was by this route that Nansen started out on his exploration of the ice sheet in 1888.

In southern Greenland local glacierization is again encountered that superficially appears to be a part of the ice sheet proper. To the south of Skjoldungen, however, the ice margin is cut off from the sea by a strip of coastland which, though narrow, is more than 3,300 ft high. It is intersected by several fjords with outlet glaciers from the ice sheet discharging into them. Southern Greenland has a very humid climate with much precipitation and heavy snowfall, and many of the mountains are more or less snow-covered. The whole of this southern part of the ice sheet is in fact made up of a number of merging local glaciers, caps of firn and ice, extensive snowfields and snowdrifts, and everywhere the peaks of the subsurface protrude through the thin ice covering. From the high Alpine country at the extreme south of Greenland and the head of Julianehåbsfjord the land drops away to the west, and sharp and rugged mountain peaks are replaced by the glacially eroded roches moutonnées, by large moraines and extensive alluvial plains. To the north of the Julianehåb district the ice margin curves to the north and is separated from the sea by a coastland some 20-40 miles wide and of no great height. Only a few glaciers descend into the deep fjords here, the most important being the glacier which flows into Sermilik Fjord; this has a considerable production of icebergs.

At about Lat. 62° 30' N. the ice sheet pushes a thick tongue of ice out to the sea. This is the fourteen-mile-wide Frederikshåb Isblink, which does not, however, calve directly into the sea as the ice margin is edged by low barrier beaches and moraines. The ice rises evenly inland from the coast; there are numerous nunataks in the upper part of the glacier: Dalagers Nunatakker are nearest the edge and J. A. D. Jensens Nunatakker are further in.

To the north, in the Godthåb area, the ice margin is again remote from the coast, leaving room for the mountainous region, some 68 miles in width with peaks up to 5800 ft high, around the long and highly ramified Godthåbsfjord. Several active glaciers descend into the inner ramifications of this fjord, but there are not many local glaciers here. This is, however, the case further to the north where the ice sheet advances and covers the whole of the inner upland area. Between Søndre Isortoq and Søndre Strømfjord there is a local glacier, Sukkertoppen Iskappe which with an area of 750 sq. miles is one of the largest independent glaciers in Greenland. Glaciers descend into Evighedsfjord from both south and north, and as the ice in Sukkertoppen Iskappe is not more than 1,500 ft thick, the relief of the ground beneath can be discerned through the ice.

At Søndre Strømfjord the margin of the ice sheet is about 125 miles from the coast, and the second largest ice-free area in Greenland is situated here. It is intersected by very long but narrow fjords which do not reach quite far enough inland to meet the icefront. There are low, undulating fells in front of the ice. Only near the coast does the land rise to any great altitude; to the south of Nordre Isortoq there are peaks up to 7,500 ft high, and a number of local glaciations are also to be found. The ice margin here therefore has the dry continental climate of the interior, and Nordenskiöld Gletscher is the only outlet glacier of any size to descend from the ice front.

Outlet glaciers from the ice sheet reach the sea at Disko Bugt and calve there. The most southerly of these is Jakobshavn Isbræ, which has a rate of ice movement of more than three feet an hour, which probably makes it the most productive glacier in Greenland and therefore in the northern hemisphere. Further to the north are the similarly productive glaciers of Torssukátaq. Both Disko Bugt and Umanak Bugt are characterized by their abundance of glaciers, and the tall, pointed icebergs that are produced by the calving of the glaciers here are to be found everywhere. The most productive of the glaciers descending into Umanak Bugt are the glaciers to Qarajaqs Isfjord in the southern part, and Umiámáko Isbræ and Rink Gletscher are the glaciers to Karrats Isfjord in the northern part of the bay.

Between these glacier-spurs descending from the ice there are narrow and steep mountains which contain numerous local glaciers of various sizes; thus on the north coast of the peninsula of Nugsuaq between Disko Bugt and Umanak Bugt more than 25 glaciers discharge into the sea. For the 25 miles across the base of the peninsula of Nugssuaq the ice margin over long stretches takes the form of an almost vertical wall of the ice some 100—130 ft high, which prevents any access to the ice sheet in that area.

To the north of the peninsula of Svartenhuk in the southern part of Melville Bugt the ice sheet sends down the most northerly of the highly productive glaciers. This discharges into the head of the 43-mile-long Upernavik Isfjord.

To the north of Melville Bugt the ice sheet sends down several outlet glaciers into the sea particularly in the upper parts of Wolstenholme Fjord and Inglefield Bredning. But in Inglefield Land, as in so many other places in north Greenland, the edge of the ice is a vertical wall some 100—130 ft high. To the north-east of Inglefield Land, Humboldt Gletscher covers a distance of more than sixty miles before reaching the sea. This is the largest glacier outside Antarctica, and it debouches into an area of quite shallow sea. The southern part of this glacier is almost motionless, and is therefore without many crevasses. The northern part is more active and is crevassed; the glacier enters the sea in the form of a thick tongue of ice, and there is a certain amount of iceberg production. The icebergs here are formed by parts of the ice front gently floating away, and these icebergs, therefore, unlike the tall icebergs of Disko Bugt and Umanak Bugt, are tabular. The icebergs from Humboldt Gletscher are easy to recognize when they are encountered later in Smith Sound or Baffin Bay.

Humboldt Gletscher is bordered on the north by Daugaard-Jensen Land which rises between Humboldt Gletscher and Petermann Gletscher almost in the form of a nunatak. With its heavily crevassed flow of ice Petermann Gletscher can be traced as a depression running far in onto the ice sheet. Its length therefore amounts to several hundred miles, and it is undoubtedly the longest glacier in the northern hemisphere. Across Hall Land the ice once more advances, and from here on, the ice front is in an almost straight line across Nyeboe Land and Peter Freuchen Land.

In many places the ice sheet is edged by an almost vertical ice wall some 70—140 ft high, which makes it almost impossible to descend from the ice sheet onto the ice-free land in front of the ice. Mostly, however, the outlet glaciers descend into the head of the long, deep north Greenland fjords. Examples are the long Ryder Gletscher, which flows into Sherard Osborn Fjord, and the wider, nunatak-filled C. H. Ostenfeld Gletscher which flows into Victoria Fjord.

The northern edge of the ice sheet is also the southern boundary of Peary Land and its adjacent areas, which form the largest ice-free area in Greenland. Geologically, north Greenland is characterized by the sandstone deposits of what is known as the Thule formation. These sandstone deposits reach a considerable thickness and in most places form an almost horizontal plateau at a

Along the glacier fronts ice dammed lakes are found at many places.

height of about 3,600 ft, which is intersected in a few places by systems of deep precipitous valleys and fjords in a direction determined by tectonic conditions. The bedrock under the northern part of the ice sheet is unknown, but it may be assumed that over large areas at least it consists of similar plateaus of sandstone, and this is also suggested by the extent of the ice. In a south-easterly direction the ice margin forms an almost straight line from Peter Freuchen Land up to Nioghalvfjerdsfjorden. On the whole of this 280-mile ice front there are only a few glaciers that emerge into the lowland, and except for the 37-mile long glacier entering Hagen Fjord, none of them is of any particular size or very productive. To the north-west the margin of the ice is 3500—4000 ft above sea level but in the south-east and in southern Kronprins Christian Land it drops to only about 2100—2500 ft. Much of the ice margin takes the form of an almost vertical wall of ice. Along the east coast of Greenland the ice margin completely changes character. In Kong Frederik VIII's Land a series of nunataks commences, and almost everywhere in north-east Greenland there are nunataks some distance in on the ice sheet. Between Kronprins Christian Land and Lambert Land broad glacier-spurs are pushed out from Nioghalvfjerdsfjorden towards Hovgaard Ø, and a smaller glacier descends to Djimphna Sund, but the main drainage of the ice sheet takes place towards the open coast between Hovgaard Ø and Lambert Land.

It will be apparent from the above survey that, although it is possible in most places to get up on to the ice sheet with dog sledges and to pick one's way with care through the heavily crevassed marginal zone, there are very few places where the ice slopes gently enough down to the foreland and is sufficiently free from crevasses for it to be possible to take tractors and motorised sledges up onto the ice. When the marginal zone has once been crossed, then the surface of the ice sheet forms a quite even, almost flat, snow field with sastrugi and low snow banks more or less regularly distributed. It is this ice sheet that is the subject of this book.

The exploration of the ice sheet

The norsemen

The Greenlander of today fears the ice sheet as much as did the Eskimoes who migrated into Greenland from Ellesmere Island four thousand years ago. There is no hunting to be had there, and the marginal zone with its deep and treacherous crevasses into which man and sledge can disappear without trace offers hazards enough. Then, far in on the ice sheet, where there are few crevasses travelling is made difficult or impossible by occasional white-out, in which a man can completely lose his bearings even in good weather on the expanse of unbroken white. The Eskimoes believed that the ice sheet was the dwelling place of the evil spirits and were afraid to enter it. The marginal zone of the ice was, of course, known to the hunters of caribou, which moved in summer to the nunataks to find refuge from the mosquitoes.

Only in the Thule district was the land in front of the ice sheet so narrow and the sea ice so difficult to travel across that the Eskimoes were forced from time to time to cross part of the inland ice, and they found their way by following a certain course in relation to the sastrugi. These Polar Eskimoes might be on the ice for days or weeks without seeing land. But apart from these routes the Eskimoes never entered the ice sheet, and their colonisation of Greenland took place along the coast, where in spring they could travel by dogsled across the sea ice and in summer sail by umiak and kayak.

In A. D. 982 Erik Thorvaldsen, known as Eric the Red, was banished from Iceland. He sailed to Greenland, where he first landed in the area of the present Angmagssalik, and later reached the vicinity of Julianehåb. He returned to Iceland and tried to arouse interest in an attempt to colonise Greenland. In 985 or 986 he was in command of 25 heavily laden ships with six or seven hundred men, women, and children on board who were on their way to colonise Greenland. In the Julianehåb area they established the Eastern Settlement, and further north, in the Godthåb area, the Western Settlement. Cattle and sheep farming yielded enough to live on, and from the long hunting

31

expeditions they made right up as far as Melville Bugten they brought back the coveted narwhale and walrus teeth, furs, and Greenland gerfalcons, which were all valuable export commodities that fetched high prices in Europe.

In subsequent years the Norse settlements flourished and reached a population of three or four thousand. However, the climate deteriorated; the Norse settlers began to clash with immigrant Eskimoes, and eventually they lost contact with the outside world. The Norsemen in Greenland gradually died out, first in the Western Settlement, later in the Eastern Settlement. The last reliable evidence of Norsemen in Greenland dates from about 1500.

For the European immigrants, on the other hand, the ice sheet was a riddle that demanded to be solved. The country had to be mapped, and there were many questions to be answered, such as: what lay hidden behind the icy coasts?, and whether the white brilliance which could be seen rising away towards the horizon continued right across the country as a mighty desert of ice and cold, or whether there might be oases with grass and flowers in the interior of the country.

The first Norse colonists knew glaciers and ice caps from Iceland. The Greenland ice sheet may have reminded them of the white dome of Vatnajökull, which for many seafarers sailing from Europe is their first sight of Iceland. The Norsemen seem also to have a fairly clear conception of the ice sheet and its character. The first known description of the geography of Greenland is found in *Speculum Regale,* which was written about 1220, and it gives such a clear account of the country that it remainded unsurpassed until the expeditions of the nineteenth century returned with their findings.

A passage from *Speculum Regale* runs like this: "But when you asked whether the land was free of ice, or whether it was covered with ice like the sea, then you must know that there is a tiny part of the country which is without ice, but all the rest is covered with it, and it is not known whether the land is large or small, because all the mountains and valleys are hidden by the ice, so that there is no opening to be found in it anywhere. In reality, there probably are some openings either in the valleys which lie between the mountains or along the coast, for the animals could not have migrated from other lands unless there were some openings in the ice and unless the land was free of ice. But men have often tried from various sides to climb the highest mountains to look about and to discover whether they could find any land that was clear of ice and habitable, but nowhere has it been possible to discover such land: there are only small strips along the coast itself."

The Greenland ice sheet probably ranks with Antarctica as the most desolate region on earth, and exploration of these ice masses did not become feasible until modern technology made it possible for all supplies to be brought from home. There is no vegetation or animal life in the interior. The lowest temperature ever recorded was — 88.3° (— 123° F) and this was recorded on the Antarc-

Greenland's nunatak landscape.

Kangerdlugssuaq in the district of Umanak. Countless outlet-glaciers discharge into Disko and Umanak Bugter.

A drained melt water lake on the ice sheet. After the water has drained away ice floes remain.

From Storstrømmen in Dove Bugt the ice sheet pushes numerous glacier spurs down towards the coast.

In north Greenland the ice front is frequently a vertical cliff of ice.

The front of the independent ice-cap Flade Isblink in north-east Greenland.

Outlet-glaciers descending from all sides into Evighedsfjord.

The first nunataks that were discovered on the ice sheet were Dalagers Nunatakker on Frederikshåb Isblink.

Dog-sledging in spring time when the sun starts melting the snow.

tic ice sheet. Although "only" — 70° (— 94° F) has been recorded on the Greenland ice sheet, it is nevertheless one of the coldest regions in the northern hemisphere.

No economic interests have been linked with its exploration, and even though great mineral wealth should exist beneath the ice, it would hitherto have been technically impossible to exploit it. The driving forces behind the many expeditions to the Greenland ice sheet have been: the desire for adventure, scientific curiosity, or an interest in something that lay outside the ice sheet itself, so that the ice sheet was merely an obstacle to be overcome in reaching the true goal. Not until modern geophysics and, especially, glaciology got under way, did the exploration of ice become a goal in itself.

As the strategic importance of the whole Arctic region has grown, the Greenland ice sheet has also come into prominence. An enormous amount of activity has arisen, particularly on the part of the Americans, aimed not only at tackling the problems of military transportation and operations on the ice sheet, but also at investigating the possibilities of living on the ice and of using the ice sheet as an enormous natural refrigerated store, where large quantities of foodstuffs could be kept in readiness, or where dangerous radioactive fall-out could be disposed of.

The purpose of exploration and research has therefore changed with the times, and it would seem natural to present the history of the exploration of the Greenland ice sheet in a series of periods, each presenting different problems and with different technical resources available for solving them.

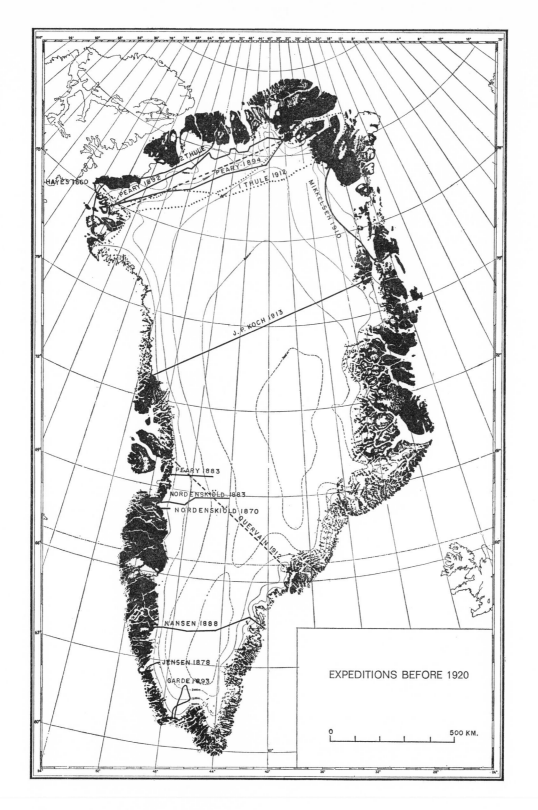

HAYES 1860
2 THULE
PEARY 1892
PEARY 1894
I THULE 1912
MIKKELSEN 1910
J. P. KOCH 1913
PEARY 1883
NORDENSKIOLD 1883
NORDENSKIOLD 1870
QUERVAIN 1912
NANSEN 1888
JENSEN 1878
GARDE 1893

EXPEDITIONS BEFORE 1920

0   500 KM.

42

Investigations before 1850

The rediscovery of Greenland

When the Norsemen died out in Greenland, the knowledge of the existence of Greenland seems to have disappeared from the general European conception of the world, and strange theories and fables came to occupy its place. After America had been discovered, a number of expeditions set out to find a north-west passage round North America to China and India, and in these attempts Greenland was rediscovered.

In 1576 the British explorer Martin Frobisher made an attempt to find the North-West Passage; he started out with three ships, but ran into a violent gale when he had got no further than the Shetlands. One of the ships sank, another was so badly damaged that it was forced to turn back, so that Frobisher was left to continue with one ship. At about Lat. 60° N. he got a sight of south Greenland, which, however, he took to be Friesland, for according to the charts of that time Friesland lay in the North Atlantic.

Frobisher sailed on to Baffin Island, which he explored, and where he thought that he had found gold. To exploit this mineral wealth, a new expedition was sent out in 1578, but this time with fifteen ships. On this voyage Frobisher made a landing in Greenland, which he still imagined to be Friesland, and he claimed it for the Queen of England. He has given a description of the natives of the country, who were fur-clad, and of the ice drift along the coast. There can therefore be no doubt that it was south Greenland that Frobisher visited.

But when he and his cartographer, James Beare, drew up their maps, they were still unaware that they had been in the country that the Norsemen had called Greenland. So they marked in both Greenland and to the south of it Friesland, and further to the west a *Meta Incognita* which is identical with the present Baffin Island.

In 1585 the English navigator John Davis visited Greenland. He realised that he was in the country called Greenland that had been inhabited by the Norsemen, but he was unaware of the mistake that Frobisher had made, so he named a strait after Frobisher, which was supposed to intersect the southern part of Greenland. This mistake was repeated on a large number of charts, among them the charts used by the British pilot, James Hall, who was engaged to explore Greenland in the service of the Danish King Christian IV. Seventeenth century charts mark another strait, Beare Sound, in addition to Frobisher Strait. Beare Sound is shown as lying a little further to the north intersecting the Greenland ice sheet from the west coast to the east coast. These cartographic inaccuracies were to be of importance later in the planning of expeditions to the ice sheet.

After contact with the Norsemen in Greenland had been severed, the knowledge of where their settlements were located was also lost, and as was natural, it was assumed that the Eastern Settlement lay on the east coast and the Western Settlement on the west coast. In 1721, Hans Egede, a Danish clergyman, sailed to Greenland to try to ascertain what had happened to the Norse colonies, and to bring the gospel to any of their descendants that might still remain. On 3 July Hans Egede landed near Godthåb, where he set up his first mission station. He also had instructions that he was to continue on through Frobisher Strait to reach the Eastern Settlement, if this should be possible. The Eskimoes informed him, however, that there was no such strait intersecting south Greenland, and he therefore abandoned the idea of reaching the Eastern Settlement. But he was told that there had in ancient times been a strait intersecting Greenland, through which it had been possible to sail with kayaks and umiaks, but that it was now ice-covered and impassable. On his map of Greenland Egede marked in this strait as a narrow channel extending eastward from Disko Bugt.

It was impossible at that time for a ship to reach the east coast because of the heavy polar pack-ice, but there was still a strong urge to reach the Eastern Settlement, and in 1727 the Danish King Frederik IV sent out Major Enevold Paars, who became Greenland's first and only military governor. With orders to make every effort to cross the ice cap and find the Eastern Settlement, Paars, with a small force under the command of a captain and a lieutenant and with twelve convicts who before leaving Denmark had been forced to marry twelve women from a house of correction, was in charge of an attempt to establish a Danish colony in Greenland. A number of attempts to reach the east coast by ship had all failed, and as Egede had found out that Frobisher Strait did not exist, Paars and his men decided to march straight across Greenland and thus traverse the ice sheet. For this purpose, Paars had brought eleven horses, and the idea was that they should ride across the ice.

On the mainland opposite the island of Håbets Ø, where Hans Egede had first established himself, a small fort was now constructed, and here Paars and his party spent the winter with Egede. The material was the worst possible, and even before they landed they had terrified the Eskimoes by having some of the convicts publicly flogged. During the winter the party went to pieces;

44

Secured by rope it is possible for an explorer
to climb down and study the crevasses.

most of the company fell victim to scurvy, disease, and fighting, and the horses also died. However, the plan to travel across the ice sheet was not abandoned.

On 25 April 1728 Claus Paars started out with Lieutenant Jesper Reichardt, a clerk named Jens Hjort, five soldiers, and two Eskimoes. They entered Ameralik Fjord by boat and from there found their way up on to the ice. The ascent took time, but at last they arrived on the ice sheet. They had brought no sledges or any special equipment with them, and after walking for some hours across the ice, they came upon a large crevasse, lost heart, and abandoned the attempt. In his report to the Danish king, Paars wrote: "As we saw no prospect of proceeding, we sat down on the ice, discharged a Danish salute of nine rounds, and drank the health of Your Most Gra-

45

cious Majesty in a glass of *snaps* in a place where it had never before been drunk; such an honour had never before been accorded the mountain of ice. After we had rested for about an hour, we returned." On 7 May they were back in Godthåb after this "ill-starred and very arduous journey", and with this concludes the first Danish military expedition to the ice sheet! The expedition marks no advance whatever in our knowledge of the ice sheet.

The First Journey on the Ice in Search of the Eastern Settlement.

The thought of travelling right across the ice sheet to the east coast and reaching the Eastern Settlement continued however to occupy the minds of many people. In 1751, Lars Dalager, a trader in Frederikshåb, heard of a Greenlander who claimed to have been so high up into the mountains that he had seen mountains "on the other side" of the ice sheet. Dalager assumed that he must be speaking of the mountains on the east coast, and in that case the distance across to them could not be so terribly far. He therefore decided to make an attempt to reach the east coast by crossing the ice sheet and to look for remains of the Eastern Settlement. On 2 September 1751 he started out with five Greenlanders to try to climb up on to the ice sheet from a fjord on the southern side of Frederikshåb Isblink. The expedition was not specially equipped for a journey across the ice, only having what would normally be used on hunting trips.

The members of the party were, however, men who were accustomed to living in the wilds of Greenland. They had neither tents nor sleeping bags with them, and they used Eskimo *kamiks* as footwear. After leaving their camp at the fjord, they continued as far as the margin of the ice sheet, and then on the fourth morning they struck out across the ice sheet, setting a course for the first peak that could be seen on the ice.

The way across the ice was very level, "almost as level as a Copenhagen street, but more slippery. Nor were we forced into the gutter in fear of the postmaster's horses," wrote Dalager in his report. On the very first day they arrived at the nearest nunatak, which lay some five miles in on the ice, and the next day they continued on to a nunatak even further in, from where they had a wonderful view towards some mountains which Dalager wrongly took to be the mountains on the east coast. Actually, they were the nunataks that were later visited by J. A. D. Jensen and which are now named after him. It soon became evident that the footwear of the expedition was unsuitable for travelling across the sharp ice; their kamiks were soon cut to ribbons, even though they had followed the Eskimo custom of having a woman with them to patch and sew their clothes: she had lost her sewing tackle.

They were obliged to return, and by 8 September they were back at their tent by the fjord. Dalager described his journey across the ice in a report published in 1752, which shows him to be a

46

At some places the ice margin is inclined forming an easy access route to the ice. The front of a local glacier in Angmagssalik district.

perceptive observer. He was thus the first to describe the surface of the ice sheet, and he mentions also the low temperatures which obtain on the ice sheet because of the high degree of radiation. He remarks that the cold there seemed more intense than anywhere else in Greenland, and that it had caused them great inconvenience. On the basis of his experiences Dalager considered that is was impossible to traverse the ice sheet, not because of the crevasses, which he did not reckon to be so hazardous, but he could not see how sufficient provisions for the return trip could be transported across the ice.

While Major Paar's attempt at setting up a colony in Greenland was being planned, a certain Lieutenant-Commander Trojel in a report submitted to the king of Denmark in 1728 had suggested that a group of young Norwegian skiers, who would be accustomed to winter hunting in the mountains, should be sent out to explore and reconnoitre in Greenland, but this suggestion never developed into anything further.

47

In 1784 Otto Fabricius, a Danish scientist in Greenland, published his treatise entitled: *Om Driv- isen i de nordlige Vande og fornemmelig i Davis-strædet* (Concerning the drift-ice in the north- ern waters and chiefly in Davis Strait), which contains not only a number of descriptions of ice- bergs and their prevalence, but also an account of ice-calving and of the deep crevasses. There can be no doubt that Fabricius had himself visited the ice sheet, but there is no evidence that he had penetrated very far on to it. The German mineralogist, Karl Ludvig Giesecke, who in 1806- 1813 travelled in south and west Greenland, paid a visit to the ice sheet at Qôrorssuaq near Ju- lianehåb, but when near the ice margin he came up against a crevasse which he sounded as being 100 ft deep, he abandoned any attempt to go further.

After Dalager's attempt a long time was to elapse before anyone else tried to travel on the ice sheet. But as knowledge of the map of Greenland increased, all thought of travelling to the East- ern Settlement through any Frobisher Strait, or overland across the ice sheet, was abandoned. During the next hundred years no journeys were made to explore the ice sheet itself.

The Period 1850-1888

Modern Glacier Research Begins

By the close of the eighteenth century and the beginning of the nineteenth the study of glaciers and the problems connected with them had commenced in Europe. In 1779—97 Benedict de Saussure, who was a professor of philosophy in Geneva, published his *Voyage dans les Alpes,* containing descriptions of glaciers and a discussion of their nature. The Jesuit professor, J. Walcher, had also — in 1773 — emphasised the connexion between climate and fluctuations in the glaciers.

About 1830, under the inspiring leadership of the geologists Johan Georg Charpentier and Louis Agassiz, there began a comprehensive investigation of the Unteraar Gletscher and of the glaciers in the Mont Blanc area. In a lecture given in 1816, the Swiss engineer, Ignaz Venetz, had given an account of his studies of the glacier transport of boulders, and in 1821 he submitted a prize-winning essay demonstrating that the glaciers in the Alps must earlier have had a considerably greater area. In 1829 he was able to report that he had found old moraines in the foothills of the Jura mountains, and he claimed that these must have originated in the Walliser Glaciers.

In 1840, Louis Agassiz's pioneering work, *Études sur les Glaciers,* appeared, laying the foundation of modern glaciology. Meanwhile, Venetz's theory about the former larger area of the glaciers was gaining support, and Jens Esmark in Norway had been publishing the findings of similar investigations made in Norway. In a lecture to the Schweizer Naturforscher Gesellschaft in Lucerne in 1834, J. G. Charpentier had supported Venetz in his theories, and had propounded his own theory that there had previously been an "ice age" in which the climate had been cold and the glaciers had covered a much larger area.

His theory found support from Louis Agassiz, who pictured the Alps as having been completely covered by a vast, unbroken sheet of ice. This had completely covered all the mountains until they had been forced upward by some sudden upheaval and had broken through the ice. In this process a mass of split-off boulders had been scattered over the ice, and the ice had subsequently transported them over the whole of central Europe. Charpentier imagined that the whole of Europe, maybe most of the earth, had been ice-covered. He regarded the presence of these erratic blocks as being a decisive proof of the theory that the glaciers had once been more extensive and that there had been an ice age.

While the Swiss scientists explained the occurence of these erratics as the result of glacier movement during the ice age, Sir Charles Lyell, a British geologist, although agreeing that there had been an ice age, submitted that the boulders had been transported by being confined in drifting ice bergs. On melting they deposited their contents of rock and gravel. The discussion for and against the ice age theory was carried on among geologists with great asperity, and the Danish geologist J. G. Forchhammer was one who rejected it. Forchhammer explained phenomena such as glacial striae and roches moutonnées as the result of marine activity in the form of erosion by stones and sand carried back and forth along the coast by the action of the waves. The well-known Danish zoologist, Japetus Steenstrup, was another who rejected the Swiss theories about a general glaciation of Europe, whereas Frederik Johnstrup, the geologist, was an early supporter of the theory.

One result of these scientific discussions was that attention was drawn to Greenland in the search for more exact information about the conditions that would have prevailed in a Europe covered by ice. Hinrich Rink, a Dane, was the particular pioneer in this. Rink had studied physics and chemistry at the Technical University (Polyteknisk Læreanstalt) in Copenhagen, and had soon shown outstanding ability as a scientist, combined with a considerable artistic talent for drawing. In 1843 Rink received the gold medal of the university for a chemical treatise, and in 1844 he took his doctor's degree at the University of Kiel. Rink was with the Danish Galathea Expedition, which circumnavigated the globe, as a mineralogist, but he was obliged to return to Denmark part way by an attack of fever contracted on the Nicobars. He managed, however, to publish a work on the geography of those islands. Rink first came to Greenland in 1848, and travelled in north Greenland to study the occurrences of graphite in the Umanak and Upernavik districts.

In 1849 he obtained further grants of money for a fresh journey to Greenland, where this time he came to spend two years. Few men have been able, as Rink could, to range over both physical and cultural fields of research. He wrote many pioneering works about the nature of the ice sheet, or *inland ice,* a term that he himself invented, and he was also one of the leading experts of his time on Eskimo culture. Further, he did outstanding administrative work for the Greenlanders as head of the Greenland Directorate. The Greenland Society was therefore justified in founding a Rink Medal to be awarded for outstanding contributions to administrative, scientific or cultural work in or for Greenland.

50

In 1852 Rink published a book entitled *Om den geografiske Beskaffenhed af de danske Handels-distrikter i Nordgrønland* (Concerning the Geographical Nature of the Danish Trading Districts of North Greenland), in which he was the first to calculate the production of icebergs from the great ice fjords. He found that five glaciers descending to Jakobshavn Isfjord, Qarajaqs Isfjord, Torssukátaq Fjord, Kangerdluarssuk, and Upernavik Isfjord, were particularly productive, and he estimated that each of these glaciers had an annual production of more than a thousand million cubic *alen* of ice. In this work he also suggest the term *isstrøm* (ice-stream) to describe the parts of the ice sheet in which the ice moves more rapidly than that around it.

Rink writes: "In such places conditions are unusual, for the movement of the ice, though present everywhere, is so unevenly distributed — being concentrated into a few arms descending into the sea, that everywhere else it can be regarded as negligible. This is particularly remarkable, as the whole surface of the ice sheet forms a uniform plateau, and it is impossible to discover from its form any reason for the ice masses to be extruded from the centre towards certain particular points on the outer margin; the cause of this must lie concealed in the interior of the ice, probably in the shape of the underlying land. I have thought it fitting to call these parts of the ice sheet that are in a higher rate of motion ice-streams, and the essential difference between these and the formations of moving ice that are known as glaciers, or in Danish *bræer* and in Icelandic *isjökler,* is that the rate of movement of the latter is directly caused by the structure of the surface and the gradient of the ground over which they are moving, so that their movement is mainly the result of gravity, whereas the ice-streams in the ice sheet are moving within the frontiers of a seemingly uniform mass with a plane surface. But the main difference lies in the force of the movement and the size of the masses of ice that are being endlessly pushed out towards the sea. For it is from these ice-streams, and, it seems, exclusively from them, that the huge colossi of ice descend which float around in the Arctic seas and bear the name of icebergs."

The following year, in 1853, an important new work appeared: *Om isens Udbredning og Bevæ-gelse over Nordgrønlands Fastland* (Concerning the Distribution and Movement of the Ice over the Mainland of North Greenland), in which a detailed description of the ice fjords and of the calving of the ice from the ice fronts is given. This work gave rise to a very comprehensive discussion of how calving actually took place, but Rink's sure powers of observation again left him triumphant.

In these works he also put forward his explanation of how the ice sheet could have been formed, and he assumed that the ice-streams marked the courses of rivers which had once drained the interior. The rivers had become frozen with the intense cold, and the layer of ice had gradually grown until it had completely covered the interior of Greenland in one continuous mass. When

51

it had reached a certain thickness, it had begun to move out toward the sea, and the ice continued to follow the old river beds which had already been formed by running water.

In 1851 Rink received the silver medal of The Royal Danish Academy of Science, and in 1864 he became a member of this academy. In 1853 he had been put in charge of the colony at Julianehåb, and at the same time he was appointed acting prefect of south Greenland, becoming prefect of the whole of Greenland in 1858. In 1868 his health forced him to resign, and Rink settled in Copenhagen, where he was soon eagerly occupied with scientific authorship. In 1872 he took over the post of director of The Royal Greenland Trading Company, but he resigned this in 1882 after meeting with strong opposition to his plans.

The Ice Age Theory is Accepted.

Rink's labours had won great recognition among all scientists, and they helped the ice age theory to become accepted. Research on the actual ice sheet had brought a fresh understanding of Arctic glaciers and had helped greatly in answering the question as to what sort of natural conditions would have dominated an ice cap covering the whole of Scandinavia or even the whole of Europe. In 1868 F. Johnstrup, professor of geology in Copenhagen 1866—1895, delivered a lecture to the Royal Danish Academy in which he supported the ice age theory and declared that Denmark must once have been completely covered by a thick ice sheet which in melting had deposited a large number of boulders and moraine deposits.

His lecture was based on Rink's findings in Greenland as well as on the work of Danish and other Scandinavian scientists, who had demonstrated that fossil remains of Arctic flora and fauna occurred in a number of Danish and Swedish bogs and that the remains of Arctic crustacea as relicts had also been found in the great Swedish lakes. In 1826 O. Torell published in Stockholm his work: *Undersökningar öfver istiden* (Investigations on the Ice Age) which presented conclusive proof that the boulders had been transported by the ice, and that they had not been transported while frozen into drifting icebergs. This meant that Scandinavia had once been covered by an ice cap. It was now clear that a better understanding of the natural conditions in Europe during the ice age could only be gained through a study of the Arctic glaciers, and in particular by investigating the geography of the Greenland ice cap, which by reason of its size was the most important parallel to the Pleistocene glaciation of Europe and North America.

There was at that time a lively interest in Arctic exploration and in mountaineering, and in October 1860 the American polar expert, I. I. Hayes, had attempted to penetrate on to the ice sheet north of Porte Foulke. According to his own account he covered 60 miles in six days before being forced to return by the cold and the wind. His claims were very much doubted by others, and sci-

52

The front of the ice sheet at Camp Tuto with the road that leads to the ice tunnels which are at the foot of the moraine in the centre of the photograph.

entifically his journey contributed nothing. But it did open people's eyes to the possibility of travelling across the ice. In 1867 a British mountaineer, Edward Whymper, "the conqueror of the Matterhorn", made an attempt to cross the Greenland ice sheet.

Earlier journeys on the ice had been mere short visits with only as much equipment as could be carried on the back, but Whymper planned to use sledges to transport his equipment. As soon as he arrived in west Greenland in the spring of 1867, he began to reconnoitre for a possible route up on the ice sheet, and in July he found what he was looking for inland of Ilordlik Fjord to the north of Jakobshavn.

He found that the surface of the ice was here quite even and easy to cross, and he was very optimistic. Unfortunately, luck was not on Whymper's side. A violent epidemic of influenza coincided with his visit to Jakobshavn, and over a third of the population of the town were badly affected,

53

and even the sledge dogs were ill. Whymper had brought some timber with him to have the sledges constructed in Greenland for he presumed that the Greenlanders would be able to build better sledges than English joiners. Because of the epidemic it was impossible to get the sledges made, and he had therefore to fall back on making the attempt using Greenland sledges which he bought on the spot. These were built for travelling over sea ice and proved far from strong enough for sledging across the ice sheet. On 20 July Whymper started out on the actual expedition. There were six members of his party, including some Greenlanders.

But since he had reconnoitred the area the snow had begun to melt in earnest, and when he and his party got up on to the ice sheet, they found that the surface of the snow was in a chaotic state, being criss-crossed by crevasses and streams of melt-water. The sledges broke up and the Greenlanders soon refused to go on. Whymper tried to push on alone, but was quickly forced to turn back.

In the years after 1850 it was not only scientific or sporting interest that caused expeditions to find their way to the ice sheet. New technical problems were to be solved. The plan for a trans-atlantic telegraph cable between Europe and America was well advanced, but it was feared that the cable would part if it was laid across the great ocean deeps, and the possibility was therefore investigated of taking it via Greenland and Iceland. In 1860 the *Fox* expedition investigated whether it would be possible to lay the cable across the Greenland ice sheet.

The expedition was led by Alan Young, a British Arctic explorer. They made an unsuccessful attempt to penetrate the belt of pack-ice on the east coast of Greenland, and a brief visit to the ice front behind Julianehåb convinced the members of the expedition that it would not be possible to lay the cable across the ice, so further investigations in Greenland were thereupon halted. Sir Leopold McClintock had come to similar conclusions after his visit to Greenland in the *Bulldog* in the same year.

In 1875 Rink published a book with the title: *Om Grønlands Indland og Muligheden af at berejse samme* (Concerning the Interior of Greenland and the Possibility of Travelling there), in which he argued that it must be possible to travel on the ice sheet with sledges hauled by the members of the expedition themselves. The question as to what conditions were like in central Greenland was still unanswered. Did the ice sheet cover the whole country, or were there also oases right in the interior of the desert of ice?

Several authorities maintained that there must be oases, for it had been observed that reindeer and other animals appeared in large numbers in certain years, while in other years they were much less numerous or disappeared completely. It was therefore thought that these herds of reindeer found grazing land right in the centre of Greenland, and from time to time migrated to west Greenland from there. It seemed probable that there was ice-free land in the interior and that Greenland should be regarded as several islands or groups of islands, as was known to be the case with Arctic Canada.

In 1870 the Swedish geographer and geologist, Adolf Erik Nordenskiöld, as part of his preparation for an expedition to Spitsbergen made an attempt to traverse the Greenland ice sheet. With sufficient supplies for thirty days, and with a Swedish-built sledge, he found his way up on to the ice behind Aulatsivik Fjord. He succeeded in getting up, but it soon proved impossible to drag the sledges over the very wet snow, so the sledges were abandoned and the journey was continued on foot, each man carrying what he could on his back. After tramping on for six days, they had to give up, for they no longer had enough provisions to continue.

They had however come 35 miles in on the ice sheet, and from there they could see that the ice was still rising inland to the east as far as they could see. This journey was made in July, while the melting of the snow was at its height, and they had difficulty, not only with the crevasses, but also with the numerous deep melt-water streams which could only be crossed with difficulty. Nordenskiöld brought back the first real measurements of temperature on the ice, and also samples of cryoconite, which, however, he assumed to be of purely cosmic origin. In 1874 the Norwegian glaciologist Amund Helland travelled to Greenland to study the ice fjords of north Greenland and to take measurements of the movement of the ice. The measurements showed that the Jakobshavn Isbræ was moving at a rate of 19.5 m (64 ft) a day, and that the glacier at Torssukátaq was moving at 10.2 m (33ft 2 in) per day.

The Commission for Geological and Geographical Investigations in Greenland is established

In 1876, on the initiative of Professor J. F. Johnstrup, the *Kommissionen for Ledelsen af de geologiske og geografiske Undersøgelser i Grønland* (The Commission for the Direction of the Geological and Geographical Investigations in Greenland) was set up, consisting of Professor Johnstrup himself, the then Danish minister of naval affairs, N. F. Ravn, and Hinrich Rink. The commission regarded it as one of its duties to organise research into the extent and nature of the sheet, for, as Johnstrup wrote in his proposal for the establishment of the commission, "very vague views are still held by various scientists about this subject, and frequently the most fantastic theories are put forward, solely because of the defective data that have been obtained in the few and limited attempts hitherto made to get acquainted with the interior of the ice sheet.

Such assertions as that an ice-free land, perhaps even inhabited by human beings, will be found in the interior of Greenland, and other such ideas can never be properly refuted, if one or several expeditions are not made across the ice from the west coast to the east. In this way, too, it will be discovered whether the ice sheet forms a continuous covering over the whole land, or whether it is interspersed with areas of mountain, or is only sporadically broken through by single peaks of rock. It is known for certain that the latter is the case in several places, but nothing is known of the structure of these mountain masses." It was therefore the intention that the commission should send out expeditions to Greenland to undertake investigations, and these would include expeditions to the ice cap.

That same summer the first expedition was sent out — to the Julianehåb district — under the leadership of K. J. V. Steenstrup, who in the years 1871—72 and 1874 had made geological investigations in Greenland. Among Steenstrup's instructions was that he was to reconnoitre the margin of the ice with a view to future journeys on the ice sheet. In 1876 Tasermiut Fjord was explored, but the margin of the ice was found to be so heavily crevassed there that it would be impossible to proceed inland by that route.

As the rate of movement of the glaciers in south Greenland had never been determined, Steenstrup made a series of measurements, and he found the ice movement here to be somewhat less than the figures Helland had obtained in investigations further north. Steenstrup was a very careful observer, and through a long series of expeditions he became one of the greatest experts on the physical geography of Greenland. In 1894 he was made an honorary doctor of the University of Copenhagen, and in 1902 a member of the Royal Danish Academy of Science. Steenstrup made many investigations on the glaciers of Greenland; he calculated the hardness of the ice and also its air-bubble content. He did not himself, however, take any part in the exploration of the ice sheet itself.

In 1877 the commission continued its research in the northern part of the Frederikshåb district, where it was planned to make an ascent on to the ice sheet by the same route that Dalager had used in 1751. But it was a very bad summer that year with a great deal of snow and fog, and the bad weather prevented this plan from being carried out. This bad luck did not however deter them from sending out a new expedition in 1878 led by First Lieutenant J. A. D. Jensen, who had been in Greenland the previous summer with Steenstrup, who was now in charge of a series of investigations in Umanak Fjord.

Apart from Lieutenant J. A. D. Jensen, this expedition to the Frederikshåb area consisted of A. Kornerup — a young geologist who managed to take part in four Greenland journeys before dying of tuberculosis which he had contracted in Greenland — and T. Groth, an architect. After successfully reconnoitring the area, they decided to go up on to the ice at Itivdleq accompanied by a Greenlander called Habakuk. They had brought three sledges with them from Copenhagen; these were five feet long, 2½ feet wide and weighed over 10 kg (22 lb) each. The sledges were made of specially selected wood and held together by leather bands. Each sledge was to be hauled by one man. They had provisions for three weeks, and unlike Nordenskiöld, who had used double sleeping bags and no tent, they had one tent that was big enough for all four to sleep in.

On the first part of the trip they had the help of a number of Greenlanders, but once on the ice sheet itself they were left to their own resources. After travelling for eleven days they had got as far as the nunataks that Dalager had seen and taken for the mountains on the east coast. On 24 July Jensen climbed one of the mountains and saw from there that the ice sheet stretched away as far as he could see still rising towards the east. However, because they were beginning to run short of food, they were obliged to turn back.

It had been a hard trip; they had been severely handicapped, for instance, by snow blindness, and on the nunatak itself they had been weather-bound for several days because of a blizzard. The whole journey on the ice had lasted 23 days, and as both Kornerup and Groth were accomplished draughtsmen, they had brought back a large number of sketches of the surface of the ice, the crevasses, etc. These illustrations soon found their way into international literature and manuals. The Commission continued to organize research in the marginal area of the ice, but the difficulties encountered by J. A. D. Jensen's expedition seem to have robbed it of its desire to send out the large expedition to the ice sheet for which the journey of 1878 was to have been the forerunner. But in 1879-80, First Lieutenant R. R. J. Hammer was sent out to spend a winter examining the ice fjords and glaciers of north Greenland. The commission was concentrating on other tasks in Greenland, and there was no great interest in Denmark for continuing the exploration of the ice sheet itself. In the period 1876—1901 the Commission sent out 28 expeditions to Greenland, and there were fourteen other Danish expeditions, but none of these had as its object the crossing of the ice sheet. It was thus left to expeditions from other countries to begin the exploration of the ice sheet and, in particular, its interior. About 35 years went by after Jensen's journey before any new Danish expedition was once more working on the ice sheet proper.

Oases on the Ice Sheet?

The most important scientific expedition to the ice sheet was that led by A. E. Nordenskiöld in 1883. Nordenskiöld was not only an outstanding scientist, but was also an an experienced Arctic traveller and a competent organizer. He was at that time one of the most distinguished Arctic explorers, and he had powerful financial support both from official Swedish sources and from private circles. For many years he was supported mainly by the wealthy Oskar Dickson. Nordenskiöld began his Arctic exploration by taking part in the expeditions to Spitsbergen led by the famous Swedish geologist, Otto Torell, in 1858 and 1861, and he himself led expeditions to the same regions in 1864, 1868, and 1872—3.

After these succesful expeditions to the then little known Spitsbergen area, Nordenskiöld turned to the explorations of the north-east passage — the sea-route round the north of Asia, and with the ship *Vega* he succeeded in 1878—1880, by wintering twice on the voyage, in carrying out the first navigation of the whole route from Kara Sea to Bering Strait. On his return he was received with great honours and was given a Swedish knighthood. As a geologist, Nordenskiöld was much preoccupied with the ice sheet, and was especially interested in finding in Greenland conditions analogous to those that had obtained in northern Europe during the Pleistocene glaciation. Nordenskiöld's first visit to Greenland, however, was made in order to obtain dogs for an expedition to the snow fields of Nordostlandet.

Like many of the early explorers, A. E. Nordenskiöld was convinced that there must be oases in the interior of Greenland. In support of this view he argued from the relative distribution of altitude in Greenland. He pointed out that unless Greenland was a huge dome rising towards the middle of the country from all sides, conditions in the centre of Greenland would be most unfavourable to the formation of glaciers. The climate of the interior would be arid, with little precipitation. It was to be assumed that under such conditions the precipitation in Greenland would fall on the mountains along the coast, so that the interior would be in the rain shadow of these mountains.

The climate of central Greenland would thus be characterized by dry Föhn winds which would melt the ice as such winds did in the Alps, and form oases. However, if Greenland was dome-shaped and the whole of the interior was a vast area of upland, then it might be possible that such oases did not exist. But this would involve a relative distribution of altitude that was unknown at that time for any large land area, and Nordenskiöld rejected this possibility. He was so strongly convinced that there was ice-free land in central Greenland, that he would not even exclude the possibility of coniferous forests of the same type as those found in central Siberia.

Nordenskiöld had had experience of travelling on ice in his expeditions across the ice cap of Nordostlandet in 1872—3. This was the first major journey made across any ice sheet, and he had planned to travel with reindeer-hauled sledges. With a lot of trouble he succeeded in bringing forty reindeer from Sweden, but only a few days after landing they escaped from the herdsmen and so the journey across the ice had to be made with man-hauled sledges drawn by members of the party. In 1883 Nordenskiöld returned to Greenland to study the ice sheet there, and on 4 July he entered the ice sheet by approximately the same route as in 1870. This expedition to the ice sheet consisted of nine men, among them two Laps. They used sledges built in Sweden, and the Laps had their skis and their bear spears with them.

They had a tent with them, and air-mattresses and a sleeping bag for each man, as well as provisions for fifty days. However, it was not long before they had to abandon part of the equipment, for the snow was melting freely at that time of year, and they were considerably hindered by sinking into the soft snow and slush, so that the equipment was soaked. After eighteen days they succeeded in covering 117 km (73 miles) and they had reached an altitude of 1,510 m (4,950 ft) above sea level. But then they had to give up any attempt to go further. However, before they turned back, Nordenskiöld sent the two Laps further on by ski to reconnoitre, and with instructions that if they saw land, they were to bring back samples of flowers and grass as evidence of the kind of vegetation.

After 57 hours the Laps returned and reported that they had travelled 230 km (143 miles) further in across the ice sheet and had reached an altitude of 1,947 m (6,380 ft) without seeing any trace of land. The following day the party set out on the return journey; after spending 31 days on the ice sheet they reached the base camp by the northern arm of Aulatsivik Fjord.

Even though the Laps can scarcely have covered as much ground as they claimed, Nordenskiöld had, in fact, disproved his own theory about the ice-free interior. But he did not see it in that light himself, particularly fastening on the fact that the Laps had seen two ravens flying from the north. Nordenskiöld considered that it was unlikely that these birds would come far from their nesting place during the breeding season, so he thought it possible that it was only a tongue of ice that crossed Greenland about Lat. 69°—70° N, but that to both south and north there might still be oases and that the two ravens could be assumed to have been flying from the northern oases.

Even though this expedition did not succeed in providing the final proof for or against the existence of ice-free oases, it did return with some important observations. They had, for instance, observed that the crevasses were confined to the periphery of the ice sheet and that the surface of the snow in the interior was perfectly even. When Nansen heard this, he began to make plans for skiing across the ice sheet. But before this was done, there was yet another expedition that penetrated some distance in on to the ice sheet, this time in north Greenland.

The same year as Nordenskiöld's expedition, Robert Peary, an American naval engineer, and Christian Maigaard, a Dane, managed to ascend on to the ice sheet from the head of Pakitsoq at Lat. 69° 30' N. Like Whymper, they had planned to use dog sledges, but at the last moment the Greenlanders backed out, and Peary and Maigaard had to make the journey on foot-hauled sledges. On the first part of the trip they had the help of a couple of Greenlanders, but after that they were left to themselves. They had with them two American built sledges of hickory wood; they were 8 ft 10 in long and only one foot wide and weighed 24 lb each. They had also skis and snowshoes with them. According to Peary's account, they travelled some 100 miles in over the ice before they were obliged to turn back through lack of provisions.

On the return journey Peary tied the two sledges together and fitted them with a sail rigged up on skis and ski-sticks, and with the wind behind them it was now possible to "sail" toward the coast at a considerable speed. Maigaard wrote an account of the journey in the journal of the Royal Danish Geographical Society, and although it is still uncertain whether Peary really did travel as far as 100 miles on to the ice sheet, his expedition was a pioneer in a travelling technique that was later to be used on other expeditions both by Peary himself and others. They observed, as others had done further south, that the crevasses were confined to the marginal zone.

Several more-or-less successful expeditions had brought back information about the marginal area of the ice sheet, but by the middle of the 1880's it was still an open question whether the ice sheet covered the whole of Greenland, or whether there were oases in the interior.

Nordenskiöld and Peary had proved that it was relatively easy to travel about in the interior, especially outside the season when the snow was melting. Unsuccessful attempts had been made to use dogs or reindeer to haul the sledges: in the case of Whymper's expedition, the sledges had not proved strong enough, and Nordenskiöld's reindeer had escaped. Hitherto, only man-hauled sledges had been used, if the members of the expedition had not themselves carried everything on their backs. The travelling had been done on foot, sinking deep into the snow with each step taken, except for Peary, who had skis and snowshoes, and for the Laps on Nordenskiöld's expedition, who had used skis.

Skiing across the Ice Sheet for the First Time

Fridtjof Nansen, a twenty-six year old Norwegian explorer and sportsman, was to be the first man to cross the ice sheet. Nansen was a trained zoologist, and in 1882 he had been on board the Norwegian sealing-ship *Viking* in a sealing expedition to east Greenland. The ship became beset in the ice, and for twenty-four days it drifted nearer and nearer to the barren coast of east Greenland. Nansen had the idea that he would be able to reach the east coast, which was then unknown, if he left the ship and made his way over the ice on foot, but he met with firm opposition from the captain of the ship, who forbade him to leave the ship for any distance.

Nansen was a keen hunter and an accomplished skier, and he had spent much time among the mountains of Norway in both summer and winter conditions. When he got back to Norway, he heard about the skiing trip that had been made on Nordenskiöld's expedition, and Nansen had

60

A Danish dog-sledge expedition. In north and east Greenland the dog-sledge is still in many places the only form of transport that can negotiate the difficult terrain.

the revolutionary idea of starting out from the east coast, for, he said, "if you begin, as all earlier expeditions have done, from the west coast, then you may be certain you will not succeed in getting across. The fleshpots of Egypt will be behind you, and only the unknown desert of ice and the east coast, which is little better, will be in front of you. And even if you were to make it right across, then you would still have just as far to return. But if you were to land on the east coast and set out from there towards the inhabited west coast, then all bridges would have been burnt behind you and there would be no need to urge the party on. The east coast would not entice anyone to return there, and the west coast would lie in front with all the tempting comforts of civilisation. There would be no choice. You would have to get across or die."

Nansen applied for a grant to the Norwegian government, and his application was backed by the University of Oslo, but nevertheless he received a refusal, even though he had only requested 5.000 *kroner*. His plans were generally described as those of a madman, but he finally succeeded in

61

getting support from Augustin Gamel, a Danish businessman, who had equipped and sponsored earlier polar expeditions, amongst them the Danish *Djimphna* expedition. Nansen received sufficient funds from Gamel to make a start on his plans. There were plenty of men eager to accompany Nansen, and the finally chose three Norwegians: Otto Sverdrup, Olaf Dietrichson, Kristian Kristiansen Thrane, and two Laps from Karasuak. There were no scientists in the party, except Nansen himself, but they were all experienced mountaineers and skiers.

The initial 5,000 *kroner* that Nansen had received from Gamel proved insufficient, but the Norwegian students' union succeeded in raising a further 10,000 *kroner* by subscription, and the rest Nansen paid from his own pocket. In the midst of the preparations for the expedition Nansen was called upon to defend his doctoral thesis on a zoological subject at the University of Oslo.

The expedition of Peary and Maigaard had proved that is was possible to manage with very primitive equipment, the essential thing was that it should not be too heavy. Nansen had first planned to use dogs or reindeer to haul his sledges and to slaughter the animals as he advanced. However, he was unable to get hold of suitable sledge dogs, and when it came to the point it proved too expensive to ship reindeer to east Greenland. He therefore abandoned the idea of using draught animals, and based his plans on the use of man-hauled sledges. Nansen realised that the heavy sledges used on most Arctic expeditions at that time would not be suitable for travelling on the ice sheet. They were quite suitable for travel on sea ice, but not on the heavily crevassed ice sheet. Sir George Nares, Julius Payer and others had used heavy sledges with narrow runners, but Nansen was accustomed to the Norwegian ski sledges with broad runners that were used for the transport of hay and firewood from the mountains. These served as models for the sledges he had built of selected ash wood with runners of maple or elm fitted with protective caps of thin steel plate. To make them as resilient as possible, they were fixed together without nails of any kind. Each sledge was to be hauled by one man; they were 2.90 m (9 ft 6 in) long and 0.50 m (1 ft 7½ in) wide.

The runners curved upward at the front and rear so that the sledges could be used in reverse if necessary. There was a curved upright of ash right at the back. Nansen took only five sledges with him, for one man was to go ahead and find the route. Nansen had learned from Peary the idea of using a sail to make quicker progress where wind and snow conditions permitted.

Nansen's plans were based on using skis, which had been little used on previous expeditions. Even though Trojel had mentioned the possibility of using Norwegian skiers to reconnoitre the country, his suggestion had not received much attention. It is true that J. A. D. Jensen had had skis with him, but he claimed that their main value had been as fuel. Nansen's expedition took nine pairs of skis, mainly made of birch; they were 2.90 m (9 ft 6 in) long and 9.2 cm (3½ in) broad, and were fitted with thin steel plates on the underside. They also took snowshoes, both the normal Canadian type, and some very short Norwegian ones. They had two sleeping bags with them, each designed for three men.

Nansen and his party came to Greenland on board the Norwegian sealing ship *Jason*. They arrived off the east coast of Greenland at the end of July and worked their way slowly northwards. On 17 July Nansen left the ship with two boats to try to force a way through the belt of drift ice, but they became beset and drifted southward again and it was ten days before they reached land. They landed at Qutdleq, much further south than they had intended, and they had therefore to begin to row northwards along the coast again. By 10 August they had arrived at Umivik, and Nansen decided to make the ascent on to the ice sheet there. Autumn was already coming on, the sledges were heavily loaded, so it was an exhausting operation to get them up onto the ice, but it was essential to start inland.

By 16 August they had sorted out their equipment and could start the ascent. It was already getting cold, and when they came up on to the ice they found no melt-water at all. Their plan had been to set a straight course for Disko Bugt, for Nansen thought it would be the easiest place to make a landfall and come in contact with the Greenlanders. But as it was now so late in the year, he decided instead to take a shorter route over the ice, and they made for Ameralik Fjord to the south of Godthåb.

The ascent on to the ice went off according to plan, and by the 31 August they had passed the last nunatak and had only the vast unbroken white plain before them until they reached the west coast. The temperature continued to fall: on 11 September they recorded $-40°$ ($-40°$ F) in the tent, and presumably the outside temperature was $-45°$ ($-49°$ F) an amazingly low figure for the time of year. On 5 September they passed the highest point on the route 2,716 m (8920 ft) above sea level.

On 7 September they were forced to lie up for a blizzard, but otherwise the little group struggled on westward, and on 17 September they saw a snow bunting — a sign that they were approaching the west coast. On 19 September they had their first sight of land, and soon afterwards the whole country to the south of Godthåbsfjord lay spread out before their eyes. The going across the ice sheet itself had not been too bad, but now their difficulties began. They had to cross the heavily crevassed marginal zone, which was also intersected by deep melt-water streams. On 24 September they reached the first nunatak, and could once more set foot on bare rock after wandering over ice for forty days.

They continued coastwards through the valley of Austmannadalen and reached Ameralik Fjord. If they were to get any nearer to civilisation, they had to construct some sort of craft in which to sail out of the fjord. Using the sailcloth from the tent floor and their ski-sticks, they made a boat. They made the ribs of osier branches that they found in the valley, and they spread the sailcloth over this and sewed it together. Nansen and Sverdrup reached Ny Herrnhut in this primitive boat, and then travelled overland to Godthåb where they fetched help to pick up the other members of the party.

It was late in the year, and the last ship had already sailed south, so that they had to spend the winter in Godthåb, but they managed to send a letter by kayak to Ivigtut and from there in Mc Clintock's *Fox* to Europe with the message that they had successfully carried out their project.

They had had to limit the amount of scientific equipment that they took with them and they could only take measurements that would not hinder their progress. Their most important finding was that there was no oasies in the interior. They had also made a series of meteorological observations and calculations of altitude, and on the basis of this data the Norwegian meteorologist, H. Mohn, calculated the mean annual temperature of central Greenland at — 25° (— 13° F) at an altitude of 2,000 m (6560 ft). He estimated the average temperature of the coldest month at — 40° (— 40° F), and he assumed that the minimum temperature might be — 65° (— 85° F). These figures were very close to the temperatures that have been recorded by subsequent expeditions wintering on the ice sheet. It was also evident that the ice sheet was not a regular dome uniformly vaulted from east to west, but that its crest must lie considerably nearer to the east coast than to the west coast. It was also clear that there were no oases in Greenland.

Nansen had proved that the ice sheet could be crossed, and this was the beginning of a new epoch in the exploration of the ice sheet.

The Period 1889-1912

Further Danish Expeditions

Nansen had proved that the ice sheet could be crossed, and this meant that it was now a possible route for several expeditions wanting to reach undiscovered parts of Greenland, in particular northern Greenland, which is not accessible by ship. Although the purpose of these expeditions was not the study of the ice sheet itself, and they often became a race with death from hunger and exhaustion, they nevertheless did bring back much useful information about the form and extent of the ice and about the weather conditions there in summer.

In 1893 an expedition operated in south-west Greenland under the leadership of Lieutenant T. V. Garde. It had been sent out by the Commission for Scientific Investigation in Greenland. It was to continue survey work and to make geographical investigation of the yet unmapped areas, and also, if conditions were favourable, to continue the study of the ice sheet, which had not been explored in south-west Greenland. It was still unknown, for instance, whether the same flat and even surface would be found beyond the marginal zone here as Nordenskiöld, Peary, and Nansen had found further north.

It was also an open question whether the high mountain region of south Greenland continued northward through the centre of Greenland, or whether the nunataks that could be seen from the coast were merely an extension of the mountainous area of southern Greenland. Only fourteen days, however, were set aside for exploration on the ice sheet itself, so the amount that could be achieved was necessarily limited.

Garde made the ascent onto the ice sheet with Lieutenant Carl Moltke and Johan Petersen, who was well known as an interpreter of the Greenland language. They found an ascent route at Sermitsialik, and they took with them two Nansen sledges and Canadian snow-shoes, but no skis. The snow had just started to melt, so the expedition found it preferable to sleep during the day and to travel at night when the snow was not so soft. As they reached higher altitudes the going became easier. They reached a point at the same latitude as Frederikshåb without seeing any nunataks, and Garde then changed course and proceeded east until the surface of the ice began to decline, then he continued on south as time did not permit a complete crossing of the ice. Instead, they explored a group of nunataks called Aputajuitsoq which K. J. V. Steenstrup had already seen on travels in the Julianehåb district in 1877.

The ice here was smooth right up to the nunataks and there were no crevasses. There was no vegetation or animal life on the rocks. Garde had spent thirteen days on the ice and had covered 37 Danish miles (173 statute miles); this worked out at a considerably greater daily average than any previous expedition. This was partly because there was a comparatively good crust of snow to walk on at night, and partly because the surface of the snow in south Greenland is generally very even, and there were not nearly so many nor such large crevasses to be overcome as J. A. D. Jensen's expedition further north had met with in 1878. In contrast to Nansen, Garde found only slight diurnal temperature variations. The highest altitude they reached was 2100 m (6900 ft). The following year, in 1894, Count Carl Moltke with a new expedition continued the exploration and surveying of the Julianehåb district, and with the geologist, A. Jessen, he made a detailed study of the ice margin along the then unknown fjord Nordre Sermilik.

Glacial-Geological Investigations

In 1892 a German expedition under the leadership of the well-known German explorer Erich von Drygalski was sent out by the Gesellschaft für Erdkunde zu Berlin. Its principal objective was to study the difference between the ice movement in an Arctic ice sheet and that in a normal valley glacier such as in the Alps. The expedition was also to investigate the physical properties of the size of the ice crystals and the form of the surface. They were also to investigate the formation of moraines with a view to gaining a better understanding of the conditions under which the north German landscape had been formed during and after the ice age. A preliminary expedition was sent out in 1891 to prepare the work in Greenland, and in 1892—93 a winter station was built on the peninsula called Qarássap nunatâ at the south of Umanak Bugt. Some very detailed long-term measurements of the ice movement in two glaciers were made, and the moraine systems here and at other places in the area were surveyed. The results of the expedition were published in two large volumes by the German geographical society that had organized the expedition.

Eskimo Travelling Techniques are Introduced

Robert Peary was eager to find a route to the north pole and therefore made a number of expeditions in north Greenland. Peary, during his travels with Maigaard, had convinced himself that

A helicopter on a reconnaissance flight for the International Glaciological Expedition has landed on the ice sheet to reconnoitre for a suitable route for weasel convoys.

it was possible to travel on the ice sheet, and he planned to approach as near to the north pole as he could through north Greenland. In 1891-92, Peary was once more in Greenland, this time with his wife and a party of five, among whom was Dr F. A. Cook, whose name was later to become tragically well known because of the dispute with Peary about who had been at the Pole, and Eyvind Astrup, a Norwegian. On board the *Kite* they reached McCormick Bugt where he established his winter quarters, and with the help of Polar Eskimoes he began that same year to reconnoitre around Inglefield Bredning.

Even on his first visit to Greenland Peary had studied Eskimo travelling techniques, and now, living as he was with this little tribe of Polar Eskimoes, he soon became more familiar with their methods of travel and decided that as far as possible he would adopt them on his journeys. However, with his technical background he also made some improvements. Instead of using sledges laboriously pieced together from whalebone and drift wood, Peary imported American timber and constructed sledges that were larger than any used previously, although they were still lashed together and were the same shape as the traditional Eskimo sledges. He also taught the Eskimoes to use iron under the runners. So that his expedition would be supplied with fresh meat, he engaged Eskimoes to hunt for him. Their old weapons were bought up to be sent to American museums, and their bows and harpoons were replaced by modern rifles, and they were given good American-made knives instead of their old knives made of lumps of meteor iron set in narwhale. Peary was a man of quite an original type. He was completely possessed with his great ambition: to reach the geographical north pole, which, after many years of struggling in vain, he claimed that he had succeeded in doing in 1909. By force of personality alone, he managed to drive the Eskimoes into helping him, and he persuaded them to accompany him into areas that they did not know — all to achieve a goal of which they understood nothing. He had succeeded in winning their admiration and devotion; they found in him a man that they could trust, but also a man whose anger they feared and whom they felt they must obey.

After wintering, Peary started out in the spring of 1892 on a journey across the ice sheet. On 14 May he left his winter station with four sledges and twenty dogs that he had obtained by barter. It was planned that he and Astrup should cross the ice sheet alone, but they were supported on the first part of the trip by Langdon Gibson and Dr Frederick A. Cook. In thirteen days of strenuous effort they succeeded in bringing the equipment up onto the ice. By 24 May they were 200 km (124 miles) in on the ice sheet behind Humboldt Gletscher, and here the party divided: Gibson and Cook returning with two of the sledges and two dogs and Peary and Astrup continuing eastward with fourteen dogs — four dogs had already died on the way. Astrup followed Nansen's example and used skis, while Peary kept to his Canadian snowshoes. Although the journey across the ice was strenuous, it was monotonous, but by 4 July they had arrived on the other side and from a cliff which they named Navy Cliff they looked out over the great fjord system which Peary, in honour of American Independence Day, called Independence Fjord. Here they managed to kill five musk ox, and after feeding the dogs, the two men started out on the return journey on 7 July. The heavy going over the soft snow and blizzards and bad weather delayed them so that they did not reach their winter station until 5 August. The homeward journey had taken them 27 days, and they had spent a total of 97 days on the ice, which was longer than any previous expedition.

Peary was back in north Greenland the following year, wintering in Bowdoin Fjord, which lies to the north-east of the present Thule. The same autumn Peary made a fresh attempt to cross the ice, but had to turn back because of bad weather. On 6 March 1894 Peary started out onto the ice sheet again, this time with six men, twelve sledges, and 92 dogs. The problem was always how to get the equipment up onto the ice, and this time Peary tried to use mules to carry the equipment the first part of the way up, but even so the journey was unsuccessful. Bad weather and difficult

68

Drifting snow and bad weather occur frequently on the ice sheet.

snow conditions forced his companions to turn back, and finally Peary himself was obliged to return. He left most of the sledges, which were loaded with pemmican and other food, on the ice. Peary reached Bowdoin Fjord on 19 April. He was extremely exhausted, and only 26 of his dogs were still alive. In the spring of 1895 Peary set out again. This time he had two companions: H. J. Lee, and his negro servant Matthew A. Henson, as well as six Eskimoes. He took a total of 60 dogs and six sledges. He had hopes of finding the sledges that had been abandoned the year before, but he did not succeed in doing this. Peary then sent the Eskimoes back, and he and his two companions went on with three sledges and 42 dogs. He succeeded in crossing the ice sheet to Navy Cliff, but by the time they arrived there, they were extremely exhausted and had only one sledge and eleven dogs left. Henson, the negro, had frostbite in both feet. They managed to shoot a couple of musk ox, and with these as food, they started out on the return journey. They had only provisions for 17 days, and there were only nine dogs left by this time. It was a race against death by starvation, and bad weather would have meant disaster, but Peary won through and on

25 June they reached Bowdoin Fjord with only one dog still alive — they had eaten the rest on the way. They brought back little in the way of scientific data from the ice sheet itself, and geographically they achieved nothing that had not been done on the previous journey to Navy Cliff. The results of Peary's journeys on the ice sheet were from that point of view a disappointment, and he now realized, too, that his route to the north pole would not lie across the ice sheet. On subsequent expeditions, therefore, he followed the sea ice along the coast. In addition to Peary's observations made on his journeys on the ice sheet — he made special note of surface forms — two American geologists in the party, T. C. Chamberlain and R. D. Salisbury, made a large number of studies of the glaciers around Inglefield Bredning and the peninsula of Kap York.

Nansen had demonstrated that it was possible to use Norwegian skiing techniques on the ice sheet, and now Peary had mainly adopted the travelling techniques that he had learned from the Polar Eskimoes. He had improved on these techniques by using better materials and more modern equipment, but the basis of all his expeditions had been — and remained — the Eskimo dog-sledge secured by lashing such as the Polar Eskimoes used. A number of later expeditions adopted the method of using dog-sledges and of supplementing their supplies by hunting when this was possible. The nature of the terrain and the state of the snow and the size of the dog teams all decided how much could be transported, but it would vary between 200—800 kg on each sledge. But of course provisions had also to be taken for the dogs. About 1 lb had to be allowed for each dog every day or every other day, so that even if many sledges were taken the effective capacity for scientific equipment was very limited. The journeys often became a race with starvation in which the explorers were forced to kill and eat dogs one by one, but in most cases they won the race.

Danish Expeditions in North-East Greenland

In order to link the surveying that had been done in east Greenland with that which Peary had carried out in north Greenland the *Danmark* expedition under the leadership of Mylius Erichsen was sent out in 1906—1908. They arrived in east Greenland on board the *Danmark* and there allowed the ship to become beset in the ice near Kap Bismarck, which was re-named Danmarkshavn. They used the ship as their winter station and it became the base for comprehensive scientific investigations of the geographical conditions, flora and fauna, archeology, etc. of north-east Greenland.

In the spring of 1907 two sledges made their way from the winter station at Danmarkshavn and proceeded northwards along the coast of Greenland until the party discovered Nordostrundingen, which they surveyed. One party under the leadership of J. P. Koch then continued straight across

Independence Fjord and along the coast of Peary Land to Kap Clarence Wyckoff and thus managed to unite the mapping done by the American expedition under Peary with the Danish, German, and Austrian surveying that had been carried out in east Greenland. The other team, with Mylius Erichsen as its leader, mapped the large fjord system between Danmark Fjord and Independence Fjord, reaching as far as Kap Glacier, where they had a view across to the cairn Peary had built on the summit of Navy Cliff.

Here they were overtaken by the sudden summer thaw, and a return journey was now impossible. So J. P. Koch reached Danmarkshavn again according to plan, but Mylius Erichsen had to spend the summer in north Greenland. Hunting was poor, and their equipment gradually became completely worn out. Their footwear, in particular, was ruined, and Mylius Erichsen and his two companions, Niels Peter Høeg-Hagen, a surveyor, and a Greenlander named Jørgen Brønlund, attempted to resole their shoes with the leather from the theodolite case. When by the beginning of September autumn began to set in again and it was possible to walk on the ice on the fjord, they started out on their return journey, ascending on to the ice sheet at the head of Danmark Fjord. Handicapped by their worn-out equipment and the polar night, they did not succeed in getting through.

In November, Høeg-Hagen and Mylius Erichsen perished of exhaustion in the descent from the ice sheet. Jørgen Brønlund dragged himself on to a depot where there was food enough. But he arrived there when the moon was waning, and frostbite on both feet preventing him from going any further. His body was found early the following spring by J. P. Koch, but the bodies of the other two could not be found, and the idea of searching for them had to be abandoned.

Jørgen Brønlund's diary was found on his body, and a number of Høeg-Hagen's sketch maps were found in a bottle, but the diaries of Høeg-Hagen and Mylius Erichsen were missing. Brønlund's diary gave an outline of what happened to the expedition, but it was obvious that somewhere in north Greenland there existed some notes hidden in cairns which would throw more light on what had happened on the journey. Two expeditions attempted independently of each other to find these notes, and both expeditions had, of course, to travel across the ice sheet.

In 1909 the *Alabama* expedition under the leadership of Ejnar Mikkelsen was despatched to search for the journals of Mylius Erichsen's expedition, and also to find the two bodies, if possible. The expedition wintered on board the ship at the island of Shannon, and that same autumn Mikkelsen made a journey to Lambert Land, where he visited Brønlund's grave. The search for the others had to be given up, as the sea ice in front of the glacier where from Brønlund's description the bodies should be found, had broken up. They had therefore to concentrate on finding any reports there might be hidden in cairns in north Greenland. The following spring Ejnar

Within Søndre Strømfjord the vegetation reaches practically to the front of Russel Gletscher, an outlet glacier from the ice sheet. Contrary to many outlet glaciers, the Russel Gletscher seems to be stationary.

Mikkelsen and Ivar P. Iversen sledged north once more, and on 24 March they ascended on to the ice by way of Storstrømmen, a glacier which flows down into the northern part of Dove Bugt.

Over the first part of the route, Mikkelsen and Iversen were accompanied by three fellow members of the expedition: Lieutenant V. Laub, C. Jørgensen, and G. Paulsen, but on 10 April they split up. The supporting party made a journey across to the west side of Dronning Louise Land and then returned by the same route they had come by. Mikkelsen and Iversen travelled northwards toward the head of Danmark Fjord, which they reached on 12 May.

The whole journey had been marked by bad weather, and their progress was greatly hindered by the numerous crevasses, for they had more or less been travelling through the whole nunatak zone of Hertugen af Orlean's Land. In the meantime, Mikkelsen's colleagues had returned to Shannon Ø, where they found that the *Alabama* was on the point of sinking. It had sprung a leak, and everything had to be moved ashore very hurriedly. By 1 August there was still no sign of Mikkelsen and Iversen, so they made a depot of what provisions they had, and returned home on board a Norwegian sealing ship *7de Juni*.

Mikkelsen and Iversen had spent the summer exploring Danmark Fjord and had found a number of Mylius Erichsen's reports in cairns. Their return journey followed the coast, and they suffered extreme hardships. When they reached Lambert Land the last of the dogs was dead, and the two men had to abandon all their equipment, even their diaries, in an attempt to reach the winter station near Danmarkshavn.

They reached there in a state of extreme exhaustion and they had to stay there for a long time to recover their strength. They then continued south to Shannon Ø, where they discovered that the ship had sunk and that the rest of the expedition had returned home. Iversen and Mikkelsen had therefore to prepare for another winter there. In the spring of 1911 they travelled north again to fetch their diaries and equipment, which they had abandoned in Lambert Land. From here they returned to the island of Shannon and then continued south to look for a depot on the island of Bass Rock.

The ship that was to pick them up the following summer did not find them on Shannon Ø. As it was late in the season it had to put to sea again. When they returned, Mikkelsen and Iversen discovered that the ship had been and gone, and they therefore had to resign themselves to yet another, their third, winter there. Not until the summer of 1912 did a Norwegian sealing ship find the two men and bring them back to civilisation.

Knud Rasmussen's Thule Expeditions

Back in Denmark there was considerable anxiety about the fate of Mikkelsen and Iversen, for it was not even known where in Greenland they were. It was thought possible that instead of returning to Shannon Ø they had continued north around the coast of Greenland to try to reach Thule, where Knud Rasmussen, the famous Danish Arctic explorer, had established a trading post in 1910. Knud Rasmussen and his manager Peter Freuchen therefore felt under an obligation to set out on a search expedition. In the spring of 1912 they started out on the long journey around north Greenland to search for Mikkelsen and to map the conjectured Peary Channel.

On 6 April in brilliant spring sunshine they set out with heavily laden dog sledges. They planned to proceed north along the coast, but they had got no further than Neqe when they were forced to change their plans. A northerly gale had broken up the ice, and there was open water right to the coast. Knud Rasmussen therefore decided that he would ascend on to the ice sheet and cross it to reach the head of Danmark Fjord and then return through Peary Channel. The ice sheet at this point is about 600 miles wide, and on 14 April they climbed up on to it by way of Clements Markham Gletscher and set a course for Danmark Fjord. By 31 May they had crossed over to Danmark Fjord. They found the cairns left by the *Danmark* expedition and were also aware that Ejnar Mikkelsen had been there, but he had left no cairn reports, so Knud Rasmussen and Freuchen decided to continue on to Independence Fjord and to look for reports there. Here, as Mylius Erichsen had done, they confirmed that the Peary Channel did not exist, but that there was only a system of valleys here occupied by a glacier that Mylius Erichsen had named Marie Sophie Gletscher after his wife. As there was no channel, Rasmussen and his companion had to climb back on to the ice sheet and return across it. They ascended on to the ice by way of Nyeboe Gletscher. They started on the return journey on 8 August, and on 15 September they reached Thule.

In contrast to other expedition leaders Knud Rasmussen had been born and bred in Greenland. His father had been a clergyman in Jakobshavn, and right from his earliest boyhood Knud Rasmussen had lived together with Greenlanders. He spoke their language like a native and he was a first class dog-team driver even by Eskimo standards. For this reason his expeditions, more than any others, were based on Eskimo techniques of travel. Peary had not mastered the Eskimo methods until late in life, but Knud Rasmussen had been at home with them from childhood, and he now adopted a number of improvements that he had learned from Polar Eskimoes, or invented himself. Peter Freuchen had taken part in the *Danmark* expedition and was now in charge of the Thule station. He was married to a Thule Eskimo and lived more like an Eskimo than a European.

The Thule expeditions were based on hunting: as they advanced, they lived as far as possible on the products of the country, just as the Eskimoes did. They took with them not only rifles, but also harpoons and bows and arrows, for many of the Eskimoes could still use them, having exchanged their old weapons for rifles only a few years before. Unlike Peary, who did not dare to rely on the Eskimoes as far as journeys over the ice sheet were concerned, Knud Rasmussen often travelled with Eskimoes, and was frequently alone with them. On the first Thule expedition there were four sledges and a total of 53 dogs. Normal Eskimo sledges with steel runners were used, but a runner of walrus hide approximately as wide as an ordinary ski was fitted over the normal runner. This was frozen hard to the runner with a mixture of snow and water which quickly froze

74

in the intense cold. Another thing Knud Rasmussen learned from the Polar Eskimoes was to form a lining of ice by simply pouring water over the runners a few times; when this froze, it formed a hard, glasslike cap of ice, giving an easy-running, almost friction-free ride over the ice. This method could only be used on the ice sheet itself, and even though the covering of ice quickly melted down, it was also quick and easy to renew. They used igloos such as the Polar Eskimoes normally used on their journeys, but they also carried tents with them on the Thule expeditions.

A few years later Knud Rasmussen was again crossing the ice sheet with his second Thule Expedition. The purpose of this expedition was to survey the yet unknown parts of north Greenland and to make archaeological and geological investigations of the Sherard Osborn Fjord and further north. After another winter in Thule, Knud Rasmussen started out north with the young Danish geologist called Lauge Koch, Thorild Wulff, a Swedish botanist, and four Polar Eskimoes. Like all Knud Rasmussen's expeditions, this one was based on hunting, but the weather was very bad and there was very little game. They did not succeed in bagging many seals or reindeer, eventhough the Eskimoes hunted assiduously. On one of the hunting trips one of the Eskimoes disappeared, and in spite of intensive search they were finally obliged to continue without finding him. He may have been killed by a wolf. They surveyed the land from Sherard Osborn Fjord up to De Long Fjord, but they had to abandon their plan to reach the most northerly point in Greenland, Kap Morris Jesup. Instead they returned to Sherard Osborn Fjord and from there ascended on to the ice sheet and crossed it to reach Thule again. On 4 August they started up Daniel Bruun Firn, and the whole expedition was in very poor shape: their footwear was worn out and there was practically no food left. With luck they could hope to get across to Humboldt Gletscher by slaughtering the last of the dogs and then try to get some hunting there.

The marginal zone near Daniel Bruun Firn was heavily crevassed and intersected by deep meltwater streams which they had to wade through, waist-deep. Completely exhausted, they managed to get up on to the ice sheet, but Thorild Wulff especially was badly affected by wading in the cold water. On 21 August they had only five dogs left, and everything that was not absolutely essential was abandoned. By 24 August they had crossed the ice to Inglefield Land, but by that time their last dog had been killed and eaten. Knud Rasmussen and the one Eskimo who was most enduring now tried to push on ahead and reach the Eskimo settlement of Etah so as to get help from the Eskimoes there. It was a journey of 270 km (168 miles). Meanwhile Lauge Koch, Thorild Wulff, and the two Eskimoes dragged slowly on.

They abandoned their collections of specimens and their diaries in a depot where they could hope to find them again. They shot a couple of arctic hares, but apart from these, nothing. After

75

three days Thorild Wulff gave up and asked them to continue without him. They had no sledge to haul him on, and they were all too exhausted to carry him, so under these circumstances Lauge Koch decided to go on and leave Wulff behind, so that there might be some chance of bringing the results of the expedition as far on as possible so as to preserve them. Wulff wrote a few letters which Lauge Koch took with him, and they parted. Meanwhile, Knud Rasmussen had reached Etah on 30 August, and the very next day a rescue expedition set out, but it was too late for Wulff. Lauge Koch had continued on with the Eskimoes. He was extremely weak and had abandoned hope, but on 2 September the Eskimoes managed to shoot two reindeer, and the little group were saved. A little later they were found by the relief party. In the autumn of the same year Lauge Koch fetched the collections and diaries that had been left in the depot in Inglefield Land, but he sought in vain for Wulff's body.

Knud Rasmussen continued his travels to investigate the culture of the Eskimoes and their routes of migration, and on the fifth Thule expedition he struck out across Canada to Alaska, the longest journey by dog-sledge ever made, but he never came up onto the ice sheet again.

The journey of Peary and Knud Rasmussen across the ice sheet in north Greenland had given a clear picture of the surface of the ice sheet, and by a coincidence Peter Freuchen had given the first real description of snow stratification. On all these journeys the ice sheet had only been an extent to be traversed on the way to the real field of work. It was the "imperial highway" for all these expeditions, but none of these expeditions had had the ice as its object of study.

The significance of these expeditions for the exploration of the ice sheet was in the technical progress that was made and which formed the basis of future expeditions to the Greenland ice sheet and of British and Norwegian expeditions to Antarctica. The polar explorers were now familiar with the special techniques of travelling, and in subsequent years the dog-sledge was used on almost all polar expeditions.

The Period 1912-1920

Wintering on the Ice Sheet for the First Time.

While Knud Rasmussen was exploring northernmost Greenland, the scientific exploration of the ice sheet itself was commencing further south. In 1912—1913 there were two expeditions working in Greenland, and the object of both of them was to study the ice sheet itself. One was an expedition from Denmark under the patronage of the King of Denmark and with Captain J. P. Koch as leader. It was called The Danish Expedition to Dronning Louise Land and across the Ice Sheet of north Greenland 1912—1913. It consisted of four men: Captain J. P. Koch, who had previously been on the *Danmark* expedition: Alfred Wegener, a German meteorologist who had been a colleague of Koch's on previous expeditions; Vigfus Sigurdsson, an Icelander who was in charge of the horses; and Captain Lars Larsen.

All earlier expeditions on the ice sheet had been made in summer; nothing was known about weather conditions there in the winter, and so the plan was to spend the winter on the margin of the ice sheet in Dronning Louise Land and to make meteorological measurements throughout most of one year, and also to make detailed glaciological studies not only on the surface of the glacier, but also drillings in the ice in order to gain a more detailed knowledge of the snow accumulation. A plan to establish a meteorological station just inside the margin of the ice sheet and to spend a winter there had already been discussed in connexion with the *Danmark* expedition, but the facilities necessary for transporting the equipment to the site had not been available and the idea had been abandoned.

The leader of the expedition, Jens Peter Koch, was a veteran of Greenland research. He had passed out of the Danish military academy and had been a member of G. S. Amdrup's expedition to east Greenland, from which he brought back the findings of an exceedingly competent survey. On his return to Denmark from Greenland, Koch had transferred to the General Staff Map Service, and had made long and strenuous journeys in Iceland surveying the area around Vatnajökull. Koch's chance to return to Greenland came with Mylius Erichsen's expedition. He was the surveyor on this expedition and did excellent work. Not only was he an enduring and experienced traveller, but his extreme accuracy and scientific sense had plenty of scope on this expedition. He carried out the survey of northern Greenland uniting the surveys made by Germans and Danes in east Greenland with Peary's survey in the north.

After his return to Denmark in 1908 Koch became a lecturer at the military academy and a company commander at headquarters in Copenhagen, but he could not give up his interest in Greenland. He succeeded in getting support from the Danish government and from the Carlsberg Foundation to carry out his plan to lead a Danish expedition to study the ice sheet. It was the first Danish expedition to the ice sheet itself since J. A. D. Jensen's journeys in 1878.

All previous expeditions that had traversed the ice sheet had been anxious to get across as quickly as possible, and with least possible load, but the outlook of this expedition was different. It was planned to take sufficient supplies, not only for a journey across the ice, but also for maintaining the winter station on the ice manned by a team of four and equipped with scientific instruments. Even at the most basic, they would have to reckon on a load of some two tons.

Previous expeditions had used sledges hauled by men or by dogs, but Koch regarded these as having too small a capacity, in view of the large amount of equipment they needed. On his journeys to Vatnajökull he had used Icelandic horses, and his experience with them had been favourable. Peary, it will be recalled, had once used mules to take his supplies up onto the ice sheet, but without conspicuous success. Using horses meant that large quantities of hay had to be transported on to the ice. So, instead of the light sledges that had been used since Nansen's time, heavily-constructed sledges were used once more. The Royal Veterinary and Agricultural High School in Copenhagen developed a special concentrated food for the expedition, but they would nevertheless need four tons of this in addition to six tons of hay, which was a staggeringly large load in comparison with what previous expeditions had taken, and Koch calculated that it would be necessary to slaughter the horses on the way. The cost of the expedition was about 80,000 *kroner,* of which about half was provided by the Carlsberg Foundation.

In July 1912 the expedition set sail for north-east Greenland on board the *Godthaab.* Like Nansen, Koch had decided to start out from the uninhabited side and cross over to civilisation. He planned to winter in Dronning Louise Land and then to travel straight across the ice to Upernavik. The ship managed to get through the drift ice without difficulty and they then unloaded their equipment at Stormkap, which is a little further inland than Danmarkshavn, where Koch and Wegener had spent the winter. The expedition had sixteen horses from Iceland and twenty tons of equipment and stores.

It was late in the year, so the unloading was carried out as quickly as possible and the *Godthaab*

American tractor convoys (known as "swings") bring in the heavy material for the stations on the ice sheet.

put to sea once more, leaving the four men on the shore. A motor boat shifted all the gear as far up the fjord as possible and by 1 September it was all assembled at Kap Stop. They could now make no further progress until in about three weeks' time they could expect the fjord to freeze over sufficiently to bear the weight of the sledges and the horses.

They were then able to continue inland through Borgfjorden to the glacier called Bredebræ, where they found a way up onto the ice sheet through a cleft in the ice wall. But to ascend this route it was necessary to build bridges over five crevasses and to carve out a roadway through the 40 m (130 ft) high wall of ice. On 30 September the ice calved and the road was ruined and all the equipment scattered around. They had to begin to construct a new road from scratch. However, they did succeed in getting up onto the ice and shifted all the gear up onto the glacier Storstrømmen from where they began to reconnoitre for a route into Dronning Louise Land — the great nunatak area that lies between two glaciers: Storstrømmen and L. Bistrup Bræ. Several of the sledges had been wrecked in these operations, so they decided, as it was late in the year, to set up their winter station on Storstrømmen itself, about 9 miles from Dronning Louise Land. From a glaciological point of view this was a very favourable site for the station, as Koch was able to drill down in the ice from the very floor of the building.

The winter station, which was named Borg (The Castle), was a sectional structure that they had brought with them. It was 6.6 m (21 ft 6 in) long and 5 m (16 ft 6 in) wide; the walls were made of a treble layer of plywood on each side of a slim wooden frame, so that there was a cavity of a few centimetres in the walls. The sections for the south and north walls of the living room were double with a 30 cm (1 ft) cavity, so that there were in all twelve layers of ply with three cavities. The roof was double and there was a board floor. The stable was an integral part of the house. To make it even snugger, a bank of snow was thrown up all round against the walls of the house. The structure had been prefabricated in the ordnance factory of the Danish army, and it marked quite a revolution in Arctic equipment in many ways.

The periphery of the ice sheet around Storstrømmen is heavily crevassed, and Koch himself fell into a crevasse. Remarkably enough, this was the first accident of this kind that had befallen any expedition to the ice sheet. It had happened before that men had fallen through and been left suspended, but they had never come to any harm. Koch, however, fell through a snow bridge and dropped 40 ft where he remained suspended on a slight projection. His companion, Larsen, had first to return to Borg to fetch ropes and a rope ladder before he could assist Koch to get out again. When finally an hour or so after the accident Koch was back on the surface again, his right leg was found to be broken. The expedition's only theodolite had been lost, and this was serious, for it was their only means of navigating across the ice. They brought Koch back to the station, but he had to lie up for three months while his leg healed.

Their winter stay went off according to plan. When all the supplies had once been brought in, all the horses except five or so were killed off, and althougth the temperature outside the stable dropped to — 50° (—58° F) these horses survived the winter well. As often as the weather permitted the horses were exercised, even when the temperature was — 40° (— 40° F). The expedition had no sextant, and so that they could find their way across the ice, Koch constructed a kind of Jacob's staff out of an ordinary carpenter's spirit-level fitted with an upright on each end. He inlaid on the inner side of the level in the uprights a celluloid scale in millimetres taken from a slide-rule. A little metal plate with a hole was sunk into each of the uprights. When he was shooting the sun with this, the image of the sun showed as a small point of light on the white celluloid scale and its angle could thus be calculated. The instrument could give the height of the sun to within 1 or 2 minutes, which was sufficiently accurate for the position to be calculated. With this as their only navigational aid, Koch and Wegener found their way across the ice sheet.

80

This was the first truly glaciological expedition to operate on the ice sheet. They carried out normal meteorological observations and made a series of special measurements of the ice. It was the first time that any great depths had been reached by drilling through the ice — they carved out a cellar in the ice under the house from which they were able to drill down. Two worm augers had been made in Copenhagen, and with these they managed to reach a depth of 24 m (79 ft), and in another drill-hole they reached 18 m (59 ft). Koch measured the temperature in the drill-holes and also studied the stratification of the snow. He was also able to determine the hardness of the ice at different temperatures by trying to scratch the ice with various minerals, and he measured the air pressure in the bubbles in the ice.

When daylight returned in the spring, they started to prepare for their journey across the ice sheet. They moved the equipment further inland and made a depot of it on the ice sheet itself. On one of these trips Larsen fell through a snow bridge and into the bed of a melt-water stream, injuring his foot. On 20 April they left Borg with five horses and five sledges. Every night they had to dig into the firn to get shelter for the horses, and thus Koch had ample opportunity to study the stratification of the snow. The weather was bad — over the whole of the first part of the way they were facing into a blizzard; it was not until they reached the central area that the wind dropped. Out of the first forty days of the trip there were only two days of good weather, and for twelve of the days they were unable to travel for the weather.

The cold affected the horses, and they became snow-blind. Three of them had to be slaughtered. On the first part of the way the snow was hard and smooth, but in the interior the snow was soft so that the horses sank into it with each pace, even though they were equipped with special snow-shoes. On 11 June they had to kill off the fourth horse, but by this time they had the wind behind them and could fit their sail to the sledge. They reached the other side of the ice sheet on 4 July and found the depot that had been set up ready for them from Upernavik.

The men and the one horse were exhausted, and over the final stretch of the route the four men had to take it in turns to pull the horse on the sledge. However, it proved impossible to get the exhausted animal through the crevasses near the edge of the ice, and only 6 miles from safety Koch had to shoot it.

The four men arrived at Laksefjorden, but in order to reach civilisation from there they had to get across the fjord, and they did this by constructing a primitive ferry out of a sledge and the coverings of the sleeping bags. They then continued over land through a steep and exhausting mountainous area. Their maps were not too accurate, and when they reached the coast once more, it proved to be the wrong place, and they had to clamber back up again. During this ascent they were overtaken by fog and a heavy snowfall, so that they had to lie up for 35 hours waiting for a break in the weather. Their strength was by now almost gone; they had no more provisions, and with a heavy heart Koch decided to sacrifice the only dog on the expedition which had been with them all the way across the ice. It was shot and cooked. Just as they had begun the meal, they heard a boat on the fjord, and they summoned it with shots. It was the clergyman from the trading post of Prøven who was on a journey through the district; he immediately set back to the trading station with the four men. They had succeeded in making their long journey across the ice sheet.

A Swiss Crossing of the Ice Sheet.

Ever since Agassiz did his pioneering work on glaciers the Swiss have been prominent in glaciological research. This was a natural consequence of their having in their own country some of the largest and loveliest of Europe's glaciers. It was therefore to be expected that their interest would extend to the Greenland ice sheet. In 1909 Alfred de Quervain with the Swiss, E. Baebler and a German, A. Stolberg, made an expedition to west Greenland, and on this they also ascended on to the ice sheet, penetrating 125 km (78 miles) on to it behind Qarajaqs Isfjord.

In 1912, de Quervain and P. L. Mercanton, a well-known explorer of glaciers who had been working on the Rhône Glacier, planned a large-scale expedition to the Greenland ice sheet to study its climatology and glaciological conditions. Part of the plan was to make a traverse from Disko Bugt to Angmagssalik, i. e. approximately the route that Nansen had originally intended to follow, and they also intended to take both aerological and meteorological measurements throughout one winter at a station outside the ice sheet but close to the glacier front. The expedition came to Greenland on board the *Fox* and disembarked at Equip sermia in the northern part of Disko Bugt.

There is a comparatively easy access route onto the ice sheet here, and they employed a number of Greenlanders to help them bring their equipment up on to the ice. Denmark had by this time established the colony at Angmagssalik, so that it would be possible to cross the ice sheet to the settlement and return home from east Greenland the same summer. The team that was to cross the ice consisted of four men with de Quervain as their leader: they were all experienced mountaineers and competent skiers. They took with them three Nansen-type Norwegian sledges and 25 dogs. While this party were crossing the ice, the three other members of the expedition were making a series of studies of the ice margin near Equip sermia, of which they made an accurate survey.

Two men continued on to Disko Island, where they spent the winter, and made aerological and meteorological measurements, while Professor Mercanton himself returned to Switzerland.

82

The journey across the ice sheet had been so well prepared for, that it went off according to plan and did not afford the amount of drama that had characterised previous journeys in north Greenland, but it did make a series of detailed and significant scientific measurements. The party started out from the west coast on 20 June and by 21 July they were able to begin the descent into Sermilik Fjord, where they met up with some Eskimoes and were taken on to Angmagssalik colony, from where they returned home by ship in the autumn. Throughout the trip across the ice they made systematic measurements of the density of the snow and the thickness of the layer of snow, so that they could determine the annual accumulation of snow. On the basis of these observations de Quervain compiled the first balance sheet for the ice, and he found that the annual snow accumulation was equivalent to an average of 35 cm (13½ in) of water, which was very close to the figures that have been determined by later expeditions.

These two expeditions, one Danish and one Swiss, marked the beginning of modern research into the material balance of the ice sheet and into the climatic conditions that had caused the formation of the great ice mass. Knowledge was being gained of the physical properties of the ice, but the First World War called a halt to this scientific work. All scientific activity in Greenland ceased; only purely routine measurements such as weather observations were carried out in the coastal area, and even during the war Knud Rasmussen continued his work in north Greenland.

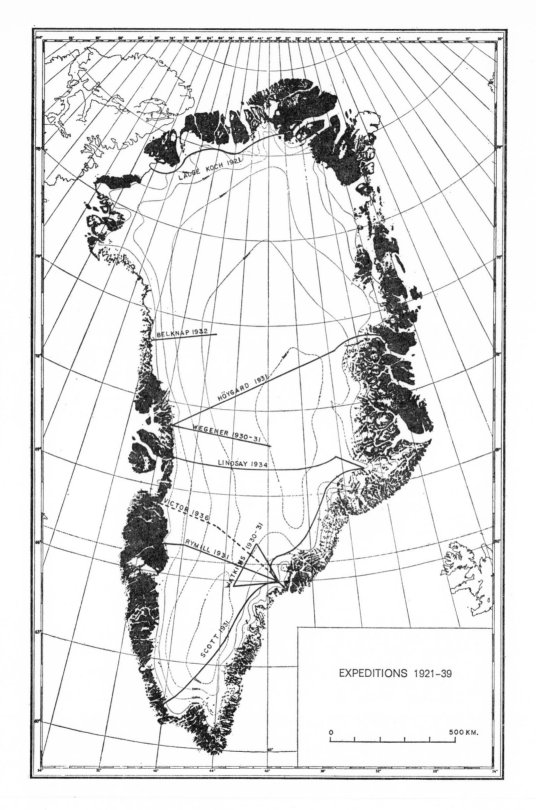

LAUGE KOCH 1921

BELKNAP 1932

HÖYGÅRD 1931

WEGENER 1930~31

LINDSAY 1934

VICTOR 1936

RYMILL 1931

WATKINS 1930~31

SCOTT 1931

EXPEDITIONS 1921–39

0   500 KM.

84

The Period 1920-1940

Preparations are Made for Air Routes over the Ice Cap.

The exploration of the ice sheet came to a complete halt during and after the First World War. Neither in Denmark or in other countries was there any interest shown in it. In Switzerland, de Quervain was busily occupied in collating the results of the expedition of 1912—1913; J. P. Koch was doing the same in Copenhagen; and Wegener was serving in the German army. Koch had returned to the general staff, and was appointed chief of staff with the 1st Division. As he was interested in aviation, he took his pilot's licence in 1917, and then was put in charge of the Danish army's flying service. However, he still kept in touch with Arctic exploration, being, for instance, a member of the committee of the Thule expeditions, and in 1930 his and Wegener's scientific report containing the results of the expedition to Dronning Louise Land and across the ice sheet appeared.

On the Danish Bicentenary Expedition North of Greenland in 1920—23, Lauge Koch continued the geological exploration and surveying of north Greenland that he had commenced during Knud Rasmussen's second Thule expedition. In 1921 he travelled along the coast of north Greenland, passed Kap Morris Jesup, and entered the ice sheet at the head of Independence Fjord and returned across the ice to Thule as Knud Rasmussen had already done. While staying at the head of the fjord he surveyed two glaciers: Academy Gletscher and Marie Sophie Gletscher. The latter occupied the valley Peary had taken for a strait and called Peary Channel.

On 26 June Koch ascended on to the ice sheet via Academy Gletscher and after months of travelling the final stretch was at last ahead of him. He was accompanied by four Polar Eskimoes, and he had four sledges and thirteen dogs. They supplemented their sparse provisions by hunting, but nevertheless crossing the ice once more became a race with starvation. They followed the heavily crevassed northern margin of the ice sheet, and on 12 August they reached Kap Heiberg — Jürgensen and continued along the north side of Humboldt Gletscher, but by this time only two of the dogs still survived; the rest had been eaten on the way.

At the end of the 1920s and the beginning of the 1930s considerable interest was being shown in America and Europe in the possibility of setting up an air route between Europe and U. S. A. via Greenland and Iceland. The Greenland ice sheet suddenly came into the limelight. If a route was to be established it was absolutely essential to have information about the climate of the ice sheet throughout the year, and not just in the summer. Up to this time, no expedition had stayed in central Greenland during the winter. U. S. A., Germany, and Britain were the three countries particularly interested in this air route, and these three countries now launched a number of expeditions to Greenland.

Wegener's Expedition Winters in the Centre of the Ice Sheet.

It was a German expedition that yielded the most important scientific results. The Notgemeinschaft der Deutschen Wissenschaft appointed Alfred Wegener to be the leader of an ambitious expedition which was to explore the ice sheet. Wegener had taken part in the *Danmark* expedition

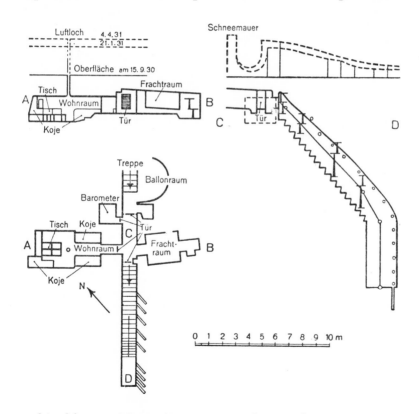

Plan of the Midice station.

and had been with Koch when he had crossed the ice sheet in 1912—13; he was a meteorologist and a versatile and original scientist — it was he, for instance, who propounded the theory of continental drift.

86

Rime crystals on the snow surface.

The plan was ambitious: to set up three stations in Greenland, one on the west coast, one on the east coast, and one at the centre of the ice sheet, and for a whole year to make meteorological measurements at the earth's surface and also, by sending up balloons, in the higher layers of air. It was thought that it would be possible by doing this to form a fairly clear picture of the movements of air over Greenland. It was also intended to study the stratification of the snow, and to determine the thickness of the ice by gravimetric and seismic measurements.

With two meteorologists, J. Georgi and F. Loewe, Wegener travelled to Greenland in 1929 to prepare for the final expedition. He was also accompanied by R. Sorge, a glaciologist. To set up their station in the interior, they planned to enter the ice sheet from a place on Umanak Fjord, and it was therefore necessary to reconnoitre the area to find a suitable ascent route. After a careful search of the whole district, Wegener chose a route up the glacier descending to the fjord Qaumarujuk, and from there made a 150 km (90 miles) reconnaissance trip across the ice sheet.

In the upper part of the glacier there was a nunatak called Scheideck where they planned to set up their base station for the coming winter. Sorge and Loewe had already started their experiments connected with the determination of the ice thickness.

They planned to base the final expedition on the use of dog-sledges, and they intended to employ a large number of Greenlanders to transport the equipment to the winter station in the interior. On the first part of the trip — as far as Scheideck — they wanted to use Icelandic horses, as on the journey Koch and Wegener had made in 1912—13. The expedition had two propeller sledges, which, however, they did not like to risk basing their plans on, for they had never been used in Greenland before. In 1930 the final expedition started out. Seventeen men, among them three Icelanders to look after the horses, took part in the expedition, and a further three men under the leadership of W. Kopp sailed to east Greenland to set up the eastern meteorological station near Scoresby Sund.

In May 1930 the main expedition sailed with the *Gustav Holm* to Umanak Fjord, where they unloaded the gear at the edge of the ice and transported it to the trading post of Uvkusigssat. Here they waited for the ice to break up, so that they could take their equipment further on by motorboat to the head of the fjord of Qaumarujuk. They had to wait for 38 days for the ice to break up, and then the great problem was how to get all the equipment from the coast up to Scheideck, which was to be the starting point for the journeys on to the ice sheet.

As on Koch and Wegener's expedition, it proved a great labour to get the gear up on to the ice. This time there were two buildings to be transported, and the propeller sledges could not be unpacked and used until they were on the ice sheet itself. The expedition had the help of 35 Greenlanders, and by stages all the gear was finally shifted to Scheideck. They transported it over the first part of the way by horse-drawn sledges, and it was necessary here to build a road through the ice, which involved using picks and shovels and dynamite, and they had also to construct bridges across the melt-water streams. However, time and time again a horse and its load would end up in the freezing water. On each stage of the journey fresh men and horses took over. The final steep part of the way up on to Scheideck itself was impassable for the horse-drawn sledges, and everything had to be hauled up by dogs. Everything was finally deposited at Scheideck, and the men set to work to construct the winter station.

Initially, the most important thing was to get the ice-cap station established. It was intended that four men should winter there, and it had been decided that 3½ tons of supplies would be sufficient. If all else failed, this could all be transported to the site on twenty dog-sledges. However, when it actually came to the point, it was found that the building and the fuel alone, apart from the scientific instruments and food supplies etc., weighed more than four tons. It had been hoped

Glaciers, with crevasses, lateral and terminal moraines and fronts furrowed by melt water, descending from the mountains of east Greenland.

For long stretches in north Greenland the ice front is a vertical ice cliff which forbids access to the ice sheet.

Terminal moraines in front of the glacier. A local glacier in Peary Land.

An American drilling attempt on the ice sheet.

The ice front descends from the 65-mile wide Humboldt Gletscher into Nares Sundet, where icebergs calve. The icebergs in the foreground are approximately 2–3 miles long.

The French station, Station Dumont, was established by parachute.

The first Danish winter station and the first station actually on the ice sheet.

Station Centrale with ventilation tower and meteorological mast protruding above the snow — the rest of the station lies below the surface.

The International Glaciological Expedition's winter station, Station Jarl-Joset, was a plastic house buried in the snow.

Station Eismitte with the weather station and in the background the snow tower from which weather balloons were sent up to record temperature and wind in the upper atmosphere.

Station Eismitte at the end of the wintering.

The British station Northice and the crashed Hastings.

The first american station on the ice sheet Site II was built in large corrugated tubes.

that most of the equipment could be transported on the two propeller sledges that Wegener had obtained in Finland, where the type had been very successfully used for travelling on the sea ice of the archipelago, but in Greenland they proved less useful. They were heavy, and on several places on the route up to Scheideck they had to be hauled up with tackle, and getting them transported to Scheideck was the work of six weeks. It was therefore late in the summer by the time they could be assembled and tried out. It was soon found that the engines were not powerful enough to cope with the steep gradients on the ice, and these propeller sledges were not, therefore, as useful as had been hoped. However, a depot of more than $1\frac{1}{2}$ tons was successfully set up some 120 miles in on the ice. On one of the trips two Danes, Peter Freuchen and an archaeologist, Dr Helge Larsen, were guests.

On 15 July the first dog-sledges started out on to the ice and headed for the site for the winter station. This was to be in the centre of the ice, and was therefore named Eismitte. The first trip was made by Georgi, Loewe, the physicist Karl Weiken, and several Greenlanders, with a total of twelve sledges each carrying 6 cwt. About 120 miles in on the ice most of the supporting sledges returned to base, and Georgi, Weiken, and four Greenlanders continued on to the site for the station on the ice. Fifteen days after they had left Scheideck they arrived at the site, and then Loewe, Weiken, and the Greenlanders returned, while Georgi started to establish the station and commenced the meteorological observations. The site was at Lat. 71° 11' W and Long. 39° 56' N. Most previous expeditions had had good weather in the interior of Greenland, but this was certainly not the case where Georgi was. The weather was a great hindrance to Georgi's work and to the transport of supplies, but nevertheless some sledge loads did succeed in getting through. On his first journey in across the ice, Georgi had marked the route by placing flags every five hundred metres, and every five kilometres he had built a cairn of snow. On 18 August Loewe again arrived at the station with five Greenlanders and one ton of equipment, and then the following day he returned to the coast and Georgi was left alone once more. On 13 September a third sledge party, consisting of Sorge, two Germans, and seven Greenlanders, arrived with a total load of $1\frac{1}{2}$ tons, mainly of food supplies and equipment for the station. They had not yet begun to bring the material for building the house itself, nor the radio equipment, and they had exceedingly little paraffin.

Wegener had planned to bring in the supplies by making three trips by dog-sledge, and two with his propeller sledges, but it had now become clear that it was going to be difficult to get all the supplies delivered in time. Sorge now remained at the station on the ice, while the other two Germans returned to the base with the Greenlanders. Some excavations in the firn showed that it was possible to winter there without any building, but even so they lacked paraffin and scientific equipment, including explosive for the seismic measurements of the thickness of the ice that Sorge had planned. Nor had they a radio, so they were out of touch with the outside world. In spite of this, Sorge and Georgi went ahead with excavating passages and a cave in the firn where they could spend the winter if necessary, and they also dug out a chamber for a glaciological laboratory and built a tower of snow blocks in readiness for the balloons they were planning to send up for making meteorological observations.

Winter was approaching, and on 30 July the midnight sun was past. On 5 October the temperature dropped to —40° (—40° F) and on 10 October to —50° (—58° F). If new supplies had not arrived by 20 October, Georgi and Sorge were to leave the station on the ice and return to the coast with man-hauled sledges. An examination of the chamber they had excavated showed, however, that the firn was excellent building material, so that they should be able to get through the winter by rationing themselves to 1¼ litres of paraffin daily. Wintering in this way would be tough, and it would mean that they could not carry out the scientific programme that they had planned, although some things would still be possible, such as taking meteorological measurements and carrying out some of the glaciological research, especially of the stratigraphy of the snow.

Wegener had spent the whole summer directing the work of erecting the coastal station. It had long been plain that it would not be possible to transport the materials for building the winter station on the ice to the site. On 4 September Wegener began to prepare for a journey inland to visit Georgi and Sorge; he planned to take fifteen sledges carrying sufficient supplies to ensure that they would have enough to carry them through the winter. It was difficult at that time to get hold of sufficient sledges and fresh dogs, so he decided to travel in himself to discuss the whole question of spending the winter there with the two men on the spot. It was autumn when he together with Loewe set out from the coastal station on 21 September, and it soon proved to be difficult for the large number of sledges to keep together, and progress was slow as they lost so much time waiting for the laggards.

By 23 September they had covered only 25 miles, but by then they were through the worst of the crevasse zone. The following morning they met one of the propeller sledges, and the crew told them that the other propeller sledge had had to be abandoned some way in on the ice sheet, and that they could not reckon on making any more trips across the ice that autumn. It was plain that the original plans could not be carried out. It was now more important than ever for Wegener himself to talk things over with the men at the winter station, and to cover the distance more quickly, they left 16 cwt of supplies in a depot on the ice.

The next day a blizzard set in and the temperature dropped considerably. The Greenlanders decided that they could not continue as they were not equipped for winter travel on the ice sheet, and they informed Wegener that they wanted to return. He managed, however, to find four who, if well paid, were willing to accompany him some way further. On 29 September the party split up: only six sledges with 69 dogs and two tons of supplies continued eastwards, the rest returned. It was difficult going across the soft new snow, and their progress was so slow that it soon became obvious that they had insufficient food supplies for even themselves and the dogs if all six sledges were to get to the station. The Greenlanders had lost heart, and 150 km (90 miles) in on the ice they announced that they would go no further and wanted to return. However, Loewe managed to persuade one of them, Rasmus Villumsen from Uvkusigssat, to continue, but the others turned back.

The three men then proceeded slowly, and the temperature dropped lower and lower, eventually dropping to —40° (—40° F) even during the day, and the amount of daylight became less and less with each day. Then the temperature dropped even further, to —50° (—58° F), and Loewe found that he had frostbite in both feet. Their daily marches were down to nine miles. It was already past the time that the two men should have left the station to return to the coast, if they had not received sufficient food supplies, and they were still discussing whether they would meet Sorge and Georgi on their way to the coast. The Greenlander, Rasmus, had again completely lost heart, but he did not dare to travel back alone. On 28 October they used up the last portion of dog food, and they did not reach Eismitte until 30 October, by which time the last of the paraffin had also been used.

Loewe's frostbite was now so serious that he could not possibly make the journey back to the coast, but Wegener, in spite of the long and arduous journey he had just made across the ice, felt fit and was in good shape; he was then fifty years old. With careful rationing, there would be sufficient supplies for three men to spend the winter there, but not enough for five; there would only be enough paraffin for cooking and lighting, but not for heating or any other purpose. Loewe's frostbite made it impossible for him to make the return journey, and Wegener offered to spend the winter alone on the ice with Loewe, but both Georgi and Sorge insisted on remaining at the station to carry out their research. It was therefore finally agreed that they should remain with Loewe. Wegener and Rasmus had therefore to return to the coast. They took with them what supplies could be spared from Eismitte (altogether 135 kg (2 cwt 80 lb) of food and 40 litres [8 gal. 6 points] of paraffin). They set out the very next day with two sledges and seventeen dogs. The wind would be behind them this time, and Wegener reckoned on gradually slaughtering the dogs and abandoning one of the sledges, and possibly covering the last part of the way on skis.

After Wegener had left, Georgi had to amputate most of the toes on Loewe's right foot with a pair of pincers, and a few days later he had to do the same to the left foot. Loewe had to lie up for the whole winter and was unable to take any part in the work of the station.

Wegener and Rasmus never reached the coastal station. When they did not appear at the west station, it was hoped there that they had remained at Eismitte. During the spring, the two propeller sledges were repaired and improved, and on 1 May they set out for Eismitte together with a dog-sledge group. The propeller sledge was the first to reach the winter station and when they saw only two men standing in the snow in front of the station, it was clear that something was wrong. On their way in from the coast the dog driver had noticed an abandoned case of pemmican about 285 km (177 miles) from the edge of the ice, at 255 km (158 miles) they had seen Wegener's sledge in the snow, and at 189 km (118 miles) a pair of skis and a broken ski-stick were stuck up in the snow. They therefore immediately set off back again, and on this trip the propeller sledge worked so well that the whole trip back was completed in only 34 hours, of which only 16 hours was spent in actually travelling.

They stopped where the skis were, and when they dug down there they found the body of Wegener sewn into two sleeping bag covers. He was fully clothed with kamiks, dog-skin breeches, a sweater and windjacket; only his gloves were missing. His clothes were in order and with no drift snow. In his pockets were his personal possessions, but not his diary. There was no sign of frost-bite, and he had presumably died in his tent of a heart-attack. Rasmus had buried him with great care and had marked his grave with the ski-stick before continuing alone to the coast. They were able to trace his camping sites for a short distance, but soon they petered out, and after 170 km (106 miles) the depots were untouched, so that Rasmus had either succumbed to the cold and his body lay in a snowdrift, or, what was more likely, he had lost his bearings and perished in a crevasse. They placed a primitive cross on the grave and then continued their journey to the coast. The work at the winter station had gone off according to plan; the meteorological measurements had been made, and Sorge had dug a 15 m (50 ft) shaft in the snow for his stratigraphic studies. In this shaft he found that it was possible to differentiate between the layers of snow that had fallen in various years, for the hard, densely packed layers were formed of winter snow, while the layers that had fallen in summer were of looser snow with larger snow grains. Working on this principle, he was able to identify the snow accumulation for the past twenty years — back to the year 1911 at the bottom of his 50 ft shaft.

The propeller sledges were used on the ice sheet in the summer of 1931, and this time with much greater success. Thus on the next journey on the ice sheet they drove from the depot that was situated 100 km (60 miles) in on the ice to the station at Eismitte — a total distance of 300 km

(190 miles) — in fifteen hours and forty minutes. The chief advantage of propeller sledges was not only that they were faster under normal conditions, but also that they consumed no fuel except when actually running. Dog teams could only take scientific parties to the scene of their observations and leave them there until a second dog sledge was sent out to fetch them back. The dogs needed too much food for it to be possible for them to remain with the scientific parties. They brought with them a radio transmitter and explosive for Sorge's seismological investigations. Georgi continued his meteorological observations and also made a number of balloon ascents to study the conditions in the layers of air at higher altitudes. The thickness of the ice beneath the station determined as being 2500—2700 m (8,200—8,500 ft), and B. Brockamp, a German seismologist, made a number af measurements of the thickness of the ice in the marginal zone. When the measurements from the various sites of investigation were collected and compared, they seemed to indicate that Greenland should be regarded as a gigantic bowl filled with ice.

Wegener's brother, Professor Kurt Wegener, had been sent up from Germany to wind up the expedition and bring back the results, and he was accompanied by a number of scientists. Throughout the summer there was great activity; they made a levelling from the coast to the winter station, and made various gravity measurements, etc. Towards autumn the expedition returned to Germany. There had been sacrifices, but this expedition had produced more scientific results than most expeditions to the Greenland ice. Modern geophysical research had begun.

Watkins's First Expedition to Greenland

While Wegener's expedition to central Greenland was operating, there was also a British expedition at work on the ice sheet. Its official name was the British Arctic Air Route Expedition, and it was led by H. G. Watkins. The plan was similar to Wegener's: that meteorological measurements should be taken in central Greenland throughout one whole year, but the British winter station was to be set up further south, and their main base would be in the Angmagssalik district. Whereas the German expedition had been particularly concerned with detailed geophysical research, the British programme covered a wider field, and was especially concerned with exploring. They also had aeroplanes with them in order to gain experience of flying under Arctic conditions. The German expedition was led by a man of fifty with scientific achievement and a long experience of Arctic exploration behind him, whereas the British expedition was led by quite a young man, Gino Watkins, who was however a man of considerable charm and originality, and with great ability as a leader. In spite of his age, he had considerable Arctic experience. In 1927, at the age of 19, he had been the leader of a Cambridge expedition to Spitsbergen, and in 1928 —29 he had led an expedition to Labrador to survey the area around Hamilton River, and here he had learnt how to drive a dog-sledge. Only two of the thirteen other members of the expedition had previous Arctic experience, namely J. M. Scott, who had worked with Watkins in Labrador, and A. Courtauld, who had taken part in two of J. M. Wordie's expeditions to east Greenland. The rest of the group were also young, most of them with military training, but they were all highly enthusiastic about the task before them.

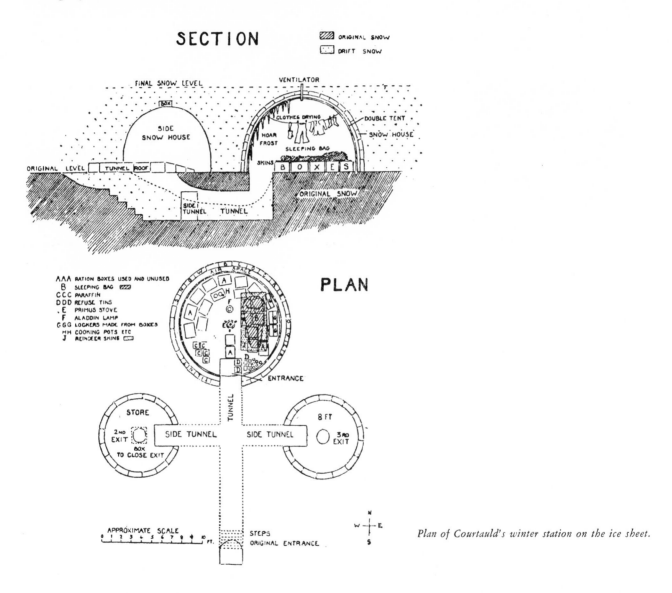

Plan of Courtauld's winter station on the ice sheet.

Watkins was supported by The Royal Geographical Society, The British Admirality, and the British Air Ministry, but as was usual with British expeditions, most of the funds came from private sources — much of it from Courtauld's well-to-do family.

102

Signals being made in the fog to guide an aircraft in so that supplies may be dropped.

They planned to make regular meteorological measurements at the main base in the Angmags-salik district, and to set up a winter station on the ice sheet at the highest point on the route across to the west coast; they also hoped to survey the lofty mountainous country of east Greenland and to make long journeys on the ice sheet in order to determine the distribution of elevation.

The expedition had with them two De Havilland Gipsy Moths for aerial photography, and they left London on board Shackleton's old ship, the Norwegian sealer *Quest,* for the Faroes, where they picked up 50 dogs from Ejnar Mikkelsen's whale station and then sailed to east Greenland. Here they turned north once more and at the end of July they were able to unload their equipment at Sermilik Fjord not far from where de Quervain had made his way down from the ice sheet in 1912. By the beginning of August they had finished constructing the base station and their work could begin.

An air route between London and America via the Faroes, Iceland, and Greenland, would have to cross Greenland by a route over Angmagssalik and then across the ice sheet to west Greenland, then on over Baffin Island and Fort Churchill to Winnipeg. It is almost this route that is now flown by Scandinavian Airlines System. It was therefore important to have exact information about the distribution of elevation along the route, so the winter station was to be sited at the highest point on this route, i. e. about Lat. 67° N and Long. 42° W. The ice cap station was to be erected with material brought on dog-sledges, but it was hoped that later it would be possible to use aeroplanes that would either land on the ice or drop down supplies. The station on the ice sheet would be isolated throughout the winter, but it was planned to keep in contact by radio.

On 11 August Scott and four others started out on to the ice sheet to set up the station. Unlike Wegener, they did not get help from the Greenlanders. Scott was the only member of this first party on the ice sheet to have driven a dog team before but he was used to the Canadian method in which the dogs follow one another in line, whereas the Greenlanders drive their dogs in a fan-shaped formation with the dogs alongside one another, and the dogs that had been obtained for this expedition had been trained for this method. The ascent up from Sermilik Fjord was extremely steep, and the surface of the ice was hard and slippery, so that they only succeeded in getting up by using crampons.

The ice above the ascent route was heavily crevassed, and the dangerous stretches had to be marked off with flags for the sake of subsequent parties, so that the rate of advance was slow. During the first week of travel they covered only fourteen miles over the ice sheet, and at this distance they established the main depot for future journeys. The whole route to the site of the winter station was marked out with flags as Wegener had done. Once they arrived on the even plain of the white ice cap and were past the crevasse zone, they covered the rest of the route fairly quickly, and on 27 August they had reached the highest point of the route. Here they set up the winter station, which consisted of a large dome-shaped tent with double walls. The entrance to the tent was through a tunnel dug down into the snow and coming up inside the tent. The tent had a ventilation shaft on top. Two men, Q. Riley and M. Lindsay, now remained at the station while the others returned.

As soon as they were alone, they set to work to improve the station and to make meteorological observations. The radio had not been brought on the first trip, and they were, therefore, cut off from the outside world. To protect the tent they threw up a bank of snow around it, and set out lines of flag from the tent so that it would be easier to find again. The temperature fell to —40° (—40° F) although it was only September, and they decided to build a proper snow house and to use the tent only as an inner lining for this.

By 3 September the first ice cap party had returned from the ice sheet to the coast, and on 21

104

An outlet-glacier from the ice sheet descending and calving in the sea. A number of smaller ice-bergs can be seen by the ice front.

September two others, J. Rymill and F. S. Chapman, started out with a fresh load of supplies for the winter station. At the same time Watkins and Scott had entered the ice sheet to reach the highest point on Nansen's route and then ascertain the distribution of altitude from there to Angmagssalik. The heavily-laden sledges were hauled up onto the ice sheet with blocks and tackle and as Watkins later changed his plans, the two parties joined up on the ice and travelled together to the winter station, which they reached on 2 October, when they relieved the two men there.

Scott and Watkins continued south, but it was already autumn and the going was hard, and the dogs, which had been working the whole autumn with untrained drivers, were worn out, so they were therefore obliged to turn back. On these two trips to the station enough supplies had been brought for two men for about a month, but not enough for the whole winter. On 26 October a third party started off inland with six sledges and forty dogs, and once again there was only one member of it that had driven a team of dogs before. It was so late in the year that there was very little daylight and the temperature was getting lower and lower. They had a load of two tons, of which about 13 cwt was just food for the dogs on the journey, and one of the sledges was completely taken up with radio equipment. All the sledges were heavily loaded, and it was not until 3 December, after six weeks' strenuous travelling, and almost four weeks later than had been reckoned on, that they arrived. By that time, however, they had abandoned the radio equipment and much of the other supplies, and the food for the dogs had almost run out.

The idea of wintering at the station would have to be abandoned unless one man was to spend the winter there alone. It had been one of the main objects of this expedition to set up this station, and Courtauld insisted on wintering there alone until his companions could come in from the coast and relieve him in the spring. The others were against it, but finally gave in and returned to the coast. When they set out on the return trip on 6 December they had only dog food for eight days at half rations and exceedingly little paraffin.

Courtauld remained behind. The weather was still bad; the snow was soft and deep; and the daylight only permitted them to make short daily journeys; but the wind was behind them. Their progress was slow, and on 14 December their paraffin ran out, and it was not until 19 December that they reached Bearbug Gletscher, which is the descent route to Sermilik Fjord, and here they met Watkins and a Greenlander who had come out to look for them.

The aeroplanes, of which they had great hopes, had not been of much use. They could only take off from the ice on the fjord, but for the whole of the autumn this ice had been too thin to bear them, and it was not until the very day that the last sledge party arrived back again that they succeeded in getting one of the planes off the ground, but the next day a gale broke up the ice on the fjord again.

The winter ran its course both at the station at the coast and the station on the ice sheet. Courtauld had six cases of provisions and 26 gallons of paraffin as well as two bottles of concentrated lemon juice and a bottle of cod liver oil. Each case of provisions was designed for one man for a fortnight, but it could easily be eked out to last for 24 days. At Christmas he discovered that 4 gallons of paraffin had leaked out through a hole in the container so that there was only enough paraffin left for cooking and none for heating the snow house. At first Courtauld took the meteorological measurements six times a day, but each time he had to clear the passage leading out from the floor of the tent to the outside, and as he could only dig himself out from within, it was a time-consuming and exhausting job, and the snow became packed harder and harder. By 4 January the passage was so drifted up that he could no longer use it. Before this, however, he had dug out a couple of side passages and some smaller store rooms.

106

Extensive moraines at the front and edges of outlet-glaciers that do not reach the sea.

The snow house was now completely covered by the winter snow, but that only made it warmer inside, and the ventilation shaft was still clear of the snow. After a snowstorm on 19 March the reserve exit was also snowed up so much that it was no longer possible for Courtauld to come out and make observations. He could now only lie in the house and wait until he was relieved. In the middle of April his paraffin ran out and he lay in the dark.

It had been difficult enough even on the last journey made the previous autumn to find the marker flags that had been placed by the tent, and it was clear that the relief party in the spring would have great difficulty in finding the station. On 1 March Riley and Scott started inland to relieve Courtauld. It was still very wintry and they ran into difficult weather. On 26 March they arrived in the vicinity of the station, but were unable to find it. Most of the time the weather was so bad they were not even able to make a search for it. So as not to tire the dogs and thus hinder a new attempt when the weather and the daylight were better, they abandoned any further search and returned to the coast. They arrived back at the camp at the coast on 18 April after the coldest journey that had ever been made across the ice sheet.

On 25 March Watkins had attempted to fly in to look for Scott but engine failure forced him to turn back. Nor was there much chance of finding the station from the air, if Scott was unable to find it in his search on the surface. On 21 April Watkins set out on a new expedition with Rymill and Chapman. They arrived in the neighbourhood of the station on 5 May, and after searching for a long time they found one of the flags that had been set out near the station; it had been torn to shreds in the severe weather.

Some time after that they spotted the ventilation shaft, but the surface of the snow was undisturbed and there was no sign of life. But when Watkins shouted down the shaft he heard an answering voice, and soon Courtauld was dug out. He looked like an apostle at Ober-Ammergau with his long black beard and hair after his long, solitary winter sojourn. The minimum thermometer showed an absolute minimum of —53° (—63.4° F), which was not as low as expected. The relief party had brought no fresh supplies with them as they had wanted to travel as light as possible. The station was therefore abandoned.

On the journey back to the coast they were met by a low-flying Junkers aircraft flown by Ahrenberg, a Swedish pilot, who had been sent out by Courtauld's family to help in the search.

After the station on the ice sheet had been evacuated, they began to carry out their plans for making journeys on the ice sheet and for attempting to climb Mont Forel, which had been previously estimated by de Quervain as being 3,200 m (10,500 ft) high. Some years previously James Wordie, a British geographer, when on an expedition from Cambridge, had climbed Petermann Bjerg, which lay further to the north and which at 2,970 m (9,750 ft) was the highest point that had been reached in the Arctic. Watkins's expedition were keen to beat this record.

All attempts to climb Mont Forel from the coast had failed, and they wanted to try to climb it from the ice sheet. On 22 May a party arrived at Mont Forel and began to search for a route up the mountain. They came to within 100 m (330 ft) of the summit, but the last piece of the way over a hard and absolutely slippery snowdrift, which could only be negotiated if they carved steps in it. The weather was bad and they were exhausted, so they did not attempt the final ascent, but they had already beaten Wordie's record.

They also had plans to map the elevation of the ice sheet by making two journeys across it. One party was to cross to Ivigtut and the other was to travel westwards to the head of Søndre Strømfjord and from there sail by kayak to Holsteinsborg.

The journey to Ivigtut was made by Scott, Lindsay, and Stephenson; they started out on 1 July

108

and the going was good right from the first. They passed the highest point of the route as early as on 20 July, and then they had the wind behind them so they could "sail" on the sledges. The wind was not strong enough for them to get up any real speed, but the sails on the sledges were a great help to the dogs. On 25 July they got their first sight of the nunataks on the west coast, and three days later they were able to begin the descent from the ice via the steep and heavily crevassed glacier called Arsuk Bræ. They then had to shoot all the dogs except one or two, as they did not dare to risk bringing the dog teams down to the colony because of the sheep in the area.

The longer, northerly route was taken by two men, Rymill and Hampton. They did not leave until 13 August as they had to wait for fresh supplies and new sledges to arrive from home. By this time it was late in the summer and the snow had already melted so much that the area at the edge of the ice sheet was almost impassable, and they had to make repeated detours to avoid crevasses. The sledges were heavily loaded, as well as food supplies and normal equipment they took with them two kayaks that were to be used on Søndre Strømfjord. When they finally got up on to the ice sheet the going was considerably easier, and the journey went off according to plan until, on 4 September, they caught a glimpse of the land behind Søndre Strømfjord.

The marginal area here is heavily crevassed, and it was hard work to bring the sledges as far forward as possible. Doing this occupied most of September; they reached the last nunatak on 24 September and then they had to abandon the sledges and carry the kayaks. The dogs, which were no longer of any service and for which they had no provisions, had to be shot, and on 15 October the two men with their kayaks reached the coast about where the present airfield is situated. Here they saw a fishing cutter lying out in the fjord and they attracted its attention with shots.

When they came on board they discovered that it was, in fact, waiting for them, for as they should have been in Holsteinsborg a month before, a search boat had been sent out. They arrived in Holsteinsborg on 19 October, but not by kayak, in a motor boat instead.

In the meantime Watkins and two others had been sailing to Prins Christians Sund and on to Nanortalik by open boat to take measurements for their surveying work. In the autumn of 1931 the work of the expedition was completed, and the whole party returned home.

On the whole the expedition had proceeded according to plan. They had carried out a considerable amount of surveying, and they had gained considerable experience of flying in the Arctic. In all they had made 74 journeys, and on some of these they had made flights of various distances by plane. They had originally planned to make a winter flight across the ice sheet from Angmagssalik to Godhavn on Disko and then on to Winnipeg, but this had to be abandoned when one of the planes was damaged in a gale and the other was damaged while landing on the uneven fjord ice. They had, however, managed to winter on the ice sheet, but the meteorological data they had gathered was very limited, and could not be compared, for instance, with what the German expedition under Wegener had achieved.

Watkins's Last Expedition to Greenland.

Even while he was still in Greenland Watkins was making plans — either to cross Antarctica from Weddell Sea to Ross Sea, or to make a three-year expedition with Rymill and Chapman across Bering Strait and along the north coast of Siberia to Franz Josef Land and from there to Spitsbergen. But he did not succeed in raising money for these rather daring enterprises, and instead Watkins was offered a smaller sum of money by Pan American Airways if he would continue his investigations in east Greenland. 1932 was the Second International Polar Year, and it was important that as many meteorological observations as possible should be made in the Arctic. Watkins was planning a four-man expedition to east Greenland and recieved a further £200 from the Royal Geographical Society and a smaller sum from *The Times* for the press rights, but this was far from sufficient for getting four men to east Greenland.

The plan was that he, Riley, Rymill, and Chapman should spend the winter in Greenland making meteorological observations and continuing their surveying work. In the spring Watkins alone would sledge across the ice sheet to Godthåb and send the results of the expedition to the Americans from there. They came to the fjord of Tugtolik on board the Greenland ship *Gertrud Rask,* and they had planned to spend the winter there. As their financial resources were very slender, they were to live Eskimo-style by hunting and fishing. As soon as they landed Watkins began to hunt for seals by kayak. He mastered the art of controlling this slim craft, and had brought with him a kayak of the Angmagssalik type.

However, on a trip by kayak on 20 August Watkins was drowned. In the afternoon of that day his kayak was found drifting; his rifle was missing, but everything else including his harpoon was there and his paddle was drifting not far off. Later his trousers and kayak belt were found on an ice floe, so he had presumably climbed onto the ice floe in search of seals, his kayak had then drifted away from him and he had undressed to swim after it but had sunk in the icy water. It was decided that the expedition should continue nevertheless, and Rymill now became its leader. They intended to carry out their programme as well as they could, although the journey across the ice sheet was abandoned.

In the spring of 1933 they made long sledge journeys to continue their survey, and during these trips they also came up on to the ice sheet. They attempted to come from Kangerdlugssuatsiaq up on to the ice near Mont Forel so that they could climb it, but the glacier inland of the fjord was

110

The vertical ice front of a north Greenland glacier. Melt water pours from tunnels in the front.

so crevassed that they had to give up. In the autumn of 1933 the expedition returned to England. The inspiring leadership of Watkins had initiated a number of British expeditions to Greenland and other Arctic areas, and some of them travelled on the ice sheet. Thus, in 1934 Martin Lindsay was once more in Greenland. On Watkins's expedition he had caught a glimpse of the unknown land between Scoresby Sund and Mont Forel. As it was almost impossible to reach it from the east coast, he decided to get to it from west Greenland by crossing the ice sheet. The expedition of 1934 consisted of three men, one of whom, Andrew Croft, had already been in Greenland in 1933 to reconnoitre in preparation for the final expedition. With the help of Greenlanders from Atâ and nearby settlements he succeeded in shifting the expedition's one and a half tons of equipment on to the ice sheet in the spring, using very much the same route onto the ice as de Quervain had used. Thus when the others arrived in Greenland everything was ready for them to start out on their journey on 3 June. But the snow began to melt strongly as early as 5 June, and

111

the surface of the snow was transformed into a bottomless slush, through which deep melt-water streams carved their way. The first part of the route up onto the ice sheet was very steep, and the heavy sledge-loads could only be managed half at a time, and then they returned for the rest.

Even on the ice sheet itself conditions were difficult. They started out with 42 dogs but five were lost in crevasses in the marginal area, and by the time they had got half way across the ice sheet on 28 June the dogs were worn out and three of them had to be shot. It was not until 20 July that they were far enough on to see one of the nunataks to the south of Scoresby Sund. They now had a view across to the lofty peaks that had first been sighted by Watkins on a flight in 1931, and they started to survey the area around the upper part of Christian IV's Gletscher. For almost four weeks they now followed the margin of the ice to the south, surveying the area as well as they could with the primitive geodetic equipment that they had. The weather was still bad and on two occasions they had to lie up for three days because of blizzards. Near Kangerdlugssuaq they came upon huge crevasse systems, and they finished their survey at Mont Forel which had previously been measured by Watkins's expedition. Absolutely exhausted they reached the descent route into Sermilik Fjord that Lindsay had used during his first stay there, but by that time they had only enough food supplies for three days for themselves and for two days for the dogs. They had travelled 1,657 km (1,034 miles) across the ice sheet and they had been travelling by sledge for 103 days, which is the longest dog-sledge journey that has ever been made in the Arctic without supply depots being set up beforehand. A Greenlander guided them across the fjord to Watkins's station and later to Angmagssalik itself.

Among the most important results of the expedition may be mentioned the carefully kept log of meteorological observations, and confirmation that the greatest altitude on the ice cap was at least 3,000 m (10,000 ft).

American Expeditions to Søndre Strømfjord.

Whereas the British and German expeditions that were investigating the possibilities of an air route had been particularly concerned with making meteorological observations in central Greenland and had, at great cost, succeeded in wintering on the ice sheet, the American investigations had been concentrated on the meteorological conditions of the marginal area.

As early as 1910 William Herbert Hobbs, an American Arctic explorer, had propounded a theory that there was a glacial anticyclone over the ice cap, and this theory was an important factor when weather conditions over the ice cap were discussed (see page 215).

In 1926 Hobbs himself came to Greenland as the leader of an expedition sent out by the University of Michigan to study wind conditions along the margin of the ice sheet. The expedition con-

Melt-water stream on the surface of a minor ice cap in northern Greenland.

sisted of six men, who arrived at Holsteinsborg on board Captain Bartlett's schooner *Morrissey* and from there struck off inland to Maligiaq where they set up camp. Here they were able to send up pilot balloons to study the air currents in the upper layers of air, and they also experimented with sending up a meteorograph in a balloon and succeeded in registering up to an altitude of 5,300 m (17,380 ft). These were the first measurements that had been made in the upper air in Greenland apart from those made with kites and balloons by A. Wegener on the *Danmark* expedition in 1907—09. Meanwhile the schooner had sailed north to Thule, where Knud Rasmussen had chartered it to take a load of skins to U. S. A., on board it was another expedition from America under the leadership of George Putnam which was making a zoological collection for the American Museum of Natural History.

Hobbs continued his investigations in 1927, but this time chose to work at the head of Søndre

113

Strømfjord, where he set up Camp Lloyd, named after the late president of the University of Michigan. From the summit of nearby Mount Evans they had a clear view across to the ice sheet and it was here that they set up the meteorological station and made the balloon ascents. The station was also to function in the winter, and the meteorologists who had spent the winter there were to be relieved the following spring.

The routine experiments were thus continued on an all-the-year-round basis, and towards spring they began to lay out depots in readiness for a journey inland across the ice sheet, for they planned to set up a camp on the ice sheet so that they could make meteorological observations and measurements of snow evaporation etc. there. So little snow had fallen in the area that it was difficult to take the sledges across the snow, but they did succeed in setting up a camp some way in on the ice and in making some measurements over a period of several months.

In March the expedition was again at Mount Evans. Helge Bangsted, a Danish photographer, had taken part in the journey across the ice, and it had originally been the intention that the Danish polar explorer Peter Freuchen should also have been in the party, but he had shortly before had to have his left foot amputated as a result of gangrene that had set in after frostbite on the Fifth Thule Expedition.

Hobbs returned in the summer of 1928 to relieve the wintering party. On this journey he collaborated with the Swedish-American aviator Bert Hassell, who had been planning to fly in one hop from Rockford to Stockholm, a distance of 4,500 miles. When Hobbs contacted him he changed his plans so as to touch down at Camp Lloyd, where it was possible to land on the delta sand flats at the mouth of the river in the fjord. Hobbs was to transport the necessary aviation fuel and spare parts to Greenland, and in return for this the aeroplane was to be fitted with self-recording meteorological instruments to register air-pressure, temperature, and humidity during the flight across the ice sheet.

Hassel set out from U. S. A. on 24 July, but he had bad luck right from the start and his plane was damaged on take-off, although no harm came to Hassel himself or his mechanic Parker D. Cramer. They tried again on 14 August, and by 18 August they were taking off from Cochrane in Ontario and heading for Greenland. On the morning of 19 August at about 10.30 a. m. the plane was seen above Fiskenæsset in Greenland, but afterwards it disappeared, and the party at Camp Lloyd waited in vain. It was evident that there had been an accident, and Knud Rasmussen, who was at Holsteinsborg in his ship *Søkongen,* started a search. They searched out from Camp Lloyd along the margin of the ice sheet, but without success.

On 2 September, when hope had long been abandoned, and the camp was being packed up and the last supplies were being taken to Mount Evans, some Greenlanders, who were out hunting

Dirt cones along the edge of the ice near a nunatak.

reindeer at the head of Søndre Strømfjord, saw smoke signals on the other side of the fjord. As they could not sail across the fjord in their umiak, they instead sailed to Camp Lloyd and reported what they had seen. A motor boat was sent across the fjord, and there the two missing aviators were found. On the flight to Søndre Strømfjord Hassell had lost his way and had come too far to the south; after getting a sight of land at Fiskenæsset they had followed the edge of the ice to the north, but shortly before Søndre Strømfjord they had run out of fuel and had had to make an emergency landing on the ice. They had made a smooth landing, and they had been able to step straight out of the plane and make for the coast .They had taken a fortnight to reach the coast, where they had lit a bonfire to keep warm. They were starving, for the only things they had shot on the way were a couple of ptarmigans and they had brought very little food with them.

The second wintering at Mount Evans went off as planned, and the work was completed during

115

the summer of 1929. By that time the station had been in continual operation for two years. During this time 776 pilot balloons had been sent up and a great quantity of data had been gathered which threw light on the weather conditions along the periphery of the ice sheet.

The fourth University of Michigan Expedition was sent out in 1930—31, but this time to the Upernavik area, where they spent the winter and made measurements at Natsiarsiorfik at the head of Upernavik Isfjord. The leader of the expedition in Greenland was William S. Carlsson, a meteorologist, and one of the members was the young glaciologist Max Demorest, who studied the margin of the ice and gathered material for his theory of the extrusion flow of the ice (see page 262).

During the Second International Polar Year of 1932—33 the University of Michigan and Pan American Airways sent out a joint expedition to the northern part of Upernavik district, where they set up a winter station, "Peary Lodge", to the north of Cornell Gletscher, and certain meteorological measurements were also made from the trading post of Kraulshavn. During 1933 they reconnoitred to find a route up on to the ice sheet and on 13 June three men, R. L. Belknap, who was the leader, Max Demorest, and Evans Schmeling, another American meteorologist, set out from the main station to set up a camp on the ice sheet at Lat. 74° 40' N. and 47° 29' W, that is to say it was situated some 170 miles in on the ice but to the west of the crest of the ice cap. The camp was called Camp Watkins in memory of the British expedition leader. They made meteorological measurements here from 2 July to 19 August, when they evacuated the station. They lived in a tent the whole time and made no attempt to establish anything more permanent.

When Belknap's expedition was completed in 1933 the American work on the ice sheet came to a temporary halt. The economic depression and the political tension in Europe during the thirties brought scientific research on the ice sheet to a general standstill.

Arne Høygaard and Martin Mehren, two Norwegian medical students, made a purely sporting expedition right across the ice cap in 1931. They came by ship from Copenhagen to Umanak, from where they travelled to Qaumarujuk, where Wegener's expedition was working at the time. With the help of Greenlanders and Wegener's party, they soon had their equipment brought up onto the ice: they had only two Nansen sledges and 12 cwt of gear. The sledge runners were covered with German silver, but otherwise all the equipment was of normal type. They had sixteen dogs when they began their journey on 10 July, and as they had to catch a ship back from the east coast that same summer because of their studies, time was short.

On 15 August they reached the east coast and made the descent from the ice via Waltershausen Gletscher which discharges into Nordfjord, one of the inner ramifications of Kejser Franz Josephs Fjord. From here they pushed on to a trapping station in time to catch the Norwegian ship

Polarbjørn which had been operating in east Greenland during the summer with one of Dr Adolf Hoel's expeditions on board.

A Franco-Danish Crossing of the Ice Sheet

There was, however, one more journey across the ice sheet during the thirties, even though it brought few scientific results. In 1936 the Expédition Française Transgroënland crossed the ice sheet from west to east with four men and three dog-sledges. The expedition was led by the Arctic explorer Paul-Émile Victor, and the others in the party were Robert Gessain, who was an anthropologist who had carried out ethnological research in Angmagssalik, the Swiss glaciologist Michel Perez, and the Danish Arctic explorer and artist Count Eigil Knuth. The three Frenchmen had spent the winter in the Angmagssalik area in 1934—35, and it was there that Knuth had met them while he was making a summer journey in 1935. He himself had plans for wintering in east Greenland to do some sculptures of Eskimoes, but Victor persuaded him to accompany him on a journey across the ice sheet that he had planned for the following summer. So in April 1936 Victor and Knuth were in Christianshåb to bring the supplies for the expedition up on to the ice cap.

With the help of the Greenlanders the three Nansen sledges and nearly 1½ tons of equipment — including a folding boat belonging to Perez who was planning to use it near Angmagssalik i. e. the boats were being carried in the opposite direction across the ice cap from the kayaks Rymill had taken — were brought up on the ice to the north of Nordenskiöld Gletscher, and in the middle of May the two other members of the expedition arrived.

On 23 May they were ready to start inland with three sledges and 32 dogs. They were planning to cross the ice to Mont Forel and to descend from the ice at Sermilik Fjord. By starting so early in the year they got through the marginal area before the thaw set in, but once they were in on the ice they met with bad weather, and conditions underfoot were difficult. They had sufficient supplies for seven weeks, but with the conditions they encountered it was necessary to shoot some of the dogs and to set a direct course for Sermilik Fjord so as to get across the ice as quickly as possible. On 6 July they had got as far as Watkins's old station. The hard going forced the four men to abandon everything that was not absolutely essential including the collapsible boat.

This French journey across the ice sheet, like several of the British expeditions, had something of the character of a sporting achievement, but for three of the four members it was to be an experience that was of great importance for their later activity. After the Second World War Paul-Émile Victor, the leader of the expedition, laid the foundation of modern French Arctic exploration, and Eigil Knuth continued his journeys in Greenland as the leader of the Danish

117

Mørkefjord Expeditions and, after the Second World War, he and Ebbe Munck were the joint leaders of the Danish Pearyland Expedition which made an important contribution to the exploration of the routes of Eskimo immigration in northern Greenland, and also made the first glaciological investigation of a true high Arctic glacier by studying Chr. Erichsen Iskappe in Heilprin Land. Perez, the glaciologist, subsequently worked with Victor on his first French expeditions to the ice sheet.

Flights over the Ice Sheet.

As we have already seen it had been Watkins's plan to make a flight right over the ice sheet, but this plan was not carried out because of trouble with the plane. In 1931 the German pilot commander von Gronau made a flight over the centre of the ice cap from Scoresby Sund to Sukkertoppen, a distance of 850 miles. The flight took eight to nine hours and was made in a Dornier Wal aircraft powered by two BMW engines each of 700 h. p. He came to Greenland via Iceland and landed in Scoresby Sund on a small ice-free space on the fjord. He took off from Scoresby Sund and after having some difficulty in reaching sufficient height to fly over the ice cap he set a course for Godthåb. Bad weather and low cloud prevented any upward view and on one occasion it was found that the radio aerial of the plane was dragging in the snow. When it was discovered that there was insufficient fuel to reach Godthåb, they were forced to land at Sukkertoppen and not until the next day could they continue the flight to Godthåb and from there on to Labrador after the plane had been subjected to thorough repair in Greenland.

Yet another flight over the ice sheet was made in 1934 by John Grierson, with his flight over the Arctic Air Route in a Fox Moth float seaplane. A previous attempt in 1933 had ended in failure at Reykjavík, but this time he did reach the coast of Greenland from Iceland but had to make a forced landing on an ice-free fjord near Angmagssalik and was not found until after a three day search. When the plane had been repaired he flew on to Angmagssalik itself and from there took off for the flight across the ice sheet to Godthåb. The actual 260 mile trip over the ice went off without incident and with good weather, and lasted only 5½ hours.

In addition to the numerous reconnaissance and surveying flights that were made across the edge of the ice cap during the Sixth and Seventh Thule Expeditions, during the Three-Year Expedition, and on Lauge Koch's other expeditions to north-east Greenland, a flight was also made across the ice sheet in 1933. It was made by the American pilot Charles Lindbergh and his wife in a small open seaplane, and his route was from America to Julianehåb and from there across the ice to Angmagssalik and on to Iceland and Europe. A number of German flights along the edge of the ice sheet in west Greenland were made in connexion with Universal, Dr Franck's

Greenland Expedition of 1932, during which a film was made and on which, too, Ernst Sorge had an opportunity to continue the research on glaciers that he had begun during Wegener's expedition.

Some Investigations outside the Ice Cap

Outside the area of the central ice sheet itself investigations were being made, particularly by Danish research workers, on the periphery of the ice and on local glaciers. Thanks to the good work done by the Danish Geodetic Institute there was gradually a good basis of maps, which are the first prerequisite for a really scientific exploration of glaciers. Besides these Danish research workers (of whom we may mention Lauge Koch, Sigurd Hansen, Keld Milthers, F. E. Froda, and A. Kiilerich) a considerable amount of surveying and investigation was done by non-Danes, particularly in the Sukkertoppen area and on Nordenskiöld Gletscher, where a Polish expedition under the leadership of A. Kosiba was at work, in Thule district, where a British expedition under John W. Wright and R. A. Hamilton surveyed Harald Moltke Bræ, and in east Greenland, where J. H. Bretz and Richard Foster Flint made studies of the glaciers in the area of Kejser Franz Josephs Fjord on the expeditions of Louise Boyd in 1933, 1937, and 1938, and where also various observations were made by the expeditions of James Wordie to east Greenland. Of greater scientific importance to the glaciology, however, was the research that was being done on the Sukkertoppen Iskappe and on Clavering Ø in east Greenland.

Sukkertoppen Iskappe forms an independent highland glacier outside the ice sheet, but the natural conditions are the same as inside the ice sheet. Its greatest altitude is 2,200 m (7,200 ft) and in the thirties a number of British undergraduates from Oxford worked there.

In 1935 a start was made on the work of surveying the then little known area to the south of Søndre Strømfjord around Sarfartoq, and in 1936 this work was continued by a new expedition under the leadership of P. G. Mott, who made a journey across Sukkertoppen Iskappe to Evighedsfjord, and another journey from Sarfartoq across to the western extremity of the great lake called Tasersiaq and from there back to the ice cap.

In 1938 another Oxford expedition was sent out under the leadership of J. G. S. Sugden and P. G. Mott, both of whom had responsibility for the geodetic work. The German geophysicist Erich Étienne, who had been on the 1936 expedition, was also on this expedition. The programme of work for this year was concentrated on actual glaciological investigation of the Sukkertoppen Iskappe and some of its outlet glaciers. They ascended on to the ice cap by way of Tâterât Gletscher, which flows down from the ice cap and discharges into the head of Evighedsfjord. In this area Mott made a photogrammetrical survey of the glacier and determined the velocity of the ice move-

119

ment. At the same time Étienne carried out a series of geophysical measurements in the firn zone of the ice cap, particularly concerning himself with the energy balance and material balance sheet of the ice.

In connexion with these investigations, radiation measurements were made and the stratification of the snow was studied in a five metre (16 ft) shaft dug in the firn, and calculations of ablation were made. In contrast to the way Sorge had interpreted the stratification of the snow at Eismitte, Étienne considered that the summer layers because of the thawing of the snow, would have a relatively high density, while the dry, light winter snow would form a layer of low density, and working on this assumption he reckoned that at the bottom of the shaft he had reached the snow that had fallen in the summer of 1930.

Later research has proved, however, that Étienne's reasoning was incorrect, and that the density is lower in the summer layers. In 1940 — during the Second World War — Étienne's results were published as a doctoral thesis at the Geophysical Institute in Leipzig. As a meteorologist with Arctic experience in Greenland, Étienne during the war was made head of a German weather station on Spitsbergen, from where weather reports were to be sent to the *Wehrmacht*. He spent the winter there and meteorological measurements were made both on the surface and with radiosondes, but Étienne was killed when flying in a German Junkers aircraft that was shot down by the British over Barentsburg in 1942.

The Swedish geographer, Professor Hans W:son Ahlmann had been making studies of the budgets of the Scandinavian and Arctic glaciers since 1918. In the years 1918—21 and 1922—26 he had particularly studied the Norwegian glaciers; in 1931 he had been working in Nordaustlandet, and in 1934 he had collaborated with H. U. Sverdrup on Spitsbergen, and 1936—38 with Jón Eythorsson on Vatnajökull in Iceland. To continue these investigations of his, Ahlmann sent an expedition to Clavering Ø in east Greenland in 1939, on which measurements were made of the 6.3 km² (2.4 sq. mile) Fröya Gletscher. Ahlmann himself was able to make only a summer visit to east Greenland, but Kåre Rodahl, a biochemist from Norway, who the same year was wintering at the nearby Norwegian trapping station of Revet to do research on vitamins in Arctic animals and plants, agreed to visit the glacier throughout the winter to measure the accumulation and ablation of snow. Thanks to Rodahl's co-operation very full data were obtained which threw light on the budget of an Arctic glacier, and although the Second World War prevented Rodahl from returning to Norway, he was able to telegraph his results to Stockholm.

The large-scale and long-term expeditions of the 1930s had given an overall picture of the surface topography of the ice sheet, and Wegener's expedition had also determined the thickness of the ice, so that with a fair degree of precision it could be calculated that the ice sheet in central Green-

120

land was resting on a substructure that was at approximately sea level. Comprehensive meteorological observations had been made, particularly at the edge of the ice sheet, but also at Eismitte in central Greenland. The investigations had shown that over the surface of the ice there was a continual katabatic outflow of cold air, and the pilot balloons that had been sent up seemed to show that this was still a factor up to an altitude of 2—3 km (1¼—2 miles), while at greater heights than this there was an inflow of air from the west. The measurements did not confirm Hobb's controversial theory about the glacial anticyclone over the ice sheet, but sufficient data had not been collected for the theory to be abandoned, and Hobbs himself continued to argue in favour of it. A number of investigations had determined the stratification of the snow and material budgets had been compiled for several glaciers outside the ice sheet as well for the ice sheet itself.

Research on the ice sheet came to a halt at the end of the 1930s. The strong interest that there had been in the ice sheet at the beginning of the decade was due to the desire there was to set up an air route between America and Europe, but development of larger and more powerful aircraft soon made it clear that in future interest would be centred on other air routes than those across out-of-the-way Greenland and Iceland. There were therefore no scientific expeditions working on the ice sheet at the close of the 1930s.

French and British Expeditions after 1940

Victor Introduces Modern Technology.

During the Second World War the Americans established a number of airfields in Greenland to safeguard the air routes across the North Atlantic. Flying across the ice cap was no longer a special achievement, but from time to time planes were lost over the ice. If possible, large-scale rescue expeditions were then sent out to bring the crews of the disabled aircraft back to the base. The weather observations that were made on these flights and at the bases were part of the material that was used in working out weather maps and weather forecasts for the pilots, and knowledge of the meteorological and climatic conditions over the ice sheet increased considerably, but no actual glaciological research was done.

Immediately after the war research on the ice sheet commenced once more, and this time France took the initiative. Back in 1936, when he had been making his journey across the ice sheet, Paul-Émile Victor had been toying with the idea of returning with a larger expedition. He had studied ethnology at the university, but had become fascinated by the expanse of unbroken whiteness that was the ice sheet. While the other members of the expedition were thrilled to see terra firma again after their long journey across the ice, Victor was yearning for the snow. But many years were to pass before he returned to Greenland.

On the outbreak of war Victor was attached to the French embassy in Stockholm, but after the fall of France in 1940 he came by a devious route to U. S. A., where he joined the American Air Force. During the war he served in Alaska and became the head of a group of the Air Force Rescue Operation. In this activity he became familiar with the various motor vehicles and sledges that the Americans used on the snow, and at the same time he made many journeys and became thoroughly proficient in flying under Arctic conditions.

The expeditions of the 1930s that had attempted to set up wintering stations on the Greenland ice sheet had discovered that the main obstacle lay in getting the equipment transported on the ice. Even when horses or dogs had been used it had still not been found possible to transport

123

much more than was consumed on the way. Wegener had tried to bring in larger quantities by using many sledges together, but he had found that so much time was wasted in waiting for one another and repairing equipment etc., that there was no real advantage in doing this. In the years before and after the Second World War the American Admiral Richard Byrd had had great success in Antarctica using modern technology to a greater extent than any other polar expedition had done. He had used aeroplanes and had flown over both the poles , and on these flights he had been able to discover new land and to reconnoitre over large areas.

His Antarctic station, Little America, was from a technical point of view better equipped than any other station, and he had in particular paid great attention to keeping in contact with the outside world with comprehensive radio equipment. Byrd had also been one of the first to use a primitive motor sledge with caterpillar tracks; he had made great use of it on the sea ice, but it had been wrecked on a tour up country.

During the Second World War the American army had experimented with various forms of motorised sledges on the ice, and in 1943 a vehicle named the Weasel was tried out in Canada. This was a small amphibious tank specially adapted for travelling on snow. On a search expedition in Greenland in 1943 it was used for the first time on the ice sheet. Since then it has been very much used on most polar expeditions.

Victor realised that further exploration of the ice sheet would have to be done with different and technically more up-to-date equipment than that used before. Wegener's expedition had certainly achieved important results both for glaciology and meteorology, but many of the observations were based on such slight data that it would still be necessary to spend one or more winters on the ice in central Greenland. Any new winter station would have to be equipped with radio and radiosonde equipment etc. This would mean that much larger quantities of equipment would have to be transported on to the ice than on any earlier expedition.

On the basis of his own experiences in Alaska and of his knowledge of the techniques used by Americans in setting up weather stations in the Antarctic during the war, Victor decided that the plans for a new expedition to Greenland would have to be based on a combination of motorised over-snow transport on the ground and aircraft, so that as much of the equipment as possible, the fuel and the food supplies could be brought in by plane and either dropped by parachute or freedropped into the snow. For the transportation over the snow Victor chose Weasels, partly because he had had good experience with them in Alaska, and partly because it was possible to obtain them at low cost from American surplus stocks. All groups would have to be equipped with powerful radio receivers so that they could keep in contact with the main base and with the aircraft.

The era had passed when one bade farewell to an expedition as it set out onto the ice and then just waited until it returned. Now, daily contact with the members of the expedition was necessary; constant weather reports would have to be transmitted to make the use of aircraft safe, and the time and place of parachute drops would have to be agreed upon.

It was therefore also quite clear that a modern expedition would be very expensive, and could only be carried out with official support. Victor managed to get this, and on 27 February 1947 he was officially appointed organizer and leader of French expeditions to the Arctic and Antarctica. He thus laid the foundation for the organization that is now called Expéditions Polaires Françaises, Missions Paul-Émile Victor. It had its own headquarters building in Paris. Each year since it has been working in either Greenland or the Antarctic, and most of the time in both.

Terre Adélie had been discovered in 1840 by Dumont d'Urville's expedition, and a number of French expeditions under the leadership of Dr Jean-Baptiste Charcot on board the research ship *Pourquoi Pas?* had made investigations there. During the Second International Polar Year he organized and established the French wintering station that was set up in Rosenvinge Bugt near Scoresby Sund from 1932 to 1933. Throughout one year observations of meteorology, the conductivity and ionisation of the atmosphere etc. were made here.

Victor came in contact with Dr Charcot and it was on board the *Pourquoi Pas?* that he paid his visit to Greenland to make ethnographical studies in Angmagssalik. On a voyage from Greenland to France in 1936 the *Pourquoi Pas?* was wrecked off Iceland and Dr Charcot and his crew drowned. After his death there had been no interest in France for continuing his research in the Arctic and Antarctica, but then Victor received support to continue French Polar research and thus took over where Charcot had left off.

Whereas earlier expeditions to the Arctic or the Antarctic had been sent out to solve particular problems, and their first task had been to get hold of the necessary equipment either by purchasing or by borrowing, Victor decided to build up a permanent organization that would have supplies of the necessary equipment and would have a reserve of engineers with specialized experience of journeys under Arctic conditions. If the same equipment could be used in Greenland and then the following winter in Antarctica, Victor could in effect equip and send out two expeditions for a much lower cost than if they worked completely independently. It would also be possible by this method to gather a group of engineers with a considerable fund of specialized experience.

Now that polar expeditions cost such large sums of money, efficiency, i. e. technical efficiency, has become as crucial as in modern industry. Victor's organization had official backing, it is true, and in many cases he could call on the French air force to make flights for him, but a large

part of the finance came from private sources or as fees for the solution of particular problems. It was therefore necessary to employ modern advertising and publicity methods to create interest in the many projects.

In 1948 Victor's first expedition began to make preparations for a new winter station in central Greenland as near as possible to the site of Wegener's Eismitte for the purpose of comparing the data that had been obtained earlier. The equipment and the 28 members of the expedition came to Greenland on board the Norwegian sealer *Force,* and then immediately began to search for a route up onto the ice sheet.

On the 1936 expedition Victor had ascended on to the ice sheet north of Nordenskiöld Gletscher, but this could not be negotiated by the Weasels, which weighed two tons apiece. Instead, he decided to investigate the possibility of getting up on to the ice near Eqip sermia where both de Quervain and Lindsay had done so and where the distance from the coast to the edge of the ice was not so great. After searching around for several days they found a route that the Weasels could manage except for one point on it, but this too could be passed if a ropeway could be used over the last part of the way. After conferring by radio with an engineering consultant in Paris,

126

Victor received sufficient information to enable him to construct a 700 m (800 yd) ropeway to bring the Weasels and the equipment 110 m up on to the edge of the ice sheet. By 9 July the cable way had been constructed and a road from the coast had been dug and blasted out of the ice. The equipment was now shifted to the edge of the ice, and they began to search for a route over the next stage of the way through the chaotic crevasse systems of the marginal area.

The whole summer had been spent in getting the gear up on to the ice and moving it the first part of the way across the ice sheet. They did not plan to build the winter station until the following year. In September the expedition returned to Paris and in October of the same year the first of the Antarctic expeditions left France to make similar investigations in Terre Adélie.

In 1949 the main expedition left for Greenland to build the new station Station Centrale in the very centre of the ice sheet. It was planned that eight men should spend the winter there and make year-round meteorological and glaciological studies, while for the summer there were considerable plans for scientific research in the area around Eqip sermia. There were 35 men in the party, and they brought with them 140 tons of equipment to supplement the 110 tons that had been unloaded the previous year. In addition to this there were 70 tons of supplies (mainly fuel and provisions) for Station Centrale and the sledge teams on the ice cap. This was brought to Keflavík in Iceland from where it was to be flown by charter plane to Greenland. By 31 May they had completed the unloading and had moved all the equipment to the edge of the ice. In 1949 the snow began to melt earlier than usual, and the margin of the ice was transformed into nearly impassable slush.

It was therefore essential to move the goods across the melting zone as quickly as possible and all other work was put aside for this. The first convoy on the ice consisted of five Weasels with eight sledges carrying a total of eight tons of cargo, and two trailers on runners in which the members of the expedition could prepare food and where some of them also slept. This first trip inland left the coast 1 July and there were 22 men. They made slow progress at first, for time after time the caterpillar tracks parted and had to be repaired.

It was obviously impossible for them to reach the station by 13 July, when it had been arranged that an Icelandic DC 4 should make the first parachute drop at Station Centrale. Instead, the plane had to be diverted to a depot called Milcent that had been set up approximately half way between the coast and Station Centrale. On 18 July they reached their goal and were then in a position to receive the 40 tons of fuel, provisions and other supplies that were to be brought in by air and either parachuted or free-dropped when the plane was flying some 20-30 ft above the surface of the snow. The second convoy set out from the coast on 30 July and the third convoy on 7 August.

American Albatross aircraft using Jato rockets can take off from the ice sheet. The plane is used for rescue operations.

The wintering station was built of flat sheets with insulating material in between. The ground plan was 8×5 m (26 ft × 16 ft) and the building was 2 m (6½ ft) high. It contained special rooms for radio operation, meteorological observations and a photographic dark room. Most of the house was, however, occupied by a common dormitory cum living room. For protection a-gainst the low temperatures and violent blizzards the house was dug down into the snow, and around it a number of rooms and corridors were dug out directly connected to the house to serve as store-rooms. A special shaft was also constructed for sending up radiosonde balloons.

The station was completed on 20 August and the 110 tons of equipment and food supplies had been stowed in. Four days later the summer team returned to the coast, and the eight men who were to winter in the station under the leadership of Robert Guillard started to make the final preparations for their stay. The station was very well equipped in comparison with the snow cave that had been used by Wegener's expedition; they had an abundant supply of food, plenty of scientific apparatus, and enough fuel for both heating and lighting. They made daily meteoro-logical observations at set times and the radiosondes brought back information about the weather at altitudes up to 20 km (12 miles) above the ice.

The winter passed according to plan. The radio station transmitted its weather reports daily so that weather maps of Greenland could be drawn up, and they were also able to maintain contact with their headquarters in Paris. Modern technology had been introduced to the ice sheet.

In the summer of 1950 a third expedition arrived in Greenland to relieve the wintering party and also to make various extensive investigations on the ice sheet. There were 39 men on this expedition and it was planned to make as extensive journeys as possible on the ice so as to study the ice thickness by making seismic measurements and determinations of gravity. Alain Joset, a French geophysicist, assisted by Jean Jacques Holtzscherer, was in charge of these investigations. In the marginal zone Jean Nevière, a geodecist, surveyed the most important crevasse systems and also fixed the positions of various points including Station Centrale.

A journey by Weasel was made across to Cecilia Nunatak, and some of the members of this party continued on foot to the coast and were then taken by motor boat across to Lauge Koch's camp on the island of Ella Ø, from where they sailed home to Copenhagen and France.

During the Eismitte wintering Sorge had excavated a shaft 15 m (50 ft) deep in order to study the snow stratification, but it was now planned to drill to even greater depths. Until 1949 the greatest depth that had been reached by drilling down through the ice with a core drill was 25 m (80 ft), but in U. S. A. and Switzerland, and also on the Norwegian-British-Swedish Antarctic Expedition of 1949—52, attempts had been made to drill as far down as was possible. At Maudheim in Antarctica Valter Schytt, a Swedish glaciologist, had reached a depth of 100 m (325 ft) with a core drill and had brought up samples of ice from that depth.

Ice drilling was also carried out at Station Centrale, and Michel Perez, the Swiss glaciologist, and Jean-Charles Heuberger, a French engineer, reached a depth of 151 m (494 ft), there using a 48 mm core drill. By analysing the samples brought up by the drill they were able to determine the temperature and density of the snow and ice and the temperature at various depths. They also made a number of deep drillings at various points nearer to the coast. To gain more detailed knowledge of the structure of the snow than was possible by drilling, they also brought with them a drilling grab which weighed one ton and was capable of drilling out a hole with a diameter of 80 cm (31 in) which was wide enough for a man to be lowered into to make measurements directly into the snow walls. With this, they made a hole 30.5 m (100 ft) deep at Station Centrale.

It was planned that the wintering party should be brought out and the expedition to Greenland concluded in the summer of 1951. In 1950 Alain Joset had travelled 2200 km (1,370 miles) from Disko Bugt to Cecilia Nunatak via Station Centrale and had determined the thickness of the ice sheet on this route by taking seismic soundings every 16 km (10 miles) so that the topography of the substratum could be recorded. These measurements had been highly successful, and in 1951 it was therefore planned to extend these investigations and to travel over the southern part of the ice sheet so that a map could be made of the thickness of the ice in the area between Lat. 63° and Lat. 74°. On this occasion Alain Joset also was in charge of the measurements, and to save time it was decided to take measurements every 20—25 km (12—16 miles) instead of every 16 km (10 miles). During the summer four groups of Weasels covered a total distance of 3,300 miles and recorded the thickness of the ice at 340 points. Hitherto everything had gone off according to plan, but in 1951 an accident occured that cost two men their lives. On 4 August Joset was travelling with three Weasels in the vicinity of Mont Forel where he was making preparations to receive new supplies by parachute drop that afternoon. They were approaching the area from the west and had not yet come across any crevasses. They were still a good distance from the eastern border of the ice and were thus not expecting to come upon any crevasses. Suddenly one of the leading Weasels was halted by an open crevasse. They were therefore forced to turn back on their tracks and find a better spot for the parachute drop. Joset's Weasel was being driven by the Danish engineer Jens Jarl, who was representing the Ministry for Greenland on the expedition.

Joset and Jarl had till then been travelling in second position in the convoy of three, but now Jarl swung the Weasel out of line so as to take over the lead on the return. In this manoeuvre they came out on to an unobserved snow bridge over a crevasse; the snow bridge gave way, and the Weasel and the sledge it was pulling disappeared into the depths. When the others came on the scene they could see the Weasel lying upside-down about 25 m (80 ft) down in the crevasse, but there was no sign of the two men and there was no answer to shouts.

All the rescue gear was unfortunately on the wrecked Weasel, and so there was nothing else to do but radio for help. Seven hours later an Icelandic aircraft was over the spot and dropped ropes and equipment. A man was lowered, and he found that the two men had been flung from the Weasel and now lay dead further down in the crevasse. The two victims' diaries and measurement records were brought up, but no attempt was made to bring up the bodies, as the Weasel was lying in such a delicate position that at any moment there was danger of it slipping further into the crevasse and crushing the rescue party.

Jean Jacques Holtzcherer now took charge of the seismic work and they continued to take measurements of the ice thickness. The meterological measurements were continued at Station Centrale until 15 August, and on 23 August the station was closed down for good. The expedition had really concluded, although some men did return the following summer to fetch the equipment from the ice sheet and to make a few supplementary measurements.

Technically, Victor's expedition had marked a revolution in expeditions to the ice cap. They were no longer dependent on dog sledges, so that large quantities of equipment could be transported, which meant that scientific observations and measurements could be contemplated of a kind that only a few years previously would have been unthinkable. While the members of previous expeditions had lived on pemmican and basic rations, Victor's team not only had had a sufficient, even abundant, supply of food, but thanks to the modern canning industry they also had a varied and interesting diet and there was even a wine-cellar at the winter station!

Whereas the men who had made earlier journeys had lived in tents or igloos it was now possible to sleep in the Weasels and to take along trailers upon which caravans of a kind could be built of canvas in which men could work, eat, and sleep in comfort. All the physically exhausting labour connected with dog sledges and man hauled sledges was now made unnecessary by motorised transport. Members of an expedition no longer needed to be outstandingly robust physically to make a journey across the ice sheet.

Drudgery had been replaced by modern comfort, but the dangers inherent in an expedition were possibly no less than before; crevasses still had to be crossed, and the accident at Mont Forel had demonstrated that these were still a hazard even at a distance from the edge of the ice and even more for a Weasel than a dog sledge. Arctic conditions in which the magnetic compass was unreliable and the lack of any fixed point on the unbroken white expanse of the ice sheet still made aviation on the ice sheet a hazardous undertaking. The modern expedition was now a matter of teamwork between a main base, the transport columns on the ice, and aircraft, and investigations could only be carried out by engineers and scientists working together. Individuals had now to make their contribution to the collective achievement, and to a much greater extent than previously: expeditions demanded of their members technical knowledge and experience as well as an ability to work together as a team.

A British Expedition Establishes Northice.

With the British tradition for Arctic exploration it was only to be expected that Britian would once again commence research in the polar regions. In 1948 Commander C. J. W. Simpson, R. N., began to make plans for an expedition to north-east Greenland to train young officers and scientists in Arctic techniques. Simpson was a member of a family which had served in the British navy for generations. His father was a rear admiral, and his grandfather a vice admiral. Simpson himself had become a cadet at thirteen and during the Second World War he had served in the anti-submarine service where he had distinguished himself on several occasions. It was his enthusiasm for mountaineering that had first aroused his interest in the Arctic. Initially, however, the Admirality showed no interest in his plans.

On a visit to Copenhagen he met members of the Danish Pearyland Expedition led by Eigil Knuth and Ebbe Munck, and in 1950 he sailed to Greenland in the *Godthaab* in order to get acquainted with the methods of approach used on the expedition. From Zackenberg, where the headquarters of the expedition were, he made a number of flights to north Greenland and in this way came to know north-east Greenland. After his experience in Greenland that summer he decided to organize a British expedition to Dronning Louise Land.

This Pearyland Expedition was the first major Danish expedition to Greenland after the Second World War. It started in 1947 and wintered twice at Jørgen Brønlund Fjord right in the north of Greenland in 1948—51. A number of journeys were made from here to explore this almost unknown part of Greenland. Technically, the expedition was based on a combination of the oldest form of Arctic travel: the dog-sledge, which was used on journeys in north Greenland, and the most modern: the aeroplane, which brought the members of the expedition and all the supplies to Jørgen Brønlund Fjord. The equipment came to Greenland itself by sea and a base was set up near Zackenberg from where it was flown on to north Greenland. This combination of new and old techniques proved workable, and it has been used by other expeditions in the Arctic and the Antarctic. Simpson learned this technique from the Danish Pearyland Expedition and was enthusiastic about it, for it not only made it possible to explore distant areas at low cost, but it also retained the use of dog-sledges, for which there had been a strong tradition in British expeditions since the days of Watkins.

Back in England, Simpson this time succeeded in getting official recognition and support for his plans for a British North-Greenland Expedition, and the Queen of England became the patron of the expedition and Sir Winston Churchill its vice-patron. The Ministry of Defence agreed to make men available for the proposed winter stay on the ice and to lay on air support.

Instead of Catalinas, Simpson used Sunderland flying boats of the RAF. In 1951 Simpson made a flight to north-east Greenland to prepare for the expedition. He landed at the lake of Sælsø and for a month they made a search of the area until a suitable site was found for the winter station on the shore of Britannia Sø in northern Dronning Louise Land.

Originally it had not been planned to do research on the ice sheet itself, but when the results of the French research were published, Simpson decided to include similar investigations in the programme for his own expedition. It thus became necessary to set up an additional station in the interior of the ice sheet in northern Greenland, and to obtain Weasels for making journeys across the ice to determine its thickness as the French had done further south.

The expedition sailed to east Greenland in the summer of 1952 on board the Norwegian sealer *Tottan.* The equipment was unloaded at Zackenberg, where they used the base that had been set up by the Pearyland Expedition. Two Sunderland flying boats arrived on 30 July, and over a three

132

week period, fifty trips were made and 165 tons of equipment were transported to Britannia Sø. The expedition's eight Weasels could not, of course, be flown up to Britannia Sø, but it had been hoped to bring them by sea as far as Danmarkshavn or Hvalros Odden. However the condition of the ice was unsuitable that year and so, instead, they had to be put ashore at Kap Rink, almost 125 miles to the south of the winter station.

While the construction of the winter station by Britannia Sø was proceeding smoothly, the work of building the station on the ice cap was commenced. It was out of the question to get the heavy Weasels up from Kap Rink during the summer, and the journey to the middle of the ice cap had therefore to be made by dog-sledge. On 21 August Simpson and five others started out with three sledges. It had been arranged that the planes would drop deposits of supplies on the ice by the last nunatak. So they set out from there with three Nansen sledges, 36 dogs, and a load of 1 ton 15 cwt. By 13 September they had reached a point 220 miles west of Dronning Louise Land; several of the dogs had died as they had not yet recovered their strength after the long voyage and none of the members of the expedition had driven a dog team before. They therefore decided to set up their winter station at that point.

Meanwhile the supplies for the winter station on the ice had been sent by sea to Thule where also two Hastings aircraft of the RAF had arrived. The plan was that all the supplies should be brought to the ice-cap site by plane, and as they could not risk landing the planes on the ice everything would have to be dropped from the air. Some of it would be parachuted, but most would be free-dropped by the same method that Victor had used.

The first plane arrived on 15 September and the drops went off as planned, but when the next plane arrived the following day, the weather was bad and visibility was about 4 miles when they arrived at Northice but dropped to 2 miles, and a grey-white haze lay over the ice. When all the parachutes had been dropped the plane came in low to free-drop the next load. Suddenly mist and white-out descended and the pilot completely lost his bearings. Before he could orientate himself properly the port wing had struck the ground. The pilot opened up the engines and managed to right the plane sufficiently to make a belly landing. The plane bumped $1\frac{1}{4}$ miles across the ice and then came to a halt; both port engines had been ripped off and smoke was coming from one of the starboard engines. As there were still several hundred gallons of fuel on board, the crew scrambled quickly out into the snow. Three of them had been injured, but not seriously.

Simpson's men had been so busy picking up the parachutes that they did not discover the accident until they suddenly saw the plane wrecked on the ice. There was neither equipment nor food supplies enough for the twelve members of the plane crew to spend the winter on the ice, nor

133

were they themselves prepared to winter in Greenland. The chances of evacuating them, however, were not very bright. There was at that time no plane fitted with skis in Greenland that could land and take off at 10,000 ft. Also the distance to Thule was so great that a Dakota would have only enough fuel for a direct trip there and back and none for circling round to find the crashed plane, and exact navigation was still a problem on the ice sheet. Helicopters were likewise ruled out for a rescue operation by the distance from Thule — 480 miles.

Both the British and the Americans were ready to do their utmost to evacuate the crew of the plane. The very next day the other Hastings flew in and dropped supplies for the stranded men. The Americans were making plans to land on the ice beside the wreck with an Albatross and then to take off again using jet-assisted take-off bottles. This had never before been done at such a high altitude. There was not enough fuel for any errors in navigation. So that the navigation could be precise, a number of Flying Fortresses covered the whole area inland of Thule, and a Flying Fortress also escorted the Albatross on the round trip. The Albatross landed and took the three injured men on board, and thanks to the JATO bottles it managed to take off again, but when it arrived back in Thule it had only enough fuel left for another half hour's flying. Some days later an American Dakota landed and the rest of the crew were taken on board and once more the plane was able to take off. The evacuation had been successfully carried out.

Another Hastings came up from Thule to replace the wrecked plane, and the work of supplying the winter station was resumed. Thirty flights were made in 25 days, and 87 tons of equipment were dropped. About a quarter of this amount was dropped by parachute, the rest was free-dropped. There was a much higher rate of damage than had been the case with the Franco-Icelandic drops, for the parachutes had been packed in the humid climate of Britain and failed to open because ice had formed in them, and also because it was impossible to make the free-drops from so low a height with the large Hastings planes that were used.

By 18 October the erection of the prefabricated station at Northice had progressed so far that Simpson returned to Britannia Sø; the dogs had been fed up well and they had been resting during their stay at the station so that they were in good shape for the journey to the coast.

Three men wintered on the ice sheet and 22 men wintered at Britannia Sø. At the main station at Britannia Sø they made meteorological measurements as well as a geodetic and geological survey of Dronning Louise Land. Hal Lister carried out a number of investigations on an outlet glacier in the area, paying particular attention to its budget and how it was affected by various climatic factors. During spring 1953 the Weasels were successfully brought up to the base, but before that was done a misfortune befell the expedition. The Danish liaison officer with the expedition, Captain H. A. Jensen, fell down a precipice and was killed. Jensen had been in charge of

134

A Peter Snow Miller Junior excavating snow during
the construction Station Jarl-Joset.

part of the geodetic programme and in descending from a peak where he had been taking a number of measurements he was crossing a hard-packed snow drift when he lost his footing and fell. By the beginning of May the Weasels were ready for the trip to the ice sheet.

Discussions they had had with the French seismologists and geophysicists had led them to expect that the work of the expedition on the ice sheet would go off smoothly, but this was not the case. They had planned to make a traverse from Britannia Sø to Northice and then on to Thule and to

135

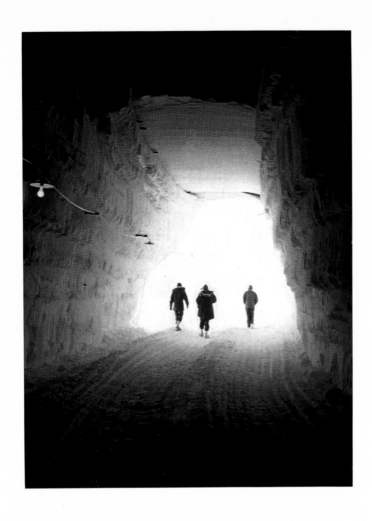

An investigation tunnel used for studies of trafficability at Camp Century.

make measurements of gravity along this profile as well as seismic determinations to ascertain the topography of the substratum below the ice. They did manage to carry out the surveying and the gravity measurements in the area between the main base and the station on the ice sheet, but the seismic measurements were unsuccessful. No matter how large a charge was used; no matter whether it was buried, set off on the surface, or placed on poles above the surface, no significant reflection was obtained from the bedrock beneath. No reflections from the ice-bedrock interface were recorded at any point on the ice sheet between Dronning Louise Land and Northice and east of a separating line running approximately 330° through 77° N, 45° W, but west of this line good reflections were obtained. A satisfactory explanation of this has still not been given.

During the summer of 1953 new supplies were brought in to both stations and some of the crew, especially the military personnel on the expedition, were replaced by others. Hal Lister, a glacio-logist, and C .B. B. Bull, a geophysicist, took part in the second wintering at Northice, and

136

they made a number of investigations on the accumulation and stratification of the snow. For this purpose a pit 50 ft deep was excavated so that they had access to layers of snow that had fallen on the ice sheet about 1879. The Weasels, which had had to cover long stretches of the route up to Britannia Sø over land, had now covered a total of more than 5,000 miles and were badly in need of repair. One had been abandoned on the ice because it was, quite simply, worn out. Another had fallen into a crevasse and been wrecked, but as the crew were wearing safety belts they had been able to clamber out unhurt, although the Weasel itself was a write-off.

The work on the ice sheet continued in the summer of 1954 and during this year they made determinations of gravity to link up with similar French and American work done at Thule. Colin Bull was in command of two Weasels which set off from Northice for Thule; they made measurements at regular intervals, but they had a lot of trouble repairing the Weasels on the way, and when they reached the American station af Sierra on the ice 125 miles north of Thule Air Base, they left one of the Weasels behind there. They managed to take the other Weasels to the edge of the ice on the peninsula of Nunatarssuaq north of Wolstenholme Fjord where they wound up their series of gravity measurements. The Englishmen, who after two winters on the ice and a long journey right across the ice sheet were worn out and had long beards and hair, now made acquaintance with the American way of expedition life with fresh food, hot and cold water, baths, and new films every other evening. The seismic group had meanwhile succeeded in getting some results from a series of measurements on the western part of the ice sheet, but could still get no results east of Long. 45° W even with fresh attempts using improved apparatus. On the return journey from making these measurements Northice was evacuated and they succeeded in returning to the coast, although the Weasels were worn-out and had to be abandoned on the way, the last of them on the tongue of the glacier that descends from the ice cap into Britannia Sø.

On 7 August a Sunderland flying boat brought the last station crew south. The expedition was concluded, and although it brought no scientific surprises, it had enlarged our knowledge of the northern part of the ice sheet, and in the coming years it was to be this part of the ice sheet particularly that was investigated by the Americans. The expedition had also been important for the training of British glaciologists who later took part in the Commonwealth Transantarctic Expedition under Sir Vivian Fuchs. C. Bull was in Greenland again in 1962 and 1963 as the leader of a series of American investigations on the Sukkertoppen Iskappe.

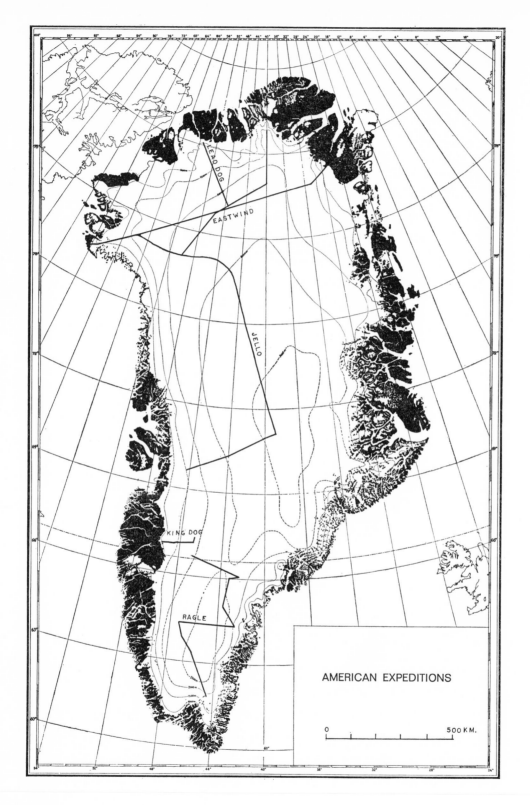

AMERICAN EXPEDITIONS

0   500 KM.

American Investigations after 1940

The First Major American Expedition on the Ice Sheet.

If we look at a globe or a map of the area around the North Pole, we cannot help observing that all the direct air routes between the industrial centres in the Soviet Union and North America transect Greenland, and that this island is the only major land mass on these strategic routes between the two great economic and political power blocks in the world. It is therefore essential that Greenland should be taken into consideration in all American strategic planning. Greenland is not only an obvious site for advance radar stations, but it is also a potential front line.

The Greenland ice sheet covers four fifths of the area, and in the winter the whole land and much of the sea around it is covered by ice and snow. It is not surprising, therefore, that the American military authorities are interested in the study of ice and snow as they investigate the problems of how men can live and travel in a high Arctic area such as Greenland.

Greenland was in the theatre of war even in the Second World War. To obtain information for the compilation of weather forecasts, the Germans set up weather stations in the uninhabited parts of east Greenland, and a Danish military patrol was initiated which with the support of the British and American air forces took part in combatting and destroying these stations. The Americans laid out a number of airfields in west and south-east Greenland to maintain their air routes between Europe and North America. They set up a hospital at the most southerly of these airfields with a view to the transport of wounded from Europe to U. S. A.

After the end of the war most of these airfields were abandoned, but two of the stations — at Søndre Strømfjord and Narssarssuaq — have remained in use until now. Søndre Strømfjord is run by the Americans and the most southerly of the bases, Narssarssuaq, has been taken over by Denmark, which now uses it as an airfield for ice reconnaissance patrols. A number of military exercises were made from these bases during the Second World War, and on several occasions emergency landings had to be made on the ice sheet and large-scale rescue actions were necessary to bring the airmen out. In 1942, for instance, a Flying Fortress crashed on the ice while trying to make an emergency landing in white-out. Some days after the accident an Albatross aircraft succeeded in landing wheels down on the snow to pick up two members of the crew.

On the next trip in, the Albatross itself crashed and all on board were killed. Two men then tried to reach the plane from the coast with two motor sledges, but when they were 100 yards from the plane one of the sledges and its driver fell into a crevasse and they were not found again. The driver of the other sledge now tried to bring three men (one of them badly frostbitten) back to the coast, but on the way another man was killed in a crevasse, and the sledge broke up, so that the remaining three had finally to winter on the ice, as did the three other survivors near the wreck of the plane. Not until the following year, five months after the crash, did a Catalina succeed in fetching them all off the ice sheet by making a belly landing on the ice. A lot of experience was gathered about the weather conditions on the ice sheet, but no really scientific investigations were carried out.

From a military point of view the main problems on the ice sheet were: how to get about on it, how to build stations, and how to keep both these stations and the mobile groups supplied.

Initially, the organization dealing with these problems was the Arctic Desert Tropic Information Center. As its name suggests, this organization was particularly concerned with gathering geographical information about almost all inaccessible and little known areas. During the war a large number of America's leading geographers, geophysicists, and geologists were working for ADTIC, and close collaboration was initiated with the American Geographical Society, which already had very large cartographic collections, and a library, etc. At the end of the war most of the scientists left ADTIC and returned to their universities and institutions, but several continued to act as advisers in future research projects. So it was ADTIC that organized the first major American scientific investigations on the Greenland ice cap.

During military operations planes fitted with plastic-covered skis had landed on the ice sheet several times. To do this was possible particularly in the winter when the snow was hard. The difficulty lay not in landing, but in taking off again from the snow. Take-off had been made in winter from the inner area of the ice sheet at an altitude of 10,000 ft, but in summer when the thaw made the snow soft it was impossible to take off from it.

Trials had been made with keeping groups of military personnel supplied by parachute drops or free drops, but this method proved unsuitable for military purposes.

It is a reliable and good method of supplying a single scientific expedition with a limited objective and relatively few men, but in large-scale military operations it is simply impossible to keep a detachment supplied in this way, and it is, besides, very expensive. It was therefore clear to the military authorities that a transport system would have to be developed that was indepen-

140

dent of air support and had sufficient capacity to operate on the basis of its own supplies. Aerial reconnaissance had shown that the marginal zone of the ice sheet was in most places heavily crevassed, which meant that to take heavy motorised transport across it would be a hazardous undertaking. This time it would no longer be a matter of taking a single expedition across the crevasse zone, but of large-scale military operations across long distances. Hitherto experimental work in this field had been neglected.

On a military manoeuvre called Snowman in 1947 it was discovered that about 110 miles east of Søndre Strømfjord at an altitude of 6,000 ft above sea level there was an area of snow with an even and firm surface that seemed well suited for a landing strip. It was decided to make a detailed investigation of the area, and this task was entrusted to ADTIC in collaboration with the American Geographical Society. A long time elapsed, however, before work was really started. Plans for an expedition were not started until 1951, and by 1953 the expedition finally started out; it was given the code name of Project Mint Julep.

It was planned that Dakotas fitted with skis should bring in sufficient supplies so that investigations could be carried on throughout the summer. It was necessary this time, as it had not been on earlier civilian expeditions, to bring such plentiful supplies that the personnel could live and work in the most comfortable conditions, and the men were not expected to live in tents but in eight Jamesway huts. These consist of a wooden framework covered with thick, heavily insulated glasswool mats, and they are heated by oil. For transportation across the ice and for reconnaissance there were two Weasels.

At the beginning of May 1953 the expedition assembled at Søndre Strømfjord; in addition to the military contingent, there were also twelve American scientists and engineers. They made a thorough reconnaissance of the area from the air and then landed with the Dakota, and 13—28 May was spent in constructing the camp at Mint Julep Site at Lat. 66° 16' N and Long. 47° 46' W. Here they made a series of investigations of the structure of the snow, its melting and run-off. The snow melted so much during the summer that the planes could not rise from the take-off strips, and for more than a month the camp had to be supplied solely from the air. By August the temperature had dropped sufficiently for the surface to harden up again so that aircraft could land once more. The camp was shut down on 21 August, but as a precaution in case any planes should be forced to land on the ice, the camp was left with sufficient supplies of food and fuel for twenty men to shelter in the camp for several weeks.

Project Mint Julep was the first major American project connected with the ice sheet, and it had proved that it was possible to construct a landing strip on which heavy aircraft could land, and it had also discovered that there were several areas, mainly located around the firn line, where the surface of the ice sheet was quite even and where the winter snowfall was so slight that it would be easy to maintain a landing strip, which, however, would be unusable in summer.

Thule Air Base is Set Up.

While Project Mint Julep was going forward in southern Greenland, the Americans were busy establishing the Air Base at Thule in north Greenland, and in future it was not to be ADTIC that was behind research on the Greenland ice sheet. After the Second World War the U. S. A. had begun to build up a system of radar warning stations in the Arctic in order to detect any attack that might be made on America via the Arctic. These stations were most frequently constructed in areas that previously had been barren and impenetrable, and the military transport organization was set a hard task in having to deliver materials and supplies to them.

At the close of the 1940s the American government realized that the chain of radar stations that was under construction in Canada and Alaska would have to be extended to include Greenland. For security reasons it would be necessary to lay out an airfield as far to the north and as far over towards the Soviet Union as possible. After negotiations with the Danish authorities, the Americans obtained permission, as part of the NATO mutual defence agreement, to establish an air base in northern Greenland.

The base was to serve several purposes: it was to be a home base for a section of the Strategic Air Command that would have responsibility for American reconnaissance flights over the polar basin; it was also to serve as a re-fuelling station and repair base for long-distance aircraft; and it was to be a supply base for the weather stations and radar stations in Arctic Canada and for the ice-floe stations that were being set up in the Arctic Ocean itself. The Americans also wanted a place where they could test Arctic equipment and make scientific studies to develop new types of equipment. A radar station was to be built in conjunction with the air base as a continuation of the North American radar chain.

The base had, therefore, to be located somewhere in northern Greenland, as far to the north as possible, but at a position where it could be visited each year by ships bringing provisions and equipment. At the same time there would have to be sufficient even land for an air-strip to be laid out. There was thus no possibility of constructing the base in north-east Greenland, where the Arctic pack-ice made navigation impossible.

The most northerly area which can be reached every year by ship in north-west Greenland is the Thule district, but there are not many stretches of lowland here. Along the whole of Melville Bugt the inland ice reaches right to the coast almost everywhere and it is only penetrated by small nunataks. To the north of Wolstenholme Fjord are the sandstone plains of north Greenland

142

which in most places present precipitous walls of rock to the coast. Thus the only area of lowland in Thule district is located around Pitugfik, a river which is fed by Store Landgletscher near to Knud Rasmussen's old station of Thule which had been in existence since 1910. By the mouth of the river there are extensive delta flats, and Knud Rasmussen himself had observed that it would be possible to land a plane there, but he can hardly have envisaged that it would become the site of an air base of such a size. Construction work began in 1951 on what at that time was regarded as the largest and most modern military base anywhere in the western world.

The construction of the Thule base presented many technical problems. Experience in construction work in Alaska and northern Canada during the Second World War had proved that it was impossible to employ traditional building techniques in the Arctic. As it was essential to have the base finished as quickly as possible, there was no time to make advance experiments before finalising the plans. The base had to be built immediately, and it had to be constructed so as to withstand the extremely low Arctic temperatures, the violent blizzards and high wind velocities. In addition it had to be built on ground that was unstable because of the effects of permafrost. As the base was to be permanent, attention had also to be paid to keeping the costs of long term maintenance as low as possible.

From the constructional point of view it was the permafrost that caused most problems. In high Arctic areas the earth is frozen to great depths, and only the active top layers thaw out during the summer. Further down in the earth the ground is permanently frozen. This layer of permanently frozen soil is called permafrost, and it may be 1,300—2,000 ft thick. Drilling work carried out at Thule suggested that it was at least 1,600 ft thick there. The boundary between the upper layers of permafrost and the lower layers that thaw in summer is very clear-cut, and its position is dependent on the thermic balance, i. e. the depth to which thawing extends is dependent on such factors as general temperature conditions, how exposed the soil is to the prevailing wind, the amount of solar radiation, the structure of the earth, what vegetation there is on the surface, and the water content of the earth. If this balance is disturbed, for instance by erecting a building on the surface or by removing the upper layer of soil, then nature will seek to restore the balance and the result will be a change in the depth of the active layer and of the permafrost resulting in soil destruction, icing on the ground, etc. The resulting soil movements can cause roadways and buildings to be completely broken up.

The destruction of the permafrost level had caused considerable damage in Siberia and Alaska. It was therefore essential to construct the buildings in such a way that the heat from them could not penetrate into the earth, and special techniques had to be employed to do this involving the use of special cooling sections built into the floors of the great aircraft hangars. All the houses on the

143

base, were therefore built with a plank foundation which permitted the free flow of cold air and prevented the heat from the house from descending into the earth. Special techniques had also to be used in excavating the foundations.

Previously, the only men to winter under high Arctic conditions had been small groups of trappers, or of scientists and weather observers, but now a military base was to be set up which would be manned by several thousand men who had been draughted there under peace-time conditions as part of general military preparedness. In the past, those who wintered in the Arctic had had a special interest in the area, but the military personnel who were draughted there had no interest, nor did most of them have any opportunity to leave the base area. It was therefore necessary to compensate them as much as possible for the isolated and tedious life on the base, providing them with the greatest comfort and with amusements and recreations in their leisure time. Thule Air Base thus came to cover a large area.

The construction of the base was one of the most fascinating, as well as one of the most costly, projects that has been carried out in the Arctic. A harbour had to be provided that could accommodate the large number of ships that would be unloading building materials and supplies for the base. This was built of pontoons which were floated up from Florida to Thule. To protect the pontoons for the quay against pack ice they were raised up above the surface of the sea. Large steel tubes were rammed through the bottom of the pontoons and into the sea-bed; then the pontoons were raised to the top of the tubes. Finally, there was also a wharf with a roadway on top which extended from the coast into deep water, so that it was possible for large ships to berth at Thule. The staff lived in barracks which were erected of sections consisting of aluminium sheets with insulating material in between. Besides these hutments, hangars, warehouses, and a gymnasium were put up. To keep in contact with U. S. A. a radio tower was erected which was 50 ft taller than the Empire State Building (and thus the tallest construction in the world until a television mast was put up on the Empire State Building). The Thule Air Base was to be manned by the American Air Force, but the planning and construction work was the responsibility of the Corps of Engineers, and as with most such American projects, the site-clearing and construction work were let out to private contractors. Many thousands of workers were required in the building of the base, and they streamed up to Thule in the summer. The work was carried out under great pressure of time, and there was round-the-clock working during the time of the light Arctic nights. It was then possible to leave the last house in a road in the morning and to discover on returning home that same evening that a new building had been erected beyond it and the road extended past the house.

Meteorological records for the Thule area covered only a few years, and the highest possible

144

The passages at Camp Century are covered with wonder arches and the ends closed with snow blocks.

wind velocities and the lowest possible temperatures were therefore unknown factors. As it was not possible to test materials out beforehand, the base had to be built to withstand the worst conditions that could be conceived as possible. Technically, therefore, the Thule base was built to much too high a standard, and would have been able to withstand conditions far worse than any that actually occur. In spite of the great difficulties in getting men and materials to such an inaccessible site and the technical problems caused by the short building season, the base was completed by 1953 when it was handed over to the American Air Force.

The choice of the site for the Thule base had been dictated solely by consideration of military strategy and accessibility by ship; no previous investigations had been made to discover whether there was any suitable route of access on to the ice sheet in the vicinity. It was clear, however, right from the first that the problems of the ice sheet would have to be studied sooner or later.

145

On grounds of military security it was necessary to know the hinterland of the base, so as to be secure from enemy attacks by low-flying aircraft across the ice sheet. It was therefore necessary to set up an advance radar station on the ice sheet itself, and it would also be necessary to devise some means of transport for travelling and moving supplies on the ice sheet. The Thule base thus became the starting point for comprehensive technical and scientific research which in nearly all fields have revolutionised our knowledge of the ice sheet and the Arctic glaciers.

Because of the long tradition there had been for Greenland exploration both by Danes and non-Danes, Greenland had already become the most thoroughly explored Polar region in the world, and now the Americans were starting the most intensive geophysical and glaciological research programme that had ever been envisaged in any area of glacier or Arctic snow. With the establishment of the northern defence area it became plain that the Americans could not avoid studying snow, ice, and frozen ground, so that troops could move about over areas which for various periods of the year were in the grip of snow and cold.

Most military activity in the polar regions is subject to the same laws that obtain for all transportation in Arctic and sub-Arctic conditions. However large the manpower and resources that are available, natural conditions are so unaccommodating and natural forces so violent that it is impossible to overcome them; it is only possible to take precautions against them and to learn to live with them.

Military planning in these regions made a knowledge of the geography, climate, subsoil, vegetation and other life absolutely vital. The Americans now moved in to obtain this information in north Greenland. They were not content with studying all the relevant literature, they also sent out numerous expeditions to study conditions at first hand, and they carried out experiments both in the laboratory and in the field to find out what principles should be followed in construction work, roadmaking, transportation and the design of equipment. They had thereby to study the effects of the Arctic climate on buildings, materials, and weapons, and they had also to grapple with such problems as how troops and bases could be camouflaged in the snow. Parallel with the technical research, purely scientific research was also set in hand in laboratories in U.S.A. and in the field in Greenland, Alaska, Canada and Antarctica. Large funds were made available for these investigations, which were also much assisted by having an existing highly developed system of military transport at their disposal.

In the following years a large number of American scientists and engineers were at work in Greenland and particularly on the ice sheet. Many of their investigations were only one phase of routine research, but others were particularly concerned with the problems of the Greenland ice sheet proper. The numbers of men and the amount of equipment that were being employed on

146

the ice now became so great that they were occupying more or less permanent stations and it was no longer a matter of individual expeditions being sent out, but rather of regular work being done on the ice. The research-workers were flown in, they made their measurements, and they left again as soon as they possibly could. The age of real exploration is past in Greenland as it is everywhere else in the world. It has been replaced by a no less exciting programme of technical and scientific research.

While the construction of the base was proceeding, The American Corps of Transport began to study the possibilities of travelling on the ice cap. The very first problem was to find a route on-to the ice sheet which could be used by tractors and motor sledges. In most places in north Greenland the ice front is precipitous, and the periphery of the ice sheet is heavily crevassed and therefore dangerous to cross. All the known routes in the vicinity of the base were only suitable for dog sledges and not for the heavy Weasels and tractors which weigh up to two tons or more a piece or for the prime movers and carriers with gross weights of 40 tons.

The American defence forces were not able to draw upon sufficient Americans with Arctic experience to solve these problems, and initially they had to call in foreign experts to act as advisers: for instance, Paul-Émile Victor, who came to Thule with some of the team that had been with him on the expeditions to the ice sheet in 1949—52, and Eigil Knuth, the leader of the Danish Pearyland Expedition. But even so there were not enough men available compared with the number that was needed. Gino Watkins on his expeditions had chosen quite young men without any experience of Arctic travel, for it was his opinion that he in this way would get hold of keen men who would not shrink from difficulties and would carry out tasks that more experienced travellers would hesitate to undertake.

However, this was not the American view of the matter, but they had no choice; having no men with experience they were obliged to send in young men with no knowledge of Arctic conditions to carry out the programme in Greenland. Officers who had led American armoured divisions in Europe during the Second World War were now put in charge of tractor and Weasel transport on the ice sheet. Pilots from Texas or Florida, who may never have seen any ice except in the ice box of the refrigerator, were now ordered to fly to Greenland and cross the ice sheet under high Arctic conditions.

Peary, Knud Rasmussen, and Lauge Koch on their expeditions to the Thule district had employed Eskimoes to help them, but under military conditions there could be no question of doing this. It was therefore essential to develop new techniques for travelling on the ice, techniques entirely based on modern motorised vehicles and making it possible to transport large quantities of equipment and building material and large numbers of men.

The Thule Air Base was built as it were on the very doorstep of the settlement of polar Eskimoes at Knud Rasmussen's old trading post, and it unavoidably ruined the hunting in the area. The military establishment also prevented several of the normal sledge routes from being used. If the Eskimo population continued to live just outside the base, it could be foreseen that it would become dependent on the base and this was undesirable.

It must be said that the Americans loyally kept the agreement prohibiting contact with the natives of the area. Nor were any Eskimoes employed in setting up the base or on the expeditions to the ice sheet. In accordance with the wish of the population Thule settlement was therefore abandoned in the spring of 1953, and a new town was laid out at Kanaq, about 70 miles further north on Inglefield Bredning. The Americans paid for the move, and instead of the old earth houses, Danish craftsmen erected modern wooden houses, and Kanaq itself was built to a regular plan and district central heating was laid on from a heating plant. It is today the most modern town in Greenland. Kanaq later had its name changed to Thule, and Knud Rasmussen's old Thule was renamed Dundas after the original name of the mountain at Thule.

The only thing left on the old site was the Danish radio station which had more recently been extended because of the flights made by Scandinavian Airlines System across the polar basin. The air base itself preserved the name Thule Air Base, or in common parlance, plain Thule.

The lack of an American tradition of Arctic exploration meant that the American technologists came back to the problems with fresh eyes, and there were many initial difficulties, and many things went wrong, but they managed to acquire a working method that would probably have caused old-fashioned travellers to raise their eyebrows, but which was nevertheless effective, even though expensive. With the large economic and technical resources that were available for solving the problems of the ice sheet, it was now possible to use equipment and techniques that would previously have been quite out of the question. Financial support had been completely lacking for such projects. This was a far cry from the small private expedition with its modest means; these expeditions were backed by the whole American defence system. In more than one respect, therefore, the American research activity on the ice sheet was breaking new ground.

It was impossible for the officers and men to take their families with them, and the base was an all-male society. The Danish liaison officer to the base was the only man to have his family with him, as also, of course, did the staff of the Danish radio station at Dundas, but that was outside the actual base area. For the Americans, this separation from their families, children, and feminine company was a great strain, and the length of service at the base, as at other overseas bases, was less than one year, so that the personnel was continually changing. New personnel had to be con-

Parachute drops are vital for all modern expeditions.

tinually trained in the techniques of Arctic living, and there was still a lack of men with the right kind of experience that can only be obtained over many years of service under Arctic conditions.

Transportation Problems

In 1952, with Victor in charge, the Americans made a reconnaissance of the edge of the ice sheet to try to find a suitable route up onto it that could be used by motor sledges. They found two possible routes close to the base. The safer route, i. e. the one on which there were fewer crevasses, was found on the peninsula of Nunatarssuaq which is situated between the ice sheet itself and the great independent ice cap of Nordisen that covers most of Stensbye Land. The other route was over Store Landgletscher within the base area itself. In both places there was a gently rising ramp of ice which allowed easy access for both Weasels and tractors. In 1952 they succeeded in taking Weasels up on to the ice by the Nunatarssuaq route, but it would be necessary to reconnoitre the Store Landgletscher route carefully for crevasses before venturing to use it.

When the Thule base had been planned, no thought had been given to the question of finding a route of access onto the ice sheet, but later investigations revealed that they had by a stroke of good fortune set up the base right beside one of the easiest ascent routes in the whole of Greenland. If the Nunatarssuaq route was to be used, this would mean laying out an extensive road network of a total of 22 miles from the fjord to the edge of the ice. All the materials necessary for constructing the Nunatarssuaq route would either have to be driven over Wolstenholme Fjord in the winter or sailed across in the summer, for there was no other way of getting to it from Thule base. It would be expensive to maintain this roadway, but nevertheless they set to work to build the road while at the same time reconnoitring for a safer route from Store Landgletscher onto the ice sheet.

While the work of constructing Thule base was proceeding, Station Nord was being erected in north-east Greenland as a joint Danish and American weather station. The station was established on a peninsula at the mouth of Danmark Fjord and was thus located north of the region that can be reached by ship, so that all supplies and materials had to be brought in by air or transported across the ice sheet and over the fjord ice of Danmark Fjord. The military transport authorities were consulted as to whether they would be able to undertake the transportation of 500 tons of equipment across the ice cap to Station Nord. Such an undertaking could only be carried out if tractors and very heavy sledges were to be used, and this had not previously been tried on the ice sheet. Experiments with tractors were therefore commenced on the ice.

Before the Second World War Admiral R. Byrd, the American Antarctic explorer, had successfully used tractors to transport supplies across the flat Antarctic ice shelf, and during the war the American defence forces had experimented with transport in Arctic regions. In 1942 comprehensive trials of caterpillar-tracked vehicles had been made on snow, as transportation problems had arisen with the construction of the Alaska and Richardson highways. In 1943 the final trials of the Weasel were carried out in Canada; this was an amphibious vehicle specially constructed for use in snow. As the Second World War did not actually lead to any sizeable operations in the Arctic, the experiments in Alaska and Canada were halted.

However, when the northern radar warning chain was built around the American continent, transportation on snow became a problem of the moment once more. From 1947 to 1950 comprehensive experiments were therefore made with sledges and tractors on the snow in Big Delta in Alaska and at Fort Churchill in Canada. The outbreak of the Korean War stopped these tests, but

150

many important results had already been obtained, and it was clear that the most suitable transport over snow was a combination of tracked vehicles and sledges; it had not proved feasible to fit caterpillar tracks to the trailers hauled by the tractors.

While the tranportation tests were proceeding on snow and ice, a more scientific and technical study of snow, ice, and frozen ground was being made. In 1944 the American army had set up a special Frost Effects Laboratory in Boston where it was planned to investigate the conditions in those regions with an annual frost period, and in 1945 a Permafrost Division was set up in St. Paul and the same year, too, a field laboratory for testing constructions and buildings under Arctic conditions was set up in Fairbanks, Alaska.

In 1949 a special research body was founded for the study of snow, ice, and permanently frozen ground, and this was given the name Snow, Ice and Permafrost Research Establishment, which was normally abbreviated to SIPRE. It was housed at Wilmette and Evanston near Chicago. As the name suggests, SIPRE was to investigate snow, ice, and permafrost in all forms both by experiments in the laboratory and by field studies. An experimental station called Keweenaw Field Station was set up in Houghton, Michigan, but the most extensive projects were carried out in Greenland, particularly in the Thule area, although also at Project Mint Julep further south. SIPRE has also done research in Alaska, in Canada, and, during the International Geophysical Year, in Antarctica. SIPRE is attached to the U. S. Corps of Engineers and employs both military and civilian personnel.

A number of foreign specialists of outstanding calibre have also been co-opted, and for a number of years its scientific leaders were the Swiss Professor Henri Bader and the Japanese Ukuchiro Nakaya, both scientists of international reputation in the field of glaciology. Most of the findings that they and their collaborators have established, have been published in a number of reports by the military authorities, and these have therefore not always had the circulation amongst scientists that was desirable. In more recent years a large number of articles and surveys of SIPRE's findings have also been published in technical and scientific journals and in the proceedings of congresses. More than 300 publications have appeared, many of them covering a very wide field.

When the strategic situation called for an extension of the defence system to Greenland, experiments with over-snow transport were resumed, and this time the trials were carried out on the ice sheet itself. The tests carried out in Canada had proved that it was possible to use tractors on snow to pull large and heavy sledges, called Otaco sledges. These sledges had a capacity of 5—10 tons each. In northern Canada the mining companies had gradually built up a considerable fund of experience with such methods of winter transport, often over bad terrain. The problem of oversnow transport in Greenland is trafficability, by which is meant the ability of the snow to sustain vehicle traffic. There are also many specialized problems that occur because of the severe weather conditions associated with snow country, because of hazards such as crevasses, thin ice on lakes and rivers, and because of the difficulties of navigation and the large distances between supply and support facilities. It was soon found, however, that the experience gained in Canada was not directly applicable to Greenland where conditions were quite different from in Canada. Both tractors and sledges sank into the loose snow on the ice cap and stuck fast, and there were other difficulties which had not been encountered elsewhere .

In Canada it had been possible to proceed without any problems of navigation, but on the featureless white extent that was the ice sheet there were no fixed points by which to find one's bearings, and it was therefore necessary to navigate by compass, establishing position like a ship at sea. But the proximity of the magnetic pole made the magnetic compass of little use, and the gyro compass proved to be too sensitive to the vibration it was exposed to in a Weasel or a tractor. In Canada, transport had been over land or on rivers, but in Greenland it was across glacier ice in which crevasses, covered by thin snow bridges, could swallow up tractors and sledges. The extremely low temperatures, blizzards, the fine Arctic snow, and the frequent white-outs were all difficulties that had to be overcome before the transportation of large quantities of supplies across the ice sheet could begin.

A large number of tractors had been used in road construction and transportation in connection with the building of the Thule Air Base, and in the summer of 1952 an attempt was made to bring a few of them up on to the ice cap to test them out with hauling some heavy Otaco sledges which had also been taken up. Initially, small ordinary tractors with narrow tracks were tried out. With great difficulty the tractors were brought up on to the edge of the ice sheet from where they continued inland, but only 12 miles in on the ice sheet the tractor that was in the lead broke through a snow bridge over a crevasse. It remained suspended so that the driver was able to climb out, but they did not dare to attempt to haul the tractor up. So as not to run any unnecessary risk, it was decided to call off all future experiments with tractors.

Instead, all efforts were concentrated on an attempt to drive by Weasel across the ice sheet to Kap George Cohn and back. Victor was in charge of this journey, and a number of his men from the earlier Greenland expeditions also took part, among them the seismic expert, Holtzscherer, who now had an opportunity to measure the thickness of the ice along the whole route across the ice sheet, and his findings supplemented most valuably the measurements made on the ice cap further south. The 1,250 mile route there and back was covered without any sort of mishap, and the French encountered no difficulties that had not already been met with on earlier expedition. On the journey they instructed the Americans in the party in their technique of travel, and at the same time they were able to test out various types of American equipment and to experiment with navigation systems for use on journeys in northern Greenland.

By late summer 1952 a relatively crevasse-free approach route to the top of the marginal area of the ice sheet had been found on Nunatarssuaq and a 22-mile road had been built from the coast at the north side of Wolstenholme Fjord to the front of the ice. Here the first heavy transport group to go on to the ice was prepared, but the coming of autumn put an end to the experiments.

An American Five-Year Plan of Research on the Ice Cap

It was plain that in 1952 the Americans did not have sufficient experience behind them and were not in possession of enough technical knowledge, nor indeed of suitable vehicles, to be able to undertake large-scale transportation on the ice sheet. It was therefore decided to initiate a five-year plan of investigation on the ice sheet and the transportation problems that were peculiar to that area. Over this period they would not only attempt to get familiar with the ice, but would also try to develop the best means of transport on the ice and the most efficient economical way of using it.

The task of carrying out the five-year plan was entrusted to the newly constituted Transportation Arctic Group, which was to collaborate with the U. S. Geological Survey, the Stanford Research Institute, SIPRE, and a large number of other military and civil research bodies, each of which had specialized knowledge that could contribute to solving the problems involved. It was also clear that if such research on transportation problems was to be undertaken it would be essential to have a much more detailed knowledge of the nature of snow and of the physics of ice, and research in this field was to be undertaken by SIPRE and other army technical laboratories. So that the technical and scientific research programmes should not be delayed by operational activities, it was agreed that Transportation Arctic Group should not be called upon to transport materials and equipment for other military organizations unless this would not hinder the actual research on the ice. All was now plain sailing for the large programme of research on the ice sheet to be carried out successfully in the years following.

In 1953 the five-year programme commenced with extensive tests of a larger variety of equipment than in any year before or since. Various military and commercial oversnow vehicles were tried out: tractors, sledges, wanigans, rolligons, and several light reconnaissance vehicles.

The safer Nunatarssuaq route was used for bringing the heavy vehicles up on to the ice sheet, and early in the spring of 1953 work was started on taking the tractors, bulldozers, Weasels, and other vehicles across the fjord ice and along the newly constructed roadway to the ice ramp, which was named Nuna Take Off or Nuto, which led up onto the ice cap itself. On the ice sheet several testing areas of both soft and hard snow had been marked out so that systematic trials of the vehicles could commence.

The Weasel, which Victor had used with such conspicuous success as an amphibious cargo carrier, proved to be unsurpassed for conveying personnel and light freight across the ice and for light sledge haulage for oversnow transport across the ice. It is fitted with a 56 h. p. Studebaker power unit and weighs 4,800 lb; it is well suited for use on reconnaissance trips and on journeys for marking out routes, but its haulage capacity is too small for it to be able to undertake large military transport operations involving hundreds of tons. It was therefore necessary to make trials with bigger tractors with 225 h. p. or even larger engines, which could haul sledges with a load capacity of 20—30 tons.

As well as trials with true tractors, tests were also made with vehicles known as Sno-cats, which had been much used at American winter sports resorts for the conveyance of passengers and also by the American forestry authorities and on rescue service in the large nature parks. The Sno-cat, unlike the Weasel and normal tractors, is fitted with four ladder-tracked pontoons which can function independently. It is therefore much more manoeuvrable over difficult terrain, and as it has a 180 h. p. Chrysler engine, it is also much more powerful than the Weasel, and has a payload of 2,300 lb. On the other hand it could not be bought from surplus stocks at the end of the war, and was therefore very expensive, but it has nevertheless been used on a large number of expeditions to the Antarctic during the International Geophysical Year, and not only by American expeditions but also by Sir Vivian Fuchs on his journey across Antarctica from Weddell Sea to Ross Sea.

Propeller sledges had been used, as we have seen, on Wegener's expedition, and during the Second World War, too, the Americans had experimented with them at bases in Greenland, but with no success. It is true that the fastest crossing of the ice sheet had been made with them when the stretch from Eismitte to the coast had been covered in sixteen hours, but they proved to be too unreliable and they did not have sufficient tractive power to transport large quantities of equipment. It was therefore obvious that no useful purpose would be served by continuing experiments with them, and instead all trials were concentrated on tractors fitted with caterpillar tracks of various types, and experiments were also made with various vehicles fitted with such large wheels that even when they carried a considerable weight they still had a low ground pressure per square inch.

There were also other types of studies proceeding on the ice cap during 1953. The Americans needed to get to know the ice and to become familiar with it under all conditions. It was there-

154

fore essential for them to make many lengthy journeys under as wide a variety of conditions as possible. As it was not at the time known how research on the ice would develop in the future, as many projects as possible were initiated, and it was hoped that some of the experiences and measurements would yield something of value. Merely to have men working on the ice cap was in itself useful, for experience was gained in transporting and supplying them. This was, therefore, a unique opportunity for scientists to obtain data and samples from the ice sheet which would have been impossible to organize in the ordinary way. In 1953 the Stanford Research Organization assumed responsibility for leading and directing the scientific research, and a large staff of geologists, glaciologists, meteorologists, biologists, and geophysicist as well as technologists of all kinds was engaged to study both the ice cap and the ice-free land in front of the ice edge.

On the ice cap, the Solo expedition under the young geologist Coleman C. Fischer studied snow accumulation. Carl S. Benson, a young glaciologist, also participated in this journey. He immediately and unreservedly lost his heart to the white expanse, and later became the leader of several expeditions sent out by SIPRE, and he is today undoubtedly one of the greatest experts on the snow of the ice cap. Another expedition was working under R. L. Nichols, a geologist, in the area between Thule and Inglefield Land where one of their objectives was to find a descent route from the ice sheet. Holtzscherer took part in this trip across the ice sheet and continued his seismic investigations of the thickness of the ice in north Greenland.

On the peninsula of Nunatarssuaq the glaciologist Professor R. Goldthwait studied several local glaciers and made very careful measurements of the ice movement and also studied the glaciological history of the area. On Nuna Take Off itself, leading up to the ice sheet, detailed measurements of the ice movement were made; these investigations were in charge of a glaciologist, Dr Laurence Nobles. At the same time a careful survey and a geological investigation of the land in front of the ice margin was carried out and the biological conditions there were also studied. In support of these investigations helicopters were available to take the men to the various places they wished to visit to collect specimens and make investigations.

Reconnaissance was continued to find a safe route onto the ice sheet from Store Landgletscher. At the edge of the ice a camp, called Thule Take Off or Camp Tuto for short, was set up as a base for this reconnaissance work, and thanks to the helicopter flights and the reconnaissance journeys by sledge the area was so well known by the end of the summer, by which time all the hazardous areas had been marked off, that it was ventured to send the final tractor convoy of the year to Camp Tuto by that route.

The summer of 1953 had yielded great results; the Americans were beginning to familiarize themselves with the ice sheet, and they had also managed to bring out the tractors that had been abandoned on the ice in 1952. It was clear that the five-year plan would allow the Americans to develop the most suitable form of transport on the ice.

The next stage of the five-year programme was planned during the winter of 1953—54. Co-operation was established between the Corps of Engineers and the Corps of Transport, and they divided the assignement between them, so that the Corps of Transport continued to be responsible for the transportation research on the ice, while the Corps of Engineers, to which SIPRE belonged, was made responsible for the scientific exploration of the ice cap and investigation of the glaciological problems there. The first year of the five-year plan had brought such good results that it was now possible to give a more definite shape to the programme of future activity and to make long term plans.

During 1954 transport trials continued on the ice cap. The best results had been achieved in 1953 with tractors pulling ten-ton sledges for transportation of heavy loads, and with Weasels and light sledges for rapid transportation when no great quantity of equipment needed to be carried. Work was now continued with improving the tractors and making experiments among other things with various kinds of tracks. The tests started in April when as many of the tractors and as much of the equipment as possible was brought across to Nunatarssuaq, for it was possible to drive across the sea ice of Wolstenholme Fjord right until the end of May. As soon as the thaw set in, the route across the fjord ice could no longer be used. Gradually, as the melting advanced, the lower zone of the ice cap was transformed into a slush of wet snow and melting ice which was impassable for the Weasels and tractors. For several weeks there could be no question of bringing convoys through this zone. So that supplies could be brought from Thule to Camp Tuto and onto the ice sheet, a road was built up to the margin of the ice, and work was also commenced on constructing a gravel road on the glacier ice itself. It was intended that the equipment should be shifted by truck and tractor to a point so high and so far in on the ice that it would not suffer from the effects of the melting snow in the summer. But even when in 1955 and 1956 the gravel road had been extended to a total of 3 miles across the ice, there was still trouble with the melting snow, but though 1954 was a heavy melt year, it was the first year in which traffic on the ice ramp was not periodically restricted by impassable melt conditions near the bottom of the ramp.

The tests that were carried out with transport on the ice cap followed the same pattern as those in 1953, and as the radar early warning stations at Site I and Site II were under construction there was plenty of opportunity of trying out different methods of transporting heavy loads on the ice cap. That summer eight convoys made trips, or "swings" as they were called, carrying building materials to Site II, about 200 miles in on the ice sheet, and thus the first experience was gained

Smoke-signalling to an aircraft bringing food supplies for the International Glaciological Expedition.

with transporting large loads. During the summer the work of reconnoitring and marking out the route across the ice from Tuto was continued, and the most dangerous of the crevasses were filled up by shovel-bladed bulldozers and were then rolled flat so that they could be driven across. By August the route was finally so well marked and tested that they risked letting the two last heavy "swings" travel by it instead of by the Nuto route.

Trials were made, not only of transportation methods and trail marking but also of navigational equipment. Proximity to the magnetic poles makes magnetic compasses insensitive, and there are also problems with gyro compasses. Expeditions must therefore have trained navigators with them who are capable of using theodolites, bubble sextants, and astro-compasses for determining positions and azimuths. On the normal routes used by the heavy "swings" the trail is marked out with flags and snow cairns, and routes used in darkness can also be marked with reflectors atta-

157

ched to flagged stakes. Both a magnetic compass and a gyro compass were tested out, and — unsuccessful — experiments were made with an electrical crevasse detector. The system employed in this is quite simple. A low frequency alternating current is set up between two groups of electrodes placed fore and aft of the vehicle. The crevasses distort the current pattern and cause changes in voltage between the signal electrodes. The instrument did not work satisfactorily at first, but after some years of testing in Greenland the Americans succeeded in developing an improved version for use in Antarctica during the International Geophysical Year, where it was considered successful.

The First Winter Journeys on the Ice Sheet

The results of the tests made in 1954 were so favourable that the Americans were now in a position, if it should be necessary, to keep a station on the ice sheet supplied in summer, but transportation across the ice cap in winter, under conditions of darkness and intense cold, was something of which they as yet had no experience. In 1955 men of the Corps of Engineers started to construct a landing strip at Site II that was large enough to take even the biggest American transport planes. This called for "swings" with heavy sledges and a large load. It was found more suitable in transporting these heavier loads to use D-7 and D-8 Caterpillar tractors which were fitted with broad (54 in.) caterpillar tracks. The heavy ten-ton sledges were fitted with wider runners and it was also found better to fit four moveable skis than two fixed runners. To provide comfortable living quarters for the crews, specially built caravans on runners were used; these were called "wanigans" and contained not only bunks and a galley but all modern comforts — most of them contained a shower with hot and cold water. They were heated by oil and had, of course, electric lighting and electric cookers, electric refrigerators and other modern comforts. In the previous years they had been chary of using tractors on routes that had not been reconnoitred and carefully marked out, but attempts were made in 1955 to take an expedition by tractor across the ice sheet to Kap Georg Cohn and back again. The East Wind expedition succeeded in making this 1,300 mile trip there and back in July and August, taking three D-7 tractors and nine ten-ton sledges, four wanigans, and three Weasels — these last were used for reconnaissance and navigation. The journey went off according to plan and without incident.

In the autumn the heavy sledge swings continued to move between Camp Tuto and Site II, and in all 24 heavy sledge swings were made in 1955. As a contribution to the programme of the International Geophysical Year, it was planned to establish six HIRAN stations on the ice sheet between Disko Bugt and the east coast, using them as measuring stations for linking the very exact surveys that had been made in east and west Greenland. They were also to be in contact

158

The crews on the American tractor convoys live in caravans equipped with every comfort – even hot showers.

with similar stations in Iceland and Canada. These measurements would give a more precise determination of the relative positions of Greenland, Iceland, and Canada. It was planned to transport at least part of the equipment for these stations by a tractor swing made in the winter and to stock it up with supplies in the same way. During the autumn preparations were made for this expedition, which was to be known as South Wind. It started out from Camp Tuto on 18 October with four large D-8 tractors, twelve ten-tons sledges, four wanigans, and three Weasels towing three one-ton sledges. It was late in the year so that there were only a couple of hours of daylight each day, and this made navigation difficult even though the Jello Expedition had marked out the route in advance. It was a severe winter and the higher they climbed, the lower the temperature fell, and they experienced minimum temperatures as low as —60 F. The men suffered terribly from frostbite, and in the intense cold they had a lot of trouble with the equipment: the heating system in the wanigans failed, there were breaks in the fuel pipes, and the caterpillar tracks parted, the electric batteries froze, and if the engines stopped for even a moment it was almost impossible to get them going again. In spite of these difficulties they managed to make the journey and deposited 30 tons of supplies at the site of the projected station Hiran 26 roughly east of Søndre Strømfjord and 660 miles south-east of Thule Air Base. But the return journey was even worse. Gradually three or four of the tractors and one of the Weasels had to be abandoned. Not

159

until 3 December did they see the lights of Site II and on 16 December they were back in Camp Tuto after covering 1,300 miles on the ice sheet and spending sixty days there.

During the summer of 1956 the abandoned tractors were brought back to Camp Tuto, but attempts to send supplies by tractor to the HIRAN stations were abandoned, and, instead, effort was concentrated on air-lifting the supplies in. The South Wind expedition had given clear proof that there was as yet insufficient suitable equipment and too little experience for long tractor journeys to be made under high Arctic conditions in winter, and apart from minor swings along the trail between Camp Tuto and Site II no major tractor convoys have since been working on the ice during the winter except in connexion with rescue operations. In 1957 an American military aircraft made a forced landing on the ice sheet inland from Thule base, and its crew was brought out by tractor, and in February of the same year a swing was made by tractor to evacuate the crew of Fistclench, which was no longer to be used as an air control and warning station.

In addition to the transportation trials on the ice sheet, scientific research was continuing both in the marginal zone and in central Greenland. In 1954 the Swedish glaciologist, Valter Schytt, had carried out on behalf of SIPRE a comprehensive investigation of the snow budget of Tuto ramp and of the ice movement there, and these studies were continued the following year by the geographer T. Griffiths, who had been Schytt's chief assistant in 1954.

Pits dug down into the ice sheet yielded information that made it possible to determine the annual snow stratification and thus the amount of annual accumulation. These investigations were carried out by Carl S. Benson, who in 1954 with Party Crystal had made examinations in the area between Camp Tuto and Fistclench, and in 1955 with the Jello Expedition had continued his investigation along the whole route from Fistclench to Station Centrale and from there to Victor's Camp VI. The expedition, consisting of eight men, took with them four Weasels, and fuel and other supplies were flown in for them on the journey and dropped by parachute.

The expedition was evacuated by an American plane that landed on the ice near Camp VI; all the equipment had to be left on the ice, where it was later taken over by EGIG (see page 207) On the journey from Station Centrale to Camp VI they carried out, in addition to the stratification studies in the pits, a re-survey and prolongation of the French aluminium markers in preparation for the work that was to be done during the coming International Glaciological Expedition.

In 1955 tests were made with helicopters flying further in over the ice cap. Helicopters had been used for research and reconnaissance in the marginal area from quite early on, but now the research teams had at their disposal two Sikorsky and six Bell helicopters in addition to two Beaver aircraft. The small Bell helicopters soon proved unsuitable for flights across the ice sheet, for they had insufficient load capacity and so could not take the navigational equipment that was

The excavated passages of Camp Century being covered with corrugated sheets.

Tellurometer readings being taken on the International Glaciological Expedition.

A specially constructed sun compass aiding navigation on the International Glaciological Expedition.

Ventilation shaft being set in place during the construction of Camp Century.

During the winters 1949–1950 and 1950–1951 9 men were wintering at Station Centrale.

Station Jarl-Joset was shaped as a round igloo but was build of plastic.

Covering one of the passages of Camp Century with wonder arches.

The Americans excavated the first tunnel in the ice sheet in the vertical or near vertical ice cliff near Camp Tuto. The ice was removed from the tunnel by conveyer belt and dumped in Tuto lake.

Ice tunnel near Camp Tuto.

Crevasse detector used by the Americans in investigations on the ice sheet.

An American "swing" on the ice sheet.

Modern expeditions on the ice sheet are based on tractors.

Members of the expeditions live in comfortable wanigans equiped with all modern conveniences.

necessary for a sufficient supply of spares in case of an emergency landing. There were thus several accidents with them: two of them as a result of forced landings during white-out.

Both in 1956 and 1957 the testing of various improved models of LGP tractors and other tracked and wheeled vehicles continued, and in 1956 experiments were also commenced with the "overland train", which was designed for impassable terrain and which, instead of caterpillar tracks, ran on four large diameter wheels fitted with low pressure pneumatic nylon tires. Trials with this proved so promising that they were continued in the subsequent years, and the system was adopted for transporting off-road cargo. Another success was the use of rolling fuel tanks which were large rubber cylinders drawn by tractors; they could hold up to 450 imperial gallons of fuel; using them not only saved weight but also time in loading and discharging the 45 gallon drums.

In 1956 the "Dishpan" electrical crevasse detector was successfully used and the testing of equipment continued. During that summer a total of ten heavy swings were made between Camp Tuto and Fistclench, and flights were also continued, although some of the tractor trials were not carried out because the material to be used in them did not arrive in time or was so badly damaged on arrival that it was unusable until extensive repairs had been carried out. In 1957 purely routine testing of the equipment continued; there were no basically new vehicles to be tried out; experiments were also continued with the electromagnetic crevasse detector and more experience was gained with this.

The Five-Year Plan is Concluded before the International Geophysical Year Commences.

The five-year plan for research on the ice sheet concluded at the end of 1957. Practically all its objectives had been attained. There was now a fund of technical experience that made it possible to operate on the ice sheet. Tractors and heavy Otaco sledges were able to transport very heavy loads so that it would be possible to erect and supply installations on the ice cap by using oversnow transport alone, and these stations could be stocked initially with sufficient supplies to make them quite independent of supplies brought in by plane. It had been proved by the research workers that it was possible to use Weasels nearly everywhere, but that on long trips they would need to be supported with supplies brought in by air and they could not operate independently of their base. Successful trials had developed an electric crevasse detector which, mounted on a Weasel or a tractor, could register crevasses that could not be seen on the surface. Experiments had also produced a navigation system that made it possible to travel outside the marked routes.

To facilitate navigation between Camp Tuto and Fistclench the route was not only marked with bamboo poles and flags, but attempts were also made to mark the route with an electric-wire trail-marking system. A cable carrying current was laid on each side of the roadway and from electromagnetic measuring equipment fitted in the Weasel or tractor it was possible to ascertain whether the vehicle was still between the cables or had left the route. But as the electric cables were frequently severed by the movement of the ice or by bulldozers digging petrol depots out of the snow, experiments with this method of marking the route were gradually abandoned. Instead, tests were made using radar to locate the marker poles in poor visibility.

The five-year programme on the ice sheet concluded as the International Geophysical Year began, during which the Americans had some important problems to solve in Antarctica. Their experience on the Greenland ice cap was of great benefit to them in carrying out their IGY programme, and it was, in fact, the basis of their highly successful effort in Antarctica. Without such a preparation they could scarcely have carried out the tasks that they undertook in Antarctica. The American engineers and scientists who were working at the South Pole had almost all taken part previously in research and transportation on the Greenland ice cap.

The undisputed advantages that the Americans had over the Russians, French, British, and other nations in Antarctica was a direct result of the experience they had gathered on the ice sheet in Greenland. In contrast to the others, they arrived with a proven technique; even the Russians had to work things out as they went along. During the International Geophysical Year more than forty stations were erected in Antarctica, and six of these were American, among them the Amundsen-Scott Station at the geographical South Pole, and the Byrd Station in Marie Byrd Land. Both of these stations were modelled on stations that had been tried out and had proved reliable in Greenland. Byrd Station was set up by means of tractor swings, using the same method that had been employed in Greenland, whereas the station at the South Pole was established solely by airlift from McMurdo Sound. It has been officially estimated that the American contribution in Antarctica during the International Geophysical Year cost more than $ 250 million; only a small percentage of this was actually spent on scientific research, which was the object of the IGY-expeditions, the rest of the sum was accounted for by the cost of transport and supplies, and of erecting and maintaining the six stations etc. This sum gives an insight into how expensive modern research on an ice sheet has become. It is a far cry from the £500—£1200 that the early expeditions across the ice sheet cost.

Access Routes onto the Ice Sheet.

Even though the five-year plan was over and its results had been good, work continued on the Greenland ice sheet. There were still technical improvements to be tested out, and there was above all a desire to gain a broader knowledge of the ice sheet beyond the narrow stretch from

One of the International Glaciological Expedition's camps on the ice sheet.

Camp Tuto inland to Fistclench. Hitherto all efforts had been concentrated in the Thule area, but now some exploration was done to discover whether there were any other access routes on to the ice sheet.

In July and August 1956 aerial reconnaissance had covered most of the marginal area in the north, the west, and the south-east of Greenland, and special interest was centred on finding new routes from the military establishments in southern Greenland, e. g. Søndre Strømfjord and Narssarssuaq, and from the Danish naval station at Grønnedal and from Frederikshåb Isblink. Several earlier visits to the margin of the ice behind Søndre Strømfjord had already convinced the Americans and the foreign scientists who were working with them, as well as the Danish scientists, that the ice sheet at this point was so heavily crevassed and intersected by so many melt-water streams that it would be absolutely impossible to take a Weasel or a tractor across it in summer.

171

It was however still an open question whether it would be feasible in the winter when snow filled all the melt-water beds and the ice was easier to negotiate.

To reconnoitre in preparation for the International Glaciological Expedition (see page 206) a small expedition was sent out from Paris in the spring of 1957 and arrived at Søndre Strømfjord. The objective was to find a possible route for travelling by Weasel from the base itself onto the ice sheet.

The expedition, which was led by Victor, flew from Paris in a French military transport plane, and had an Alouette helicopter for reconnaissance. With this they did actually succeed in finding a possible route, but it was only passable in the spring when the winter snow still filled the stream beds so that it was possible to drive on top of the drifts. The Americans were also interested in the route, and in the spring of 1958 they started Operation King Dog, on which four Weasels were driven over the route and penetrated 100 miles onto the ice sheet. They left Søndre Strømfjord on 21 March and they were back again by 17 April after surveying the route and making some investigations of snow accumulation, ice movement, etc.

A similar search for a route onto the ice sheet was made at Narssarssuaq in the summer of 1957. Here the Americans succeeded in finding a route leading from the base to the margin of the ice and then inland across the ice sheet, but the part of the route that lay across land was very uneven and would require extensive and very costly earth works if Weasels and tractors were to cross it. About this time it was decided that the Americans would give up this base and hand it over to Denmark, so that the plans for developing an access route onto the ice sheet here were set aside. No Weasel was ever successfully taken up onto the ice sheet at this point.

The Large Expedition to Peary Land.

Plans were also being worked out for a more detailed exploration of north Greenland. It was planned that Operation Lead Dog should study the ice-free land in front of the ice in Nyeboe Land, Peary Land and Kronprins Christian Land, and also compile an overall picture of the transportation environment under the wide range of conditions encountered in north Greenland, both on the ice sheet and on the sea ice. The expedition was expected to last for several years, for it would only operate in Greenland during the summer. The expedition was planned on the basis of tractor and Weasel transport across the ice sheet from Camp Tuto to the edge of the ice. This was to be their base for reconnaissance work by helicopter in the hopes of finding a descent route from the ice sheet to the ice-free coastland.

While travelling across the ice, they intended to map the snow accumulation and the topography of this part of the ice sheet, which was very little known. During 1958 they were to explore Nye-

172

Frequently repairs and the replacement of caterpillar tracks have to be carried out on the ice sheet.

boe Land, but as the equipment was very late arriving at the base that summer, they had to post-pone this journey until the following year and limit themselves to reconnoitring the first part of the route and setting up a large depot of fuel, food, and various kinds of equipment. They were also able to test out a number of new electronic navigational aids at the same time. Over part of their route they followed the tracks of the 1955 East Wind expedition which were still visible.

In May of 1959 Lead Dog started out again, this time in real earnest, the largest expedition ever to operate on the Greenland ice sheet was being organized. The whole time there were more than forty men on the ice sheet, even though some members of the expedition were relieved from time to time by plane. Six large D-8 Caterpillar tractors, four Weasels, one of the new Pole-cats, four

173

Overland Trains, fourteen 10-ton Otaco sledges, one 20-ton sledge and five wanigans were taken, and also at the disposal of the Lead Dog expedition were two aircraft (one Beaver and one Otter) as well as a Chickasaw helicopter. The great convoy departed from Camp Tuto on 15 May and for the first 300 miles they were able to follow the trail that had been made the previous year, but when they came to the depot they changed course and turned due north towards Nyeboe Land.

They were now covering terrain that had never previously been visited. On 1 June they reached the edge of the ice behind Nyeboe Land and set up camp about 4 miles from the edge of the ice so that they had a view of the ice-free land in front of the ice sheet. They laid out a landing strip with tractors, and the two aircraft and the helicopter that were at the expedition's disposal were assembled there. It was now a matter of finding a route that was suitable for taking the Weasels and tractors down from the ice sheet and on through the ice-free land. At most places the front of the ice sheet resembled a 100—130 ft wall which completely excluded any chance of descending.

After making many reconnaissance flights they succeeded in finding a route through the crevasses and down over the edge of the ice. This route looked as if it might be just about possible for Weasels to use, although probably not for the tractors. It turned out, however, to be of very little value to them, for it led only to a high plateau which was bounded on all sides, except the side where the ice sheet was, by deep and precipitous canyons which prevented any further advance. They were therefore obliged to abandon the idea of reaching Nyeboe Land, and on 24 June the convoy struck camp and continued north-east towards Peary Land.

The journey on the ice sheet went off according to plan, although they were frequently delayed by white-outs, but as they approached Peary Land their difficulties began in earnest. To make sure the route was safe for the passage of the heavy convoy, a Weasel fitted with a crevasse detector drove on ahead and examined it. When they were once more near ice-free land they entered the crevasse area, and the Weasel with the crevasse detector broke through a snow bridge over a crevasse, and only with a great deal of trouble and difficulty did they succeed in getting the Weasel and its crew safely onto firm ground again.

A fresh attempt to find a safe route through the crevasses was made the next day, but they had the same experience again — the Weasel fell through another snow bridge and again was only rescued with great labour. Further reconnoitring showed that access to Peary Land by this route was even more difficult than access to Nyeboe Land. Even though they should succeed in finding a route through the dangerous crevasse area, the descent into Peary Land itself would be so difficult, if it were not impossible, that further attempts were abandoned, and on 20 July they started on the return trip along the tracks they had made on the way out, and they reached Camp Tuto on 1 August.

The Lead Dog expedition had been carried out without loss of human life or equipment in spite of the difficult and perilous crevasse area that they had crossed. Considerable experience had been gained in using tractor convoys across unknown terrain, and new navigational equipment had also been tested out. The American glaciologist Chester Langway had made detailed studies of the snow along the whole route, and had collected data about the annual amount of snow accumulation in that region, about which nothing was known previously, but unfortunately seismic measurements had not been made to determine the thickness of the ice.

It was therefore still uncertain whether the valley that near the coast was occupied by Humboldt Gletscher extended far into the inland ice area. Nor had they succeded in finding any descent route into either Peary Land or Nyeboe Land, and had therefore been unable to explore these areas.

The transportation that had formed the basis of the expedition to Nyeboe Land and Peary Land had been D-8 Caterpillar tractors, which on a number of expeditions to Antarctica had proved well suited for long journeys as they were able to carry large quantities of fuel and were thus independent of air supplies. The expedition had also had one Pole-cat and four Overland Trains. The Pole-cat is an articulated two-unit carrier for personnel and light cargo. It has four-track drive and consists, in fact, of two Weasels. It has a 120 h. p. engine, and with a cruising speed of 10—11 m. p. h., a maximum speed of about 20 m. p. h., and a load capacity of 1—1½ tons, it is the fastest vehicle that has been used on the ice cap and is also considerably more comfortable to travel in than the Weasel.

The Overland Train consists of four units: a driving unit and three goods trailers which can carry some 15 tons. Each of the units is fitted with four large wheels of a diameter of 10 ft 6 in covered with very large tubeless tires of nylon. The train is powered by diesel engines which drive two generators, each of which supplies power to the sixteen 40 h. p. electric motors fitted one to each wheel.

In addition to the payload capacity of 50 tons the train can also pull one or more off-road trailers, which, like the train itself, are fitted with large wheels. Its great length and its even distribution of power and weight give the overland train considerable manoeuvrability and greater safety when crossing crevasse-covered terrain. It can be used on ordinary roads or on snow, and it is therefore possible to load directly onto it at Thule Air Base and then drive it up onto the ice sheet under its own power, so that no time is wasted in transferring the load, which would otherwise have to be done at Camp Tuto. On trials with the Overland Train and the off-road trailers it had been found possible to transport a payload of 71 tons on one train. Figures show that the train has a maximum speed of over 15 m. p. h.

Experience on the Lead Dog expedition had shown that it was impossible to use Weasels or tractors to enter Peary Land, and no detailed exploration of Kronprins Christian Land had yet been carried out, either. In 1960 a camp was set up on the ice sheet near Centrum Sø at the head of Danmark Fjord, and all equipment and supplies for it were transported to it by tractor, and helicopters, too, were able to follow the trail to the main camp. During the summer most of northern Greenland was explored by American geologists and glaciologists, and these scientists were transported around by helicopter, so that they were able to collect their samples and take measurements in many places.

These investigations seemed to confirm Lauge Koch's theory that the eastern part of Peary Land had not been glaciated during the Pleistocene glaciation. Precise measurements of the lake ice at Centrum Sø were made as well as measurements of snow accumulation and the temperature of the snow in pits along the whole route from Camp Tuto to the main camp.

The tractor convoys went through according to plan, but they did not succeed this time either in finding a route suitable for taking the Weasels down from the ice sheet to Jørgen Brønlund Fjord in Peary Land, where the Americans on Operation Groundhog in 1958 had set up an emergency landing ground on the north side of the fjord about opposite to the old winter station that had been used by the Danish Pearyland Expedition.

The same year heavy swings began to bring in building materials and supplies for Camp Century which was under construction. Among the equipment was a heavy and not easily transportable atomic reactor which was brought in by sledge train. Every year until now tractor swings have continued to supply Camp Century, and tractor and Weasel convoys have each year visited the abandoned camp at Fistclench to resurvey it so as to keep a check on the deformation of the drill holes and corridors in the snow.

A continuation of Carl S. Benson's measurements in the snow in southern Greenland was made in 1959 and 1960 under Richard Ragle, who drove by Weasel across the southern part of the ice sheet and took systematic measurements of the snow accumulation there. By comparing Benson's earlier investigations with observations from northern Greenland, a general idea has been obtained of the snow accumulation and snow temperatures on the ice sheet. The objectives of the five-year plan and subsequent research have now been achieved, and American activity in exploring the ice sheet has since decreased.

American Stations on the Ice Sheet

Old Ice Cap Stations

Even when Thule base was first built it was clear that one or more advanced radar warning stations would have to be constructed on the ice sheet to give warning in case of attack. All previous stations on the ice sheet had been built to last for only one, or at the most two, winters, but the radar stations had to be planned to have a useful life of a number of years.

All previous constructions on the ice had been quite primitive — the expeditions of Wegener and Watkins had dug themselves into the snow — and it had never been a matter of more than two or three men living on the ice. A somewhat larger station but nevertheless still of a very primitive kind, had been used in Nordaustlandet when the Oxford University Arctic Expedition wintered there in 1935—36. The French expeditions under Victor had used a prefabricated building dug down into the snow from which they had dug out long passages for use as store rooms and for radiosonde measurements.

On Admiral R. Byrd's Antarctic expeditions in 1928—30 and 1933—35 and on the U. S. Antarctic Service Expedition 1939—41 a large amount of experience had been gained by the Americans in living conditions under high Arctic conditions, but not even on these expeditions had there been any experience of more permanent stations, for each expedition had established a new station.

There are manifold problems and difficulties in the planning of stations on the ice sheet. They must be able to keep the cold out and to resist the violent arctic blizzards. To protect them it is therefore most to the purpose to dig them down into the snow and allow them to be covered in by the winter snow, only letting chimneys, ventilation shafts, and exits remain exposed. As time passes the stations will gradually come to sink deeper and the weight of the accumulating snow will finally be enough to crush the strongest construction. An example of this can be seen in Station Centrale, which was constructed in 1949. By 1959 it was 10 m (33 ft) below the surface and had been partially crushed. In addition to this, the walls had been squeezed together from the side;

the passages, which had once been more than three feet wide, were found on a visit in 1959 to have been compressed to half their original width.

Just keeping the cold out is not enough; insulation is also necessary so that the heat cannot escape from the station and melt the snow around it and thereby possibly ruin the foundations of the base. Another problem was that the difficulty of transporting materials to the ice sheet made it necessary to keep the weight and dimensions of the building down to the minimum. The average snow accumulation for the whole of the ice sheet is about one metre annually, but in northern Greenland it is somewhat less than this. Even so, it must be assumed that buildings erected on the surface of the snow would in ten years' time come to lie under seven to eight metres of newly laid snow and that everything that projected above the snow would cause the formation of huge snow drifts that would soon conceal everything. It was no longer a question of building a station to be used by a small group of scientists with very limited scientific equipment; now stations were to be constructed that would have room for all the equipment that a modern military radar station needs, manned by troops who were to live as comfortably as conditions on the ice sheet permitted.

The Ice Cap Station in Tubes.

New and quite untraditional methods had to be adopted. The first two radar installations were erected in 1952-53. One of them, Site I, was situated on the ice cap north of Thule Air Base fairly close to the ice front. The other, Site II, was 200 miles inland on the ice sheet east of Thule Air Base, 7,000 ft above sea level.

To protect the stations against wind and cold and to prevent them from being crushed too rapidly by the accumulating snow, the buildings were erected inside gigantic tubes made out of corrugated iron sheets "floating" in the snow. The tubes were eight metres (26 ft) in diameter and were assembled from sheets that had previously been tailor made for the purpose. At the time the stations were constructed, the tubes were only half submerged in the snow, but they were soon completely covered by snow drifts.

A plank base was laid in the tubes and the actual hutments were built on this. Standard prefabricated units could be used for the hutments, for they were not exposed to any special pressure or load. These buildings in the tubes were fitted out with billets, bathrooms, radio rooms, etc. for the use of the crew; only the radar aerial itself had to project above the snow, and this was raised up so much that it was reckoned that it would be a long time before it was covered. Apart from the radar tower, the whole construction was only connected to the outside world by a number of air ducts and some vertical tubes that served as entrances and exits for the crew. These were fitted with trap doors to prevent the drifting snow from penetrating down.

178

As the building was buried deeper and deeper under the snow, these ventilation shafts and access tubes had of course to be extended. In Danish newspapers these two radar stations have often been compared with submarines floating in the snow. To walk about the long galleries with their gleaming metal struts on which the ice crystals were sparkling and on which the conduits and electrical installations marked out their own particular pattern, was to feel that one was in a submarine, and one was, indeed, far enough beneath the surface to have no glimpse of daylight. The only contact with the inhabited world was by radio and aeroplane. But once one had entered the barracks themselves with their billets, mess rooms, library, table tennis, and blaring radios, one had come into the normal world of an army camp.

It was an almost normal life that was led there; both the crew's and the officers' quarters were well fitted out, there were showers with hot and cold water, and no canteen in America or any-where else could have served a better meal than one could get at the two stations under the Greenland ice sheet. In a way one was isolated, of course, surrounded by one of the world's most barren landscapes, but the sense of isolation and boredom was offset by the frequent tractor "swings", air connexions with Thule Air Base (at least in summer) and the all-the-year-round mail connexion with America. The latest American films were shown at the base, often before they were on general release.

Site II was an important starting point for the scientific exploration of the ice sheet. A number of expeditions started out from there, and a long series of technical and glaciological tests were made. In laboratories in America, Britain and Switzerland comprehensive studies had been made to discover how snow and firn react when as a block or cylinder they are exposed to stress or strain. All these experiments had worked with pressure or load in one particular direction, and no similar tests had been made on the mechanical and physical properties of snow and firn in situ, where it is not merely a matter of a top load, but also of pressure from all sides. Such tests were now made at Site II.

In 1954 the most comprehensive tests that had ever been attempted on the pressure and deform-ation of snow and firn were commenced. A number of snow tunnels were dug out and also several trenches that were afterwards covered over. A deep pit was also excavated which was fitted with instruments that could record the changes that would take place over a five-year period. Near Site II a cylindrical tunnel with a diameter of 2.5 m (8 ft 2 in) was excavated in 1954; from the surface the tunnel descended with a gradient of 1:3¾ to a depth of 8 m (26 ft) and then con-tinued horizontally for another 9 m (30 ft). So that the stratification of the firn could be studied and the relationship between the size of the load and the amount of deformation could be deter-mined, a vertical shaft 30 m (10 ft) deep was excavated and from the bottom of this shaft a hole was drilled down for a further 20 m (65 ft) with a core drill, so that a continuous series of samples could be obtained to a depth of 50 m (165 ft).

In addition to this excavation work, attempts were also being made to find a relatively cheap method of roofing over the 2—3 m (8—10 ft) wide trenches which had been dug out in the surface of the snow. To carry on this research, a special camp, called Fistclench, was erected, where the Corps of Engineers was active during the summer. However, the men whose task it was to take readings of the instruments during the winter remained at Site II.

It had been reckoned that Site II would last for five years, and the principles of construction had proved good enough for that, but it had gradually come to lie so far down in the snow that it had become uncomfortable to live in. In 1957 the station was abandoned and evacuated, but every year since, the station has been visited to that re-measurements of the amount of deformation could be taken. On a visit made by the author in 1962 the corrugated iron tubes of Site II were found to be still usable, but they lay 11 m (36 ft) beneath the surface. By and by, as the station was covered by more and more snow it became more and more difficult to locate. In 1965 despite a thorough search it was not possible at first to find it; neither by ordinary reconnaissance on the ground nor with the aid of a helicopter. It was not until help was obtained from an aircraft which was equipped with radar designed for submarine search that the station was located and what were probably the last re-measurements of the station undertaken.

The results of the studies at Fistclench showed that snow is a cheap and good building material and a good heat insulator. Tests with a Swiss snow clearing machine, called the Peter Snow Miller, had proved that it was possible to excavate long trenches mechanically, and if these were then covered over with arched sheets of corrugated iron, it was a simple matter to construct long tunnels, The corrugated sheets were strong enough to support the accumulated snow and to keep it from falling into the passage ways, and after a time the snow became so hard that it could, in fact, support itself. If, instead of letting the new snow cover the passages, the excavated snow was thrown back over them, a snow cover that could support itself was very soon obtained. It was thus possible to erect hutments and buildings inside the passages and so avoid the construction of great tubes of corrugated iron.

Such snow-covered passages are difficult to locate from the air, and the snow on top of them is a good protection from air attack. There was thus considerable interest in military circles in constructing a major experimental station somewhere on the ice sheet. Site II had been situated some 350 km (200 miles) from the edge of the ice, and supplies had been brought to it partly on tractor swings and partly by air, but in the winter particularly it had proved difficult to keep the station supplied, and there had also been a number of air crashes on these flights.

180

CAMP CENTURY

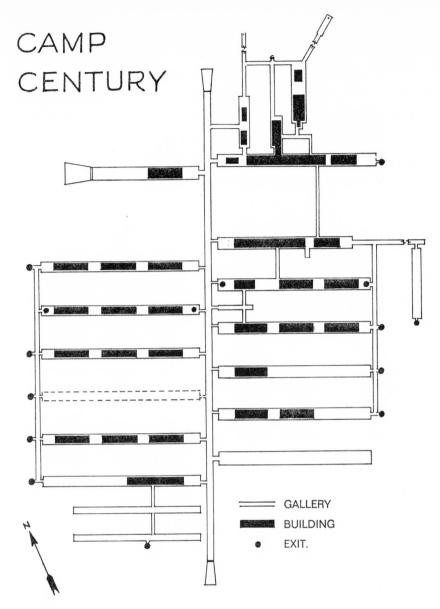

Camp Century, "The City under the Ice", is constructed

It was therefore intended to make use of the experience gained at Site II and at Fistclench in the construction of a larger experimental station named Camp Century — to be about 100 miles from Camp Tuto. The station was to be the starting point for a large number of scientific glaciological tests and experiments, and from a military point of view it was hoped to gain practical experience of how such a permanent station could be run and maintained. To ease the problem of transportation to it, it was therefore to be built nearer to the ice margin than Site II and Fistclench had been, but because snow was to be used as a building material, it had to be built far enough on to the ice sheet for summer snow melting to be an insignificant factor. The station was actually built about 220 km (140 miles) within the margin of the ice sheet at Camp Tuto, and over 6,000 ft above sea level. Preparatory work was started in 1958, and during the summers of 1959 and 1960 building work was completed.

Diesel oil for heating and for generating power had been a significant part of the supplies that had had to be transported to Site II. It would therefore be considerably easier to supply the station if diesel oil was not required. For a number of years the possibility had been examined of supplying the station with oil by pipeline, but the results had not been promising. It was therefore decided that instead of using oil heating the station would be equipped with a modern atomic power plant.

Whereas the life of Site II had been reckoned at five years, the new station was to last for at least ten years, and it was planned that it would have a staff of about a hundred men in the winter and accommodations for double that number in summer. It was thus a matter of building a whole township under the snow. The station contains a 400 m (¼ mile) long "main street" from which a series of side passages branch out at right angles to each side. The passages were excavated by a Peter Snow Miller, which cuts its way down into the snow which it flings up to the side. Using this machine, it is possible to cut 20—30 ft deep trenches of varying width and length, and under ideal conditions it can shift up to 900 m³ (1,200 cub. yds) of snow per hour.

If the machine traverses the excavation several times, the passages can be widened and deepened. When the desired dimensions have been reached the passages are covered over with corrugated iron sheets, and after that some of the excavated snow is thrown back again to make a layer about 3 ft thick on top of the sheets. At first this snow is quite loose, but it soon cinters and becomes very hard with a considerably higher density and greater tensile strength than natural snow of the same age. It is, therefore, soon able to support itself, and in many cases it has been possible to remove the corrugated iron sheets. This "Peter snow" is suitable material for many construction works, and by changing the elevation of the blowing tube, the snow can be made to fall at various distances, which alters its tensile strength and other properties.

By the Peter method snow can very quickly be obtained that after a few hours is suitable for construction, having the same strength as very old and hardened snow. This hardening of the snow is partly due to the fact that the large snow grains have a tendency to grow at the expense of the small grains. When the snow is milled up, it is mainly the large grains that are preserved, and thus the "Peter snow" has the same constituency as snow that is much older.

The long "high street" is the main traffic route of the camp with an entrance at both ends, and it is so wide and high that tractors and Weasels can drive in and unload direct at the spot where

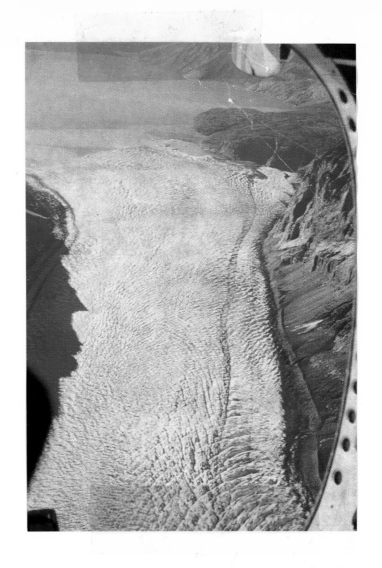

An outlet-glacier from the ice sheet at Kangerdlugssuaq, west Greenland.

their loads are to be used. To protect this "street" from wear, it is paved with planks, and to improve traffic flow it is a one-way street. On each side there are some passages running off at right-angles, fourteen in all.

In these side passages are the billets and mess-rooms of the crew. Buildings of various types are used, most of them are the normal American hutments of T-5 type which are used in Arctic areas and are assembled from prefabricated units. Plastic houses, cast on the site, are also used. The raw materials for these is transported in barrels in powder form or as a solution, and the houses themselves are built of cast units. The raw material — essentially polyurethane plastic and fibre-glass — is a polyester blend which expands into a light foam and forms very durable and strong panels and is a good heat insulator. In view of the great advantages of thus transporting building materials in barrels and bringing only single moulds for casting, it may well prove to be

The author is standing in a sub-glacial melt water tunnel which was formed by the draining of an ice-dammed lake. The process of draining drew the very large ice blocks into the tunnel.

the case that plastic houses will be much used in ice sheet stations of the future, but at present they are still at the experimental stage.

The nerve centre of the station is the nuclear power plant at the northern extremity of the camp. It has a capacity of 1500 kw, and the camp is also equipped with 300 kw diesel generators as reserves in case the atomic reactor should fail. It took an enormous amount of effort to get the heavy reactor and power plant to the station by sledge, but it arrived during the summer of 1960, and in October of the same year it was started up. In spite of some odd troubles it has functioned so satisfactorily that the Americans have now installed one of the same type at McMurdo Sound in the Antarctic.

The amount of heat developed by the installation is very great, and cooling is done by sucking in cold air, and the warm air is discharged through three large glycol cooling towers. The formation

184

The colour-play of the ice in the tunnels can
be most impressive.

of hoar frost was a great problem here, and trials have been made with using cooling wells: by
leading the hot glycol liquid through a 50 m (160 ft) shaft which widens out to a 150 m (500 ft)
wide basin designed to take the surplus heat.

The camp is heated by electricity alone, because of the danger of fire. Water supply has caused
considerable problems. Normally, water had been obtained on the ice sheet by melting snow with
an oil burner. But at Camp Century the consumption of water is so great that other methods had

185

to be used. Attempts have been made to make a well in the snow with steam, and a 150—200 ft shaft has been melted out, and at the bottom of this a large drop-shaped basin was formed by piping in steam. By regulating the supply of steam it should be possible to keep a certain quantity of water constantly in the well and to slowly extend the bulb-shaped container, but it seems to be difficult to achieve a suitable balance between the supply of steam and the consumption of water. The daily consumption of the camp in summer is around 10,000 gallons, but in winter it is less.

The passages in the ice camp at Camp Century will, of course, get deformed in the same way as those at the other stations on the ice sheet, and if the camp is to be maintained it will from time to time be necessary to scrape the passages free of the snow that has been gradually pressed in to them, but the colder the passages are, the less maintenance there will be, for the rate of deformation of snow becomes greater at the temperature rises.

If the temperature rises above —6° (—21° F) the snow loses a considerable amount of its bearing strength, and it is therefore important to make sure that such temperatures are not reached. In the long passage the temperature is very nearly the same as that of the air outside, which means that it drops right down to —50° (—58° F) in winter, but in summer can rise to as much as 0° (32° F). In the side passages the temperature depends very much on the amount of warmth that is given off by the buildings there.

The power plant and the water pipes in particular radiate considerable heat, but a considerable amount of heat is also given off by buildings themselves, perhaps not so much because of poor insulation as because a lot of warm air streams out every time a door is opened, and there is a very high temperature inside the hutments. The amount of heat actually given off is much greater than had been assumed beforehand, and deformation therefore takes place more rapidly than had been anticipated. Thus, the problem for Camp Century is not how to keep the buildings warm, but how to cool the passages and corridors adequately. During the winter it is, of course, possible to ventilate the whole camp with cold air from the surface and in this way keep the temperature low enough to offset the heat loss from the inner buildings, but in the summer the air temperature is usually too high for it to be of much use. Since snow is permeable and the temperature 30 ft down is practically identical with the mean temperature of the place, i. e. very cold, it has proved possible to construct a summer cooling system whereby cold air was sucked from the pores of the snow beneath the tunnels of the camp. Holes of 12—14 in. diameter were bored to a depth of about 40 ft in the floors of the tunnels and steel casing was sunk to a depth of 16 ft or so. Air was drawn in from the lower, uncased portion of the hole by a fan set in the casing.

By this method it is possible to lower the temperature in the passages by 6—7° (10—12° F) but it would probably be more effective still if the main passage could be closed to the "warm" summer air and left open only in the winter.

Experience in running the station has been favourable, and constructions of a similar type have now been put up in the Antarctic. It is true to say that Camp Century is equipped with every comfort: the officers' quarters are fitted with deep leather-covered armchairs, mahogany chests-of-drawers with bronze fittings, standard lamps etc. in accord with modern American trends in interior decoration.

By constructing this modern town under the ice technology has proved that it can make it possible to live and work in and on the ice. The camp is designed for 150 men, but there is nothing to prevent a larger installation from being built. Both the principle of building the dwellings in large buried systems of tubes and the system now used of covered passages have proved feasible, but neither of them has completely overcome the difficulty of the continual accumulation of snow causing the constructions to sink further and further from the surface. Because of the risk of fire and of an accident with the atomic reactor Camp Century has been spread over as large an area as possible, but this has made long passages necessary and has also meant that there is a large heat loss to the snow. A better heat balance could certainly be achieved if a more compact camp were built, and if instead of building it in horizontal passages, it was laid out in a vertical shaft, it would be possible, by continually extending upward, to keep pace with the accumulating snow. It is therefore possible that the dwelling of the future on the ice may be a tall tower dug in the snow. When the International Glaciological Expedition built Station Jarl-Joset it was the first time that a two-storey building had been erected on the ice, but it was very small. In Greenland, where there are large ice free areas, it will not be usual practice to build large bases or establishments on the ice sheet, but conditions in Antarctica are different.

The development of air routes in the southern hemisphere will probably sooner or later necessitate the building of one or more stations in the Antarctic, and these will presumably have to be built on the ice sheet, for that would be the only place where landing strips could be built that would be useable in both winter and summer. The experience gained with such establishments on the Greenland ice sheet will be extremely valuable when similar structures are envisaged for the much more remote Antarctic regions.

It became apparent from the success of Camp Century that the principle of the camp's construction was correct and that it would be valid in the future, it was therefore decided to close the camp earlier than had been planned. The atomic reactor was brought out in 1964: the dismantling of the camp began in earnest in 1965 and in August 1965 Camp Century was officially closed. Before then what was at the time the deepest drilling in the ice had been carried out and in order that certain special radio measurements might be made a 1,000-foot tunnel had been excavated. The tunnel had a declination of 1:3 and at a depth of 100 m (330 ft) below the snow's surface reached a layer formed from snow which must have fallen in 1690. The deep drilling will probably be continued in the coming year and likewise the deformation of the station's passages and rooms will be under surveillance, but the necessary personnel for these operations will live in wanigans on the surface and will only go down into the camp to carry out their work.

During the Antarctic summers of 1960—61 and 1961—62 the U. S. Navy built a new Byrd station as an undersnow complex building to replace the earlier IGY station of the same name. The design is broadly similar to that of Camp Century, and it has been possible to make comparisons between the environments of Greenland and Antarctica.

The Station on Stilts.

While Camp Century was being built, the system of radar warning stations named Distant Early Warning Line (usually abbreviated to DEW line) was being extended. This line stretches across America from the Pacific to the Atlantic and is intended to warn the U. S. A. if any enemy attack should come from the north. The eastern flank of the U. S. A. would, however, still be unprotected if the system were not extended to cover Greenland and Iceland.

This would mean building one station on Iceland and four in Greenland, two of which were to be on the ice sheet, one on the east coast and the fourth on the west coast. Compared with the older radar stations, Site I and Site II, the new ones were to be very large and modern warning stations — of quite another order of size and range — and of course the radar scanners would have to be installed much higher above the surface of the ice. An excavated site like that of Camp Century or those of the older stations could not be used; building would have to be done on the surface of the snow. The stations were to be situated on a line approximately between Søndre Strømfjord and Angmagssalik, so they would be in an area of relatively high precipitation where snowdrifts would soon cover everything. Tests made at Site II and elsewhere had shown that 90 % of drift formation takes place less than six feet from the surface. If it could be possible to raise the building on pillars above this drift layer, then the formation of drifts would be avoided. It was also important to avoid wind eddies at the corners of the buildings. Wind tunnel tests were made to find the most suitable shape for the building, which proved to be a building on stilts about 30 ft above the surface of the snow. This would solve the problem of drift formation, but would not, of course, prevent the steady accumulation of snow with each fresh fall.

Thus if the building with the radar scanners was to remain at a constant height above the surface, it would be necessary to raise the building continually. The stations, which were named Dye sites, were therefore built on a large platform supported on eight columns, in each of which a hydraulic jack was installed. These jacks were able to raise the whole platform as the snow accumulation increased. To anchor the building it was necessary to consolidate the pillars to a depth of 33 ft below the surface, and then to fill in the excavation again to prevent any changes in the load bearing capacity of the ice. During 1960 and 1961 the erection of the two stations was completed, and Dye 2 and Dye 3 were brought into use. Power was generated by two diesel generators, and the oil for them was pumped up from a 100,000 gallon tank in the snow near the station.

Like Camp Century, the stations themselves are equipped with all modern comforts, and each man has his own room. Unlike the other stations, the personnel here are civilians, and apart from a few technical specialists they are recruited in Denmark. From the windows of the station there is a view across the white snowfield, but life indoors is very much like that on a large ocean liner, and a large part of the personnel, or crew, have in fact previously spent much of their lives at sea. The surroundings are monotonous — very monotonous — there is nothing to be seen but the unbroken whiteness of the ice. There are Weasels and tractors for transporting the gear from the landing strip to the station. All supplies are brought in by air, for the difficult nature of the approach route on to the ice cap from Søndre Strømfjord makes tractor convoys impossible. Instead, everything is brought in by large Hercules aircraft which take both passengers and freight. The staff arrive at Dye 2 and Dye 3 with their suitcases; they go straight from their planes to the station, where they live and work under comfortable conditions, and many of them leave again on the expiration of their contracts without ever having gone more than a hundred yards from the station. There is nothing to go on to the ice sheet for, it is monotonous and therefore without any interest for most of them.

In no place in Greenland or Antarctica has there been such a great departure from the age and spirit of the first explorers as at these Dye stations. The ice sheet is here invaded by men in lounge suits, collars and ties, carrying brief-cases. They arrive and depart in the same way. The ice sheet is now part of the technical equipment of the modern world — at least as long as one does not move far from the stations, for only a mile or two from them living conditions and travel techniques are the same as they have always been.

Ice Drillings.

Drilling in glacier ice is technically very difficult, and to date no one has succeeded in drilling right through either the Greenland or the Antarctic ice sheet. As the glacier is in constant movement, the drill hole will also shift, and the rate of movement will vary from the upper to the lower part of the hole. Because of the plasticity of ice, the drill hole will gradually deform and

An outlet-glacier with ice-dammed lake and moraines in north Greenland.

will eventually be completely compressed. Either a mechanical drill can be used which gradually cuts its way down in the same way as an earth drill, or a thermoelectric drill which melts its way down. Whichever method is used, melt water will form in the hole, and if the drilling work is stopped for any length of time the drill will freeze solid and it will be very difficult to prise it free again.

The first attempts at drilling through a glacier were made with great labour at the close of the last century by the famous German glaciologist, H. Hess, on the small glacier called Hintereisferner which has been the object of much intensive glaciological research. Hess wanted information about the thickness of the ice and the shape of the basin occupied by the glacier. Using a snail bit, he succeeded in making a number of drillings of which the deepest reached 800 ft, and he was able to determine the ice thickness and also the topography of the substratum. Other drillings were made in the Alps, and on his expedition to Dronning Louise Land, J. P. Koch used a worm auger at his winter station to gain information about the temperature of the ice at great depths, but he drilled to only 70 ft.

190

Modern theories about the dynamics of ice movement have made it important to study the deformation of drill holes. In order to study the relationship between the rate of ice movement and the thickness of the ice, M. F. Perutz and A. Roch made in 1948 a deep drilling with an electrically heated boring bit on Aletsch Glacier just below the international research station at Jungfraujoch. They melted their way down to a depth of 445 ft, where they struck rock, and they had presumably cut through the ice far enough to reach the substratum. The drill hole was lined with a thin steel tube and its deformation was measured with a specially constructed clinometer. Similar drillings were made on the Malaspina Glacier in Alaska by the American glaciologist, Robert P. Sharp, who reached a depth of 305 m (1000 ft) without penetrating right through the ice, and as part of the research programme of the American Geographical Society called Project Juneau Icefield, a seven ton drilling rig was flown in to the glacier and various tests were made with drilling. A core drill was used for this, and it was possible to bring up the ice core for analysis.

If crystallographic and glaciochemical analyses are to be made it is important to have samples of the ice, and ice specimens are also essential for a proper description of the stratigraphic conditions. In Greenland both J. P. Koch on the expedition to Dronning Louise Land and Sorge on Wegener's Eismitte had made pits in the firn to study the snow stratification and temperature conditions etc. On the basis of his investigations Sorge had even been able to establish a formula for the relationship between the density of the snow and its depth beneath the surface. But none of these excavations had reached a sufficient depth to penetrate through the firn to the glacier ice proper. It was therefore important that drillings should be made to even greater depths, preferably of course right through the ice to the subsoil beneath.

It was, however, not until after the Second World War that financial resources and technical facilities were available in sufficient quantities for such drillings to be made. A prerequisite for them was of course that the heavy drilling equipment could be transported on to the ice. On the French expedition under Victor, J. Heuberger and M. Perez made a number of drillings: they used a 57 mm core drill and at Camp VI they reached a depth of 126 m (415 ft) and at Station Centrale 151 m (495 ft). At the same time the Swedish glaciologist Valter Schytt, was also beginning to make drillings: first experimentally in Lapland and then later at Maudheim, the winter station of the Norwegian-British-Swedish Antarctic Expedition, where with an 80 mm core drill he reached a depth of 100 m (328 ft).

With the International Geophysical Year particular in mind, a number of drillings were made on the Greenland ice sheet, and an attempt was made to use modified oil-drilling techniques. The experiments were made at Site II; a form of diamond drill was used which in 1956 reached a depth of 305 m (1000 ft), but it was not possible to bring up a complete series of samples. In

1957 a new attempt was made, and this reached a depth of 411 m (1350 ft), and samples were obtained from almost the whole of this depth.

With an average annual snow accumulation of about 34 cm (13 in) of water equivalent for the lowest 300 m (1,000 ft) of the drilling, and a somewhat larger amount of precipitation for the upper part, this meant that at the bottom of the drill-hole they had reached the layers of ice that had originally fallen on the ice sheet as snow some thousand years before — i. e. about the time that Eric the Red was beginning to colonize southern Greenland.

During the International Geophysical Year the Americans made a drill hole to a depth of 304 m (996 ft) at Byrd Station, and the Russians reached 370 m (1250 ft) at Mirny. But none of these drillings penetrated right through the ice sheet. An intensive programme of drilling was commenced in 1962 on the approximately 420 m (1,400 ft) thick Schucherts Gletscher in north-east Greenland in connexion with the search for molybdenite there, and for that purpose it was necessary to bore right through the ice to the bedrock below. The movement of the ice in this glacier is small, and the temperature at the bottom of it is probably about 0° (32° F).

The great interest in the lower zone of the ice sheet, and the widely differing ideas about the nature of the ice at these depths makes it natural that there should be particular interest in drilling right down through the ice to study the temperature conditions and the physical properties of the ice in the zone of contact with the substratum. Attempts to do this were made at Camp Century, where the presence of the atomic power station meant that sufficient electricity and technical assistance were available for a really deep drilling to be made. Seismic measurements show that the ice there is only 1,600 m (5,250 ft) thick, and attempts have been made to drill right through it. It was obvious from the start that conventional drilling methods could not be used, for the drill would freeze solid in the hole. Instead, experiments were made with an electrically heated drill head lowered into the hole on a cable.

The drill head itself is a six metre (20 ft) high cylinder fitted at the lower end with a drill shoe with built-in heating elements. When the current is switched on the lower edge of the drill melts its way down, as the head moves downwards the core of the drilling slides up into the hollow cylinder. Thus, the drill-head must be raised every two or three metres so that the core sample can be removed.

Tests with this method of drilling have demonstrated that there are many difficulties. In 1961, for instance, the cable to the drill parted, and it was only with great difficulty that they succeeded in raising the drill head again. In 1962 the attempt continued, and a depth of about 100 m (325 ft) was reached before the drill head froze solid in the hole. When they attempted to free the drill head, the drill shoe snapped off and prevented any further drilling in that particular hole! In

192

1963, however, a new attempt was made. Even this time they did not succeed in drilling right through the ice, but in the autumn they filled the drill hole with a mixture of diesel oil and trichlorethylene of the same specific gravity as ice to prevent the hole from closing up again. When they returned to Camp Century again the following spring they found the hole in good order, and were able to continue with the drilling, which during that summer reached a depth of 1,500 ft before work had to be called off again and the drill hole filled up once more with fluid.

The depth drillings of 1964 were continued in 1965, however, with the application of another technique. Instead of the previous electrically heated thermo-drill, a rotary drill worked by electricity was used, and the drilling was made as a normal liquid drilling, as the drill hole was filled with glycol. This technique has been used in oil drilling and had proved very efficient. By working round-the-clock a depth of 50 feet a day was drilled. Previously, the core samples taken up were of a rather bad quality, whereas they now came up undamaged. Before the camp had to be closed and the drilling suspended, they had reached as far as 3200 feet below the surface. This is the deepest drilling with core samples that has ever been made on any glacier. To prevent compression of the drill tube the hole was filled with diesel oil and trichlorethylene and sealed for the winter. The drilling will be resumed in the summer of 1966 and they hope — a hope which is justified, no doubt — to penetrate the ice sheet and reach the substratum.

In connection with the depth drilling trials were made with a thermal sonde constructed by the German physicist Bernhard Philbert. The principle of the sonde is a spool wound with a thin electric wire, and when the current is switched on the wire and spool melt their way down the ice. During this process the wire is wound off and at various depths the current can be switched off and the ice temperature measured by means of the electric resistance. As long as the sonde is working in the firn the latter will absorb the melt water, but in proper ice the sonde will be surrounded by melt water, which freezes again, however, as the sonde penetrates further down. It is the plan of Philbert to make measurements of the temperature at the bottom of the ice sheet; and co-operation between Philbert and the Swiss glaciologists of the EGIG has been initiated. A number of trials have thus been made on Swiss glaciers. In Greenland considerable technical difficulties have been encountered, and during the summer of 1965 a depth of only 80 metres was reached, at which depth the sonde was abandoned.

Dr. Philbert believes, however, that these difficulties will gradually be corrected, and undoubtedly, it is a good principle to try different techniques for measuring the temperature at great depths as well as for taking up core samples; but it is obvious that a large number of tests must be made before the sonde will prove advantageous for an expedition of a more civilian character.

Drill samples are of rather small diameter, so it would obviously be still better if measurements and investigations could be made directly on the sides of the drill holes. The French expedition under Victor brought with them a specially constructed drill grab which weighed one ton and which could cut out a hole 80 cm (2 ft 7 in) in diameter, i. e. large enough for a man to be lowered into it and to make measurements, remove samples etc., directly from the sides of the hole. At Station Centrale they reached a depth of 30.5 m (100 ft) but unfortunately the findings of these experiments have never been published, and on a visit to the site in 1959 the International Glaciological Expedition was unable to locate the hole again, so that it has now been completely lost.

194

The American Is Tunnels

Natural Ice Tunnels

When in the summer of 1955 the American Corps of Engineers started to excavate a tunnel into the edge of the ice cap near Camp Tuto, it sparked off wild rumours that even found their way into the world's press. German newspapers, for instance, published a very fanciful artist's impression of trains running into the platforms of subglacial railway stations "somewhere" on the ice cap. In fact, the ice tunnels at Camp Tuto are of much more modest dimensions, though it is possible to drive cars and Weasels through them.

In modern glaciological research it is extremely important to have information about the structure of the ice and its physical condition at great depths, and in many glaciochemical investigations it is necessary to have samples of the ice for analysis. It is no longer adequate merely to study the surface structure of the ice, but it is technically very difficult to get the necessary samples from great depths.

In minor valley glaciers it is, of course, possible to make certain investigations and take certain samples from the sides of the deep glacier crevasses, and from glacier moulins, but even so it is not possible to find out anything about the firn area. As far as the ice sheet is concerned, information could only be gained in this way for the marginal area. In 1891 an American explorer, J. R. Russel, succeeded in penetrating several miles in under the Malaspina Glacier in Alaska by making use of a natural tunnel in the ice formed by a melt-water stream, and similar tours under the ice have been made under several other glaciers.

In Greenland, for instance, the British glaciologist, W. R. B. Battle studied the glaciers of Clavering Ø by taking advantage of the melt-water streams and crevasses in the *Bergschrund* and in this way he collected information about the temperature conditions in the contact zone between the ice and the substratum. Such observations can, however, be only sporadic and random, and the personal risk involved in entering these subglacial channels is out of all proportion to the meagre data that is gathered.

Systematic studies of the ice at depth must be based either on direct measurements using ice drillings and tunnels in the ice, or indirect information must be obtained by analysing geophysical data such as the reproduction of seismic shock waves.

Artificial Ice Tunnels

It is plain that a better method of studying the structure of the ice than to drill down into it would be to construct a tunnel into the ice. Not only could measurements be taken inside it, but the way the tunnel became deformed would be an indication of the way the ice moved and of the pressures that acted within it. During the First World War the Austrian and Italian Alpine troops used to dig out holes in the ice on the Dolomites for their armoured positions, and in the years 1931—1941 an American prospector in Alaska, L. Thornton, is said to have excavated a number of small tunnels in the ice of some glaciers on the border between Alaska and British Columbia in order to search for outcrops of ore in the contact zone with the rock base.

Ice tunnels of any major dimension were, however, first constructed in the years after the Second World War, and this was done as part of the exploration work for the construction of the large Swiss hydro-electric works. To exploit the water power it was necessary to ascertain how the water inside a glacier moved throughout the year, and to do this it was decided to dig a tunnel into the ice. So during the winter of 1948—49 three tunnels were carved out in the ice, one about 1,100 yards long through the small Z'Mutt Gletscher which is 7,850 ft above sea level, and two other tunnels: one in the upper part and one at the foot of Mont Collon Gletscher at Arolla in Switzerland. The lower of these tunnels especially, with a diameter of 7¼ ft, extending 220 yards into the ice and making contact with the rock wall behind the glacier, gave a unique opportunity for studying the movement and structure of the ice.

Also in 1949 a tunnel was dug through the 160 ft thick ice cap on the 11,342 ft high Jungfraujoch, and as the temperature at this altitude is below freezing point the whole year round, it was possible to use this glacier cap as a kind of miniature model of a polar glacier. In 1952 the American physicist, Joel E. Fisher, began the construction of an ice tunnel on the steep glacier which covers the north side of Monte Rosa (15,400 ft high). Helped by mountain guides and by undergraduates from Cambridge, they worked their way in from the steep ice wall, but in 1954 the tunnel had to be abandoned because of the danger of an avalanche and they began a new tunnel further down. Here they excavated 300 ft in through the ice and made contact with the mountain behind the ice.

The ice in the high-altitude ice field was very cold with a surface temperature of —7.8° (18° F) and a temperature in the middle of the ice tunnel of —13.3° (8° F). In order to study the structure of the ice and the occurrence of dirt bands and other structural elements, some British un-

196

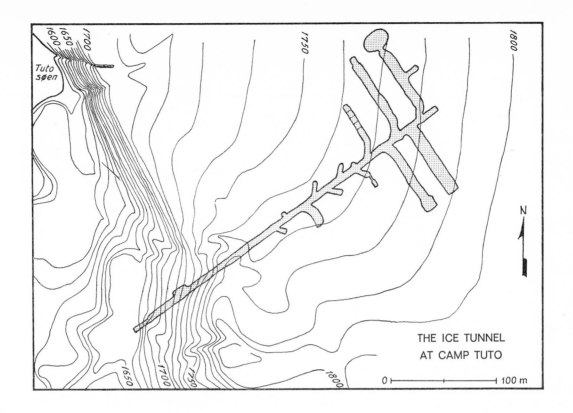

THE ICE TUNNEL
AT CAMP TUTO

0 |——————————| 100 m

dergraduates carved out two tunnels in the small Norwegian corrie glacier of Vesl Skautbreen in 1951. In the spring of 1962 a 200 ft tunnel was carved along the bottom of Isfallsglaciären in Swedish Lapland to study the formation of the moraine more closely, and several other ice tunnels have been excavated in recent years as part of glaciological research projects.

As part of their programme of research the American Corps of Engineers decided to construct a tunnel in the ice front at Camp Tuto, and their plan was not only to study the structure of the ice and its relation to moraine occurrence etc., but also to examine the possibility of constructing tunnels and chambers in the ice of such dimensions that they could be used for storing military equipment of various kind and for troops to live in.

When buildings were erected above the surface of the ice sheet they had to be protected against the fierce winter cold and the violent blizzards, whereas if they were built down in the snow or ice, they could be well protected from blizzards and the low temperatures. However, experience at the French winter station, Station Centrale, showed that although lighter building materials could be used with this method, the buildings gradually became so deeply buried as fresh snow fell each winter that in the course of a few years the whole station would be crushed.

From a strategic point of view it was, of course, preferable that the buildings should not be clear-

197

ly visible from the air as easy targets for attack. If the buildings could be constructed directly in the ice, not only would low temperatures be avoided, but they would also be well concealed from an enemy. The American ice tunnels were the first to be excavated purely so that the problems of tunneling in the ice could be investigated.

In 1955 work was commenced on sawing and hacking a way into the wall of ice at the margin of the ice sheet some 1½—2 miles from Camp Tuto. On the opposite side of the lake at Camp Tuto about ½ mile west of the route up on to the ice sheet there were a number of moraines which partly protected the ice from melting, and a row of 100—180 ft high, almost vertical, ice fronts had formed here which were almost stationary. In one of these ice fronts they began to construct a tunnel with an opening 5 ft 6 in × 6 ft 6 in and with a gentle upward gradient reaching 170 ft from the ice front. A large experimental chamber was constructed connecting with this tunnel and the dimensions of this were 33 ft long, 12 ft wide and with a headroom of 6 ft 6 in.

Experiments had been made to find the best method of excavating; part of the tunnel had been dug out using pick axes and shovels alone, for some of the work they had used chain saws, and the tunnel had been extended in length by the use of explosives. It was soon found that there was no advantage in using explosives, partly because the results were meagre in proportion to the amount of explosive that was needed, and partly because the explosions caused damage and cracks in the ice which meant that the roof became liable to cave in.

In 1956 the tunnel was enlarged to a section 6 ft × 8 ft 2 in and was further extended by about 130 ft. Another chamber was excavated here measuring 65 ft × 65 ft with a height of 25 ft. Two years of excavation work in the margin of the ice at Camp Tuto had proved that it was possible to hew out galleries in glacier ice by using the same techniques that were normally employed in coal mining. It would be possible to construct long galleries and fairly large chambers in the ice. Picks, shovels, and chain saws were used, but experiments with the use of explosives had shown that such large quantities were necessary that violent vibrations were set up in the ice which thereupon cracked, which often meant that the roof of the tunnel would cave in or other mishaps occur. The deformation of the galleries had been measured and it had been found that the factors causing the galleries to close were partly dependent on the thickness of the layer of ice above, and partly on the size and shape of the opening, but that the rate of closing was not too rapid for the chambers to be used for a considerable length of time. By spending a small amount on maintenance it would also be possible to use these chambers as store rooms and it might even be possible to build a camp in the galleries. If a large camp were to be constructed in the ice, it would be too slow and laborious to carve out the galleries by hand, and experiments were therefore made using machines similar to those used in coal mining.

198

In 1957 an appliance called the Joy Coal-Cutter arrived in Camp Tuto: using rotary chains this can cut out large blocks of ice and work much faster than the small electrically driven hand saws that had been used previously. The machine proved to be extremely efficient as long as it was working on pure glacier ice, but the teeth of the saw snapped off if it was used in glacier ice with much moraine material in it.

The removal of the excavated ice was also systematised, for it was no longer possible to remove the ice by man-hauled sledge. Instead, a small, battery-driven locomotive had to be installed, which could pull wagons loaded with the ice out to the ice margin where the ice was tipped over the edge. In the summer of 1957 the galleries were extended to a total of 350 m (1,150 ft) and to give enough room for working with the machinery the dimensions of the galleries were also enlarged to a 6½ ft wide by 7½ ft high tunnel and two rooms with dimensions of 60 ft×60 ft with a roof height of 20 ft were excavated.

One of the problems with the camps in the galleries would be supplying them with fuel, and from a military point of view it made the oil tanks extremely vulnerable to have them on the surface, so experiments were made with storing diesel oil and petrol directly in cisterns carved out of the ice.

As the mining work advanced, instruments and measuring points were installed so that the movement of the ice could be constantly checked and measurements could be made of how fast the walls of the galleries were being pressed into the chambers. These showed that the floor, because of the greater pressure, was being forced upwards at a more rapid rate than the roof was being pressed downwards, and the ice movement in the walls of the galleries varied from quite small amounts to as much as one metre per annum. The entrance to the tunnel lay in a vertical wall of ice over which melt water ran down, and gradually the tunnel was filled with melt water which froze, and this had constantly to be removed. As the tunnel was situated in a place where there was a rather active movement of the ice, there was a fairly great inward pressure of the ice walls into the tunnels, so it was decided that a new tunnel should be constructed at a better site higher up in the ice where there was less hydrostatic pressure, which would mean that the walls would close more slowly.

The coal mining machine had proved most effective, and during the summers of 1958 and 1959 a new ice tunnel was constructed to replace the first one, and an even higher capacity mining machine, a Joy continuous miner, was selected to cut the new tunnel. This was situated higher up in the ice at a spot where there was no melt water to speak of. The new tunnel was larger, having a section of 18 ft×15 ft. At the end of the main tunnel four or five side tunnels ranging from 60 —75 m (200 ft—250 ft) long were excavated. These were wider than the main tunnel, and in

199

addition to them large experimental chambers were dug out. Some of the rooms were 24 ft×200 ft and 7½ ft high; one room was 24 ft×200 ft and 15 ft high, and several more rooms were 200 ft long, 7½ ft high and more than 30 ft wide. The ice tunnel was lengthened by degrees to a total of 1,100 ft and was fitted with doors to stop the snow from drifting into it in the winter and to prevent the temperature from rising too much in summer. A total of thirty-one thousand cubic metres of ice had to be removed, and it was therefore necessary to install a conveyor belt for moving the ice out as the blocks were sawn off by the coal cutter.

The galleries were so long that continuous ventilation was necessary, and with galleries of that size it was natural to think of the possibility of building a camp inside the ice sheet. So a camp was built for 25 men with all conveniences. It was intended that this camp should be used for one whole year, but this did not in fact happen. In spite of its unique position in the Greenland ice sheet and its equipment with all comforts, it was used for only a few months in the spring of 1962. This was, however, sufficient to demonstrate that such a camp could function, and that also, if necessary, it could continue to function in isolation throughout long periods of time, but the tests were not of sufficient duration for the psychological studies of the reactions of the personnel living in and under the ice sheet to be carried out as had been planned.

The ice tunnel is a gigantic laboratory in which experiments can be made with long-term storage of equipment, fuel, food, etc., and where also, of course, measurements of ice deformation can be carried out and methods of preventing the closing up of the tunnel can be tested out, by, for instance, excavating chambers in the ice and examining their behaviour under pressure so as to find a method of avoiding deformation.

The International Glaciological Expedition

A French Parachute Expedition to the Ice Sheet.

On 27 August 1956 a French military aircraft of Nord 2501 type took off from the aerodrome at Keflavík for Greenland. Besides the crew and a Swiss observer there were four young Frenchmen on board who were intending to parachute down onto the ice sheet and establish a base there where they would spend the winter. Then the following spring they planned to ski across the ice to the east coast with sledges, and it had been arranged with Lauge Koch that they would be picked up there. The leader of the group was Jean Dumont, a thirty-year-old engineer who had spent the winter of 1950—51 with Victor's expedition at Station Centrale; the second-in-command was a thirty-seven-year-old captain from the Foreign Legion's Parachute Corps, named Michel de Lannurien; and a doctor and a radio operator completed the party.

After the machine had circled the spot selected the men got ready to jump. The weather was clear, but there was a heavy wind. It was late in the summer and it was essential to have the station set up before the severe cold set in — it was already —40° above the snow. In spite of the high wind, therefore, the men jumped and landed safely.

In the following days they received a total of seventeen tons of equipment, food supplies, and building materials dropped to them, and this was sufficient for them to get through the winter, for the house was to be dug down into the snow to protect it from the wind and the cold.

Dumont had had a great deal of trouble in getting financial support for the expedition, which had no real scientific object beyond, of course, taking daily weather observations. So as to obtain money for the project, Dumont had got in touch with the International Glaciological Expedition (see page 206) which was planning to operate later in the same area, and he had undertaken to dig a pit for their use in future glaciological investigations in return for cash aid to the tune of 30,000 Swiss francs.

The little group of troglodytes therefore at once set to work to dig, and with an almost unbelievable industry they succeeded during that winter with only picks and shovels in constructing a

201

Ice blocks piled up by the sudden draining of an
ice-dam beside the ice front.

sixty metre (200 ft) tunnel in the ice which reached forty metres (130 ft) below the surface and
had a two metre (6½ ft) square section. They removed the snow with a sledge drawn upon a
runner, and they fitted out the pit with steps cut out in the snow.

On a reconnaissance flight for the International Glaciological Expedition in April 1957 (see page
206) supplementary equipment was dropped to the station so that the site could be marked and so
that measurements could be made of the pit before it was abandoned. After they had set up a
number of measuring points so that a subsequent re-measurement could determine the deforma-

tion of the pit, the four men left the station and went on foot to Cecilia Nunatak and from there down to Røhss Fjord, where a motor boat picked them up. Two years later de Lannurien was back in his old station as the leader of the Jarl-Joset winter station on the International Glaciological Expedition.

International Co-operation

Whereas the American research bodies have usually published their findings first in military reports so that they have not found their way into the international journals until some years later, the private expeditions (particularly the French and British) have published their findings or made them available at various congresses and international meetings at an early stage.

The tenth General Assembly of the International Union of Geodesy and Geophysics was held in Rome in 1954; studies of snow and ice are internationally organized by a special Commission on Snow and Ice under the International Association of Scientific Hydrology, itself one of the several component bodies of the Union, and here the results of the French investigations under Victor were discussed.

All previous civil expeditions had just left the ice sheet without giving any thought to a continuation of their work, but markers had been set up which by being continually re-measured, could yield important information about the movement of the ice and about the accumulation and ablation of the snow. The question of the balance of the ice sheet could, in fact, only be answered if a long series of continuous measurements could be taken at fixed points on the ice sheet; the ideal method would be to take measurements along several lines crossing the ice sheet from coast to coast. Such careful determinations of accumulation and ablation have been made on several glaciers in the Alps, the longest and most detailed of them on the Rhône Glacier, where surveying has been continuous since 1874.

There was a wish expressed by the Swiss that the Greenland investigations should in some way be carried further by continuing the measurements of accumulation along the marked profile from the coast to Station Centrale.

Victor was, of course, interested in continuing the French research, but he had not himself the necessary finance, nor a sufficient number of scientists available, and so he suggested that the work might possibly be continued on an international, or at least an inter-European basis. A committee was set up with representatives from Germany and Switzerland, and with Victor himself, of course, and he applied to the Danish Embassy in Paris for Danish permission for such an expedition. When this permission had been obtained, a meeting was called in Switzerland in April 1956, and plans were made for an International Glaciological Expedition, In French: Expédition Glaciologique Internationale au Groenland, or EGIG to work on the Greenland ice sheet. The technical side of the expedition was made the responsibility of Expéditions Polaires Françaises under the leadership of Paul-Émile Victor, while the scientific programme was worked out by a board of control, whose first chairman was the Swiss glaciologist, Professor R. Haefeli.

To calculate changes in the volume of the ice, it is not sufficient to know the extent of the ice sheet and the distribution of altitude of the surface; the thickness of the ice must also be known. The object was therefore to make exact measurements along a marked profile right across the ice sheet. The thickness of the ice would be determined along this profile, which would be marked in such a way that when it came to be measured some years later, it could be possible to determine whether the ice had increased or decreased. The problems to be solved were delegated to the participating countries, so that each land undertook to solve its particular part of the common investigation, and France placed aircraft, Weasels, and other technical equipment at the disposal of the expedition. It had been hoped that Britain would participate, but as she did not, the expedition came to comprise five countries: Denmark, France, Switzerland, Germany, Austria.

The technical and operational realization of the International Glaciological Expedition was a matter of prime importance, as most of the scientific work had to be carried out during the four months of summer in 1959. Two problems had to be solved: how to travel on the ice sheet, and where to establish a base for the whole expedition.

The technical realization was the responsibility of Paul-Émile Victor as director of Expéditions Polaires Françaises. The expedition was based on Weasels, which Victor had available already, since large tractors for use in Greenland were beyond the resources of the expedition.

To reach the planned profile, it was necessary to set up a base that could be served by the heavy French Nordatlas 2001 aircraft. It was therefore absolutely essential to make use of one of the existing airfields in west Greenland, Thule Air Base, Søndre Strømfjord, or Narssarssuaq.

Earlier reconnaissance of the marginal area of the ice, in which both Victor and the present author took part, had shown that the route up on to the ice sheet from Camp Tuto was one of the best in Greenland. It was also possible to ascend at Narssarssuaq, and in 1957 this route was surveyed and measured by the Americans, but it would only be usable if large earth works were carried out, and such work was beyond the resources of EGIG. The route up from Thule Air Base was, of course, a possibility, but this would mean that a very long distance would have to be covered before the field of operations was reached, for the profile was to extend from Victor's old starting point at Eqip sermia via Station Centrale and Station Dumont to Cecilia Nunatak with an additional north-south profile running approximately parallel to the ice margin inland of Disko-Umanak Bugt.

From the mountain sides in the marginal zone of the ice
sheet avalanches crash down onto the ice.

Another point was that the harbour at Thule Air Base is only open for two summer months each
year, and it was, besides, as far from Europe as it could be. From a technical point of view, Søndre Strømfjord would make the most suitable starting point, but previous reconnaissance had
shown that in summertime access to the ice by Weasels was impossible because of the deep melt
water streams and numerous crevasses. It was through this zone that Rymill and Hampton had
descended with their kayaks in 1931, but it was impassable for Weasels, at least in summer, and
the question was now whether it would be passable in early spring when snow filled most of the

205

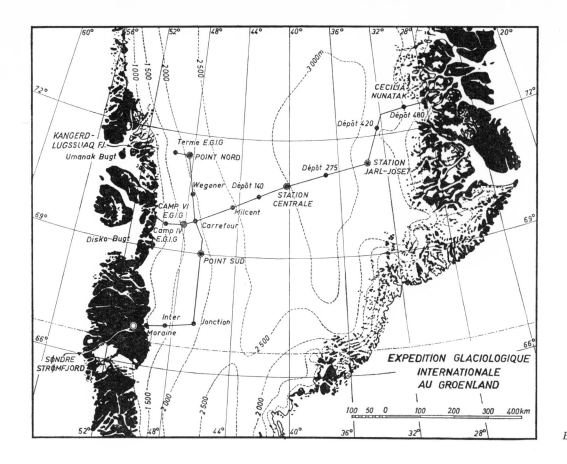

stream beds. From a reconnaissance by plane and helicopter and on foot in April 1957 it was clear that it would be possible to take Weasels both across the relatively flat land between the base and the edge of the ice and through the marginal zone of the ice itself. But when in 1959 the expedition tried to ascend by this route, it proved much more difficult than had been anticipated, for there had been little snow the previous winter and the summer thaw during 1958 had been considerable, so that the melt water streams were very deep and therefore not completely filled by snow.

Reconnaissance and various preparatory tasks were carried out in Greenland during the summers of 1957 and 1958, and in August 1958 the Weasels and the other equipment of the expedition were brought by ship to Søndre Strømfjord and stored there for the winter. In April 1959 the thirteen Weasels, nine caravans, and sixteen sledges of the expedition started out from Søndre Strømfjord and made their way slowly up on to the ice. The going was hard, and at some places they had to hack and blast their way across the ice, but they managed to get through.

The technicians alone saw to bringing in the Weasels; the scientists did not arrive until every-

206

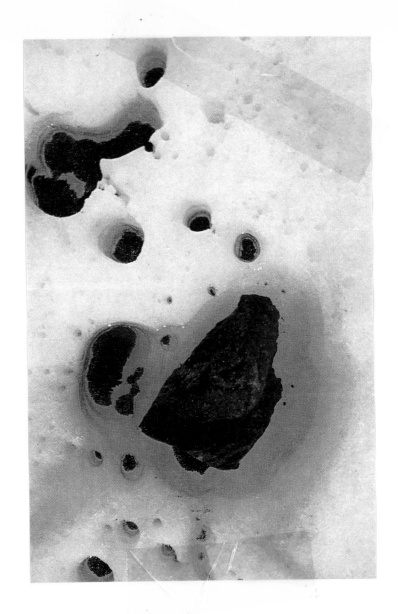

Cryoconite holes in the surface of the ice formed by pebbles and gravel which absorbed heat and so melted down into the ice. The first explorers thought the material to be of cosmic origin but modern investigations have shown it to be terrigenous.

thing was ready for work to begin, when they were flown by helicopter to Camp Jonction from where the whole expedition continued northwards. On 1 May the expedition was gathered at Victor's old Camp IV, or at least near it. As we have mentioned on page 160, Benson on Expedition Jello had abandoned four Weasels here, and these with all their equipment, were placed at the disposal of EGIG.

After they had managed to locate the Weasels by magnetic measurements, could they start to hack and dig them free of the ice and get them ready for operation. In the meantime their last supplies had been parachuted and free-dropped to them, and their work of establishing and

207

measuring the profile could begin. The profile was marked out with ten-metre-long aluminium stakes placed at an average distance of 10 km (6¼ miles) apart; they were somewhat closer in the marginal zone where the gradient prevents sights being taken from one stake to the next at ten kilometres. The positions of the poles were determined by tellurometer measurements — it was the first time this method had been used on the ice sheet. When EGIG was planned, it had been intended to use normal geodetic triangulation, which would have needed the participation of a large number of geodecists, but in the meantime the tellurometer had been invented, and it immediately won acceptance for making measurements in difficult country.

Tellurometer measurement is a kind of radar measurement. In the normal impulse radar system, one very short impulse is transmitted which it reflected from the object or is re-transmitted from a radio beacon; the time lapse between the transmission and the reception of the impulse is thus a measurement of the distance between the radar transmitter and the object. In tellurometry, on the other hand, continuous impulses are transmitted which are constantly being reflected and received, and the phase difference between the signals transmitted and the signals received is measured. Tellurometer measurements can therefore only be made between two stations both equipped with tellurometers.

The distance between the two stations can be measured with great accuracy; on the measurements made by EGIG, distances of about 10 km were used, and the distance between the stations was calculated with such accuracy that the error was below 50 cm. The apparatus was originally constructed in South Africa, where it was used for surveying trackless country, but more recently it has been used in many other places, among them Canada and Antarctica.

In 1958 the Danish Geodetic Institute obtained a set of instruments for use in Greenland, and although they were originally constructed for use under quite different climatic conditions, it was found possible by making some slight alterations to use them under Arctic conditions, too.

As well as determining the relative positions of the markers, it was also necessary to fix their altitude above sea level, and this was done by ordinary geometrical traverse from the coast inland. The area between the coast and Camp IV is heavily crevassed, and it was therefore only possible to work there on foot with man-hauled sledges, and then only early enough in the year for snow melting not to have started. In spite of support from helicopters, etc. it was necessary here to use the old techniques with man-hauled sledges, but anyway the measurements were obtained; a total of 65 km (40 miles) of traverse was done on foot, and in support of this operation fourteen depots were laid out by helicopter. As soon as the levelling party reached the coast, where they met up with firm rock again, they were helicoptered back and continued their levelling across the ice sheet by Weasel.

208

In addition to this geodetic work, seismic and gravity measurements were also made on the ice sheet, and at Station Centrale a 1,5 ton of explosive was set off in order to study the influence of the ice upon the substratum. Detailed investigations of the snow and ice were also made, by, for instance, collecting samples for oxygen isotope examination.

While the scientific programme was being carried out, work was being started on building a winter station near the French Dumont Station, for the shaft that Dumont and his team had excavated was to be utilised. The start of the building work was rather dramatic. As the radio operator was busy rigging up a radio beacon, he saw a polar bear coming towards him. He had previously been a sailor in the Orient, and had never before seen a bear except in the zoo, so he thought the bear's visit to be rather fun, and tapped it lightly over the snout with the aerial.

The next moment the bear had knocked him flat and was proceeding to drag him off. He yelled for help, but he did not dare to shout the word "bear" for fear the others would think he was pulling their legs, so instead he just screamed. Fortunately he was heard, and when his companions arrived on the scene the bear already had the man's head in its jaws. They managed to drive the bear away with some iron bars that were used when the tracks of the Weasels were changed and get the man free. The bear was groggy after the blows of the iron bars, but not otherwise injured, and they had no firearms with them. The radio operator was immediately treated by the doctor while the others tried to run the bear down in the Weasels, but it was much too quick in its movements for them to succeed. The radio operator had got away with some deep flesh wounds on his chest and shoulder, but by a stroke of luck neither his carotid artery nor any nerves had been severed, so that he suffered almost as much from the shock as he did from the actual lesion.

The bear continued to prowl around the Weasels and from time to time it jumped up and put its nose to the windows to watch what was going on inside. They spent a confused and abnormal night, and the next morning the two French planes arrived bringing a rifle which was dropped by parachute. But the bear seemed to know that something was afoot, for he kept out of range. They began, therefore, to hunt it by plane, flying low over the head of the bewildered animal until a Weasel came within range and the bear was shot. From a safety point of view it had been absolutely essential to kill the animal, which proved to be a comparatively young male. This is the only time that a man has been knocked down by a bear on the ice, but possibly it is not so unusual for bears to prowl on the ice sheet as was previously thought. In any case, on the EGIG they also came across fresh tracks within the Cecilia Nunatak, and at several of the American stations on the ice sheet, it has been necessary to kill bears. The radio operator soon recovered, and — naturally — had the skin to take home as a souvenir of his encounter with Arctic fauna.

209

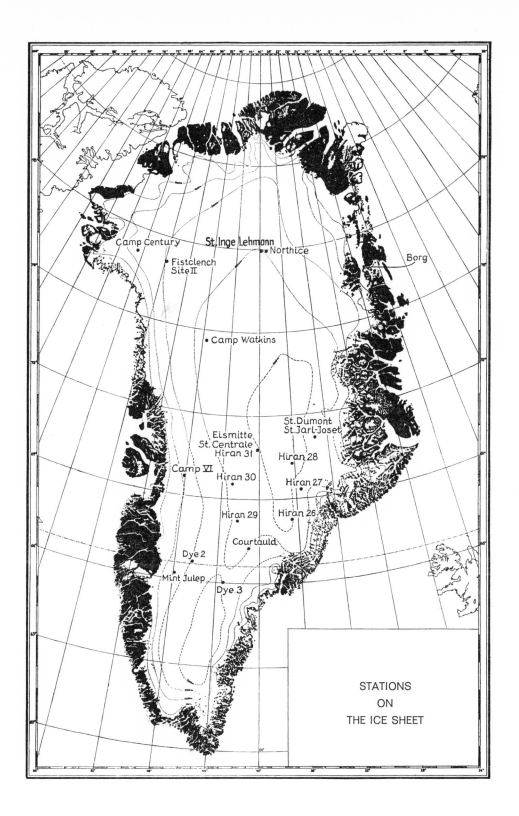

STATIONS

ON

THE ICE SHEET

210

Alouette helicopters of the International Glaciological Expedition outlined against the sky.

The winter station was erected of prefabricated plastic plates and had the same shape as a Greenland igloo, but it had two stories. Downstairs it had a kitchen and a common living room, and upstairs each man had his own bedroom, and there was also a radio room and a meteorological room. The house was heated by oil with warm air circulation, and was, of course, dug down into the snow so that only the ventilation shafts projected above the surface.

The cooking was by bottled gas, and a French firm had been persuaded to supply very modern and colourful furniture for the rooms as an advertisement. So all in all, it must be admitted that life there during the winter was relatively comfortable. Through the radio connexion with the expedition headquarters in Paris it was possible for the French participants to telephone to their wives and families.

The station was connected to the glaciological pit at Dumont station by long passages, and a number of chambers were excavated for the glaciological investigations, among them a refriger-

211

ation laboratory 8 m (26 ft) long in which the drill samples could be studied. Outside, a meteorological measuring mast was erected, fitted with anemometers and thermo-electric measuring spots, etc. The entering of this data was done continuously in the meteorological room inside the station, but when the regular synoptic measurements were to be made, the observer had to go out and read his instruments, which were placed in a meteorological hut of the usual kind, and he had also to climb up the mast to check that the instruments there were functioning satisfactorily. In winter, in pitch darkness, with the temperature at —50° (—58° F) it was no outstandingly pleasant job to be a meteorologist there!

The winter party consisted of six men: three scientists and three technicians; the leader of the group was M. de Lannurien, who had previously spent a year there as a member of Dumont's parachute expedition. There was also a French mechanic, C. Marinier, who had previously wintered at Station Centrale, and a French doctor, Dr. Sypiorski, who was completely free of professional duties during the winter, as everything went off without a hitch, but while the station was being erected he had had to carry out an appendectomy on one of the mechanics who had had such acute appendicitis that an immediate operation was necessary. He carried out the operation confidently in a temporary theatre made in one of the snow corridors. The scientific leader of the wintering party was Dr Fritz Brandenberger from Switzerland, who undertook the glaciological investigations together with a young French glaciologist, René Schneider, and a German meteorologist, Oskar Reinwarth.

The summer programme was completed by the end of August 1959; the winter party was installed and the rest of the expedition set off for home. Most of them were evacuated from the ice by a helicopter which landed them on board the German marine research ship, *Gauss,* which in connexion with EGIG was making a calculation of the run off of melt water from the ice sheet by making a close investigation of conditions in Kangerdlugssuaq Fjord. The rest of the party travelled by Weasel down to Jonction beyond Søndre Strømfjord, and were picked up there by helicopter, the equipment being left behind on the ice.

The first year's work was concluded. The six men wintered at the station, which was named Station Jarl-Joset in memory of the Danish engineer Jens Jarl and the French geophysicist Alain Joset who had lost their lives in a crevasse near Mont Forel on one of Victor's earlier expeditions (see page 130).

In the summer of 1960 a little group was once more working on the ice sheet. Just as the previous year, they were flown out to Søndre Strømfjord from Paris in the spring and then brought by helicopter to the Weasels that had been left on the ice from the previous summer. They then drove further inland to fetch the six men of the party at the winter station and to gather together the expedition's equipment so as to have it ready for shipment to France. The plan had actually been to leave the equipment on the ice inland of Søndre Strømfjord once more, for it would only be possible to cross the marginal zone of the ice in spring; the men could in this way have been flown out by helicopter and then the following spring a new group of mechanics could have brought out the equipment.

But as it was discovered that large American Hercules transport aircraft were flying in large numbers to the radar warning stations with supplies and returning empty, EGIG were given permission to take the Weasels and the equipment to the radar station Dye 2, and from there it was all flown out by American planes. It took only two days to fly all the equipment out, for the planes were so large that they could take two Weasels and one caravan on each flight.

EGIG had now finished the first round of its labours — the work done on the ice sheet itself, and the processing of the data is now going forward in Europe. In fact, however this expedition will only come to have great significance if it is repeated, for a re-measurement of the markers would give information about the movement of the ice and alterations in its volume.

Up until now, the results of EGIG have been a more detailed knowledge of the thickness of the ice than was possessed before and some detailed stratigraphic snow studies and rheological determinations. We now have a mass of data throwing light on the transformation of the ice and snow and on the physical processes which operate, and there now exists a very detailed calculation of the energy quantities going into and coming out of a particular area of the ice sheet. But the great question of the balance of the ice sheet — whether it is in surplus or in deficit, and of the velocity of movement of the ice, will not be solved unless the work of the expedition is continued.

To judge from the experience already gained, it should be possible to continue the work on an inter-European or even wider basis. It would not be the first time that research on an ice sheet has been carried out in collaboration between several countries. In 1949—51 a Norwegian-British-Swedish expedition was working in Antarctica, and during the International Geophysical Year there were several expeditions of an international character; among others to Spitsbergen, but EGIG is the largest of such international civilian expeditions, and both as far as the number of participants is concerned and the amount of data produced, it is the largest non-military expedition that has worked on the ice sheet. The foundation work for a series of future measurements has been laid by the investigations carried out in 1957—1960, and if these are followed up in years to come, very important results may materialize. In the summer of 1964 six men under the leadership of Robert Guillard were once more working in Greenland with the Weasels to lengthen the stakes that had been put up in 1959. They re-located most of the stakes on the east-west profile and some of those on the north-south profile, and they re-visited Station Jarl-Joset, which they found in good condition. After being lengthened, the stakes will remain for a number of years so that it will not be necessary to make the final re-measurement before 1967 or 1968. During the summer 1966 the weasels and the equipment of EGIG is again en route for Greenland to be stored for the winter 1966—67 so the actual resurveying will be carried out 1967 and 1968, but it is still uncertain if a new wintering will take place.

Sporting Expeditions

A purely sporting achievement was carried out, in the summer of 1962 when two Norwegian students, Bjørn Staib and Bjørn Reese, skied across the ice cap by the route that Nansen had followed in 1888. They arrived in Angmagssalik from Copenhagen on the *Kista Dan,* and from there continued their journey to Umivik by schooner. On 22 July they left Umivik: like Nansen they travelled by ski but they used dogs to pull the two sledges that they took with them. On 21 August the two students had crossed the ice sheet and were passing through the margin's hazardous crevasse zone down towards Austmanndalen. The crossing had gone according to plan.

In summer 1965 a Scottish expedition consisting of Dr. Hugh Simpson, his wife, and two other members crossed the ice sheet using only man hauled sledges. They started from Johan Petersen Fjord on the east coast and crossed to Søndre Strømfjord. On arrival here their physical condition was such that they were able to continue their journey, partly by kayak, to Christianshåb. A Finnish expedition of five man with dogteams was carried out along the same route in the summer of 1966.

Now that it is no longer so difficult to get to Greenland, a number of mountaineers from all over the world have come to the country and made ascents, particularly in east Greenland, but a few sportsmen have also turned their attention to the ice sheet proper.The large scientific expeditions are so expensive that similar journeys cannot be made for purely sporting reasons, but the old travelling techniques of skis and dog sledges are within the bounds of possibility for fairly well-off sporting expeditions. Another point, however, is that these expeditions are rather hazardous, and there is risk connected with them when they are carried out by men not used to Arctic conditions, and the risk is out of all proportion to the results.

214

The Climate of the Ice Sheet

The Movement of Air over the Ice Sheet

When we look at a map of the northern Arctic region, there are three things that strike us: that the whole of the central area around the North Pole is occupied by the Arctic Ocean; that Greenland is the only area of real highland; and that this is mainly occupied by an ice sheet. It is these factors, in combination with the very northerly latitude of Greenland, that cause the particular climate that reigns over the ice sheet.

The general air movements of the Arctic are brought about by the exchange of air masses between the "Iceland low" to the west, south-west, or west of Iceland, and the "polar high" over northern Greenland and further north. In particular, the position and extent of the Iceland low pressure area determines the air movements over the North Atlantic region, which includes both Greenland and western Europe. It is a well-known fact that a year with a severe winter in Denmark will most usually be a relatively mild year in south Greenland, and vice versa. This is due to the position of the tracks followed by the wandering depressions.

The map shows us that Greenland is almost the first high mountainous area east of the Rocky Mountains that is encountered by air masses coming from the west. The steep coastal range and the mighty dome of the ice sheet are an insuperable barrier to numerous wandering cyclones, which are thus forced to turn northwards along the Greenland coast.

This is particularly typical of the wandering depressions that reach Greenland across Davis Strait; they cannot penetrate in over the ice sheet, so they follow the coast northwards until they reach Melville Bugt, where they gradually weaken and disappear. In contrast to what was previously thought, weather observations and the numerous air flights that have been made across the ice sheet have proved that there is a passage of fronts across the ice sheet too; this has been confirmed both for the southern part of the ice cap, and also, rather less frequently, for the northern part.

Our conception of weather conditions and air movement over the ice sheet was governed until a few years ago by a theory known as the *glacial anticyclone theory*. This was put forward by the

American geologist and Arctic explorer William Herbert Hobbs in 1910, i. e. at a time when there were very few summer observations from the interior of Greenland available, and no measurements at all had been made in winter. Hobbs had fastened on the fact that over the edge of the ice there is a strong outflow of cold air from the central parts of the ice sheet.

He assumed that the air over the central area would cool very rapidly, and that therefore heavy air masses would flow out towards the lower parts of the ice. As this air flowed out towards the edge of the ice sheet it would reach such a low altitude that diabatic warming would mean that it was no longer colder than the surrounding air masses, so that the process would cease and air would be stationary. But now radiation would once more become a factor, and the air would cool down and once more move outward.

The centrifugal movement of the air over the ice would contribute to the formation of a vacuum over the central part of the ice sheet, so that at great heights air would come streaming in and would then be sucked down to the surface of the snow at the centre of the anticyclone. On the way down the air would become dry and warm to some degree, but on contact with the snow surface it would nevertheless cool down again and precipitate snow, hoar-frost crystals, and fine ice needles. This accumulation of hoar frost would be carried by the wind to the periphery of the ice, so that the ice sheet should be increasing along the edge by this constant accumulation. Hobb's glacial anticylone, which is not an anticyclone in the normal sense of the word, would mean that there should be fine and settled weather in central Greenland, but this was not confirmed when Wegener's expedition wintered at Eismitte nor on other later expeditions.

Present-day knowledge of weather conditions and climate over the ice sheet is based both on information from radio-sonde measurements at the Greenland coastal stations, and on the observations made on various winter expeditions, but these latter have only covered short periods. The longest and most complete series of observations that exists were made at Site II; other all-the-year-round observations have been made in the areas of: Eismitte — Station Centrale; Station Dumont — Station Jarl-Joset; Northice; Camp Century.

Observations were also made in winter by Courtauld, but these were not complete. Observations made at the two Dye stations, have not been published. No data from winter observations on the southern dome of the ice sheet exist, and only very brief series of observations have been made in summer. There is much fuller summer data for the northern part of the ice sheet, partly from the semi-permanent American stations, and partly from the numerous expeditions that have crossed the ice sheet. In addition to the direct meteorological measurements, information about temperature and precipitation can also be gathered by studying the stratification of the snow, and from the temperature of the snow in pits dug in the firn. Where there is no significant summer melt,

216

A halt during a reconnaissance expedition on the ice sheet. The bamboo poles to the left of the photograph are used in measuring ablation.

the annual temperature variations will not penetrate deeper than 7—8 m (23—26 ft) down, and below this depth it can be reckoned that the temperature of the firn will be practically identical with the mean annual temperature of the place, and at 10 m (33 ft) depth the temperature measured differs no more than 0.3° from the local mean temperature.

The Cold on the Ice Sheet

The annual temperature conditions over the Greenland ice sheet are shown by the accompanying curve of the monthly average temperature at the most important stations, and from the map on page 230. This map was drawn up from data published by Carl S. Benson, R. W. Gerdel, Marvin Diamond, C. Langway, H. Bader, and others. The isotherms are partly based on the observed mean temperatures of the winter stations and the snow pits, and partly, where such data were insufficient,

217

on observations from the coastal stations by reckoning that the temperature will drop by 0.7° (1.2° F) for every 100 m (333 ft) of increased altitude.

It will be seen that the annual mean temperature on the ice sheet varies between — 20° (—4° F) and — 30° (—22° F) and that only in the marginal zone is the temperature higher. The whole of the northern part of the ice sheet has relatively homogeneous mean temperatures around —28° to — 30° (—18° to — 22° F.) The coldest monthly mean temperatures were —40° (—40° F) at Station Centrale, and —43.3° (—46° F) at Northice, whereas only —37.7° (—35° F) was recorded at Site II. In all cases the coldest month falls late in the winter: for Station Jarl-Joset February is the coldest month, while March is the coldest for Northice and Site II. That the coldest month comes so late is due to the relatively strong radiation from the surface of the snow. Throughout the period of darkness, i. e. in the northern part of the ice sheet from November to February, there is no insolation, since the sun is below the horizon, but radiation occurs, so that the snow cools down considerably. When the sun returns, insolation commences, but while the sun is still low in the sky, this is very slight, and 70—90 % of the insolated energy is reflected from the white surface of the snow. Thus long after the sun has returned, radiation will continue to exceed insolation, and the surface of the ice sheet will continue to grow colder.

February or March are in all cases the coldest months, but the absolute minimum temperatures for the year depend to a much greater degree on local air movements, and they occur almost always after a long period of strong radiation and stable weather conditions. The absolute minimum for the year may occur in any of the actual winter months. The lowest temperature recorded on the ice sheet occured on 8 January 1954 at Northice, when the thermometer fell to —70° (—94°F), whereas the lowest temperature at Station Centrale was "only" —65° (—85° F) which was recorded on 22 February 1950. At Site II —56.1° (—68.9° F) has been recorded, and at Station Jarl Joset —55° (—67° F). Since the observations made at the winter stations all cover only a short period, there can be no doubt that in future even lower temperatures will be recorded on the ice sheet, especially in view of the fact that the coldest station, Northice, was situated at only 2,300 m (7,550 ft) above sea level; it must be assumed that the higher parts of the ice sheet in the north have even lower temperatures.

The climate over the Greenland ice sheet is neither so cold nor so extreme as that in Antarctica, where the Russian station, Vostok, recorded —88.3° (—126.9° F), the lowest temperature recorded on earth, and where the average temperature of the coldest month is —55° (—67° F). The lowest temperatures in the northern hemisphere have not been recorded in Greenland, but in the northern continental part of Siberia, where at Oimekon —78° (—108.4° F) was recorded, and where, too, the coldest month has lower temperatures than Greenland. But on an overall view

218

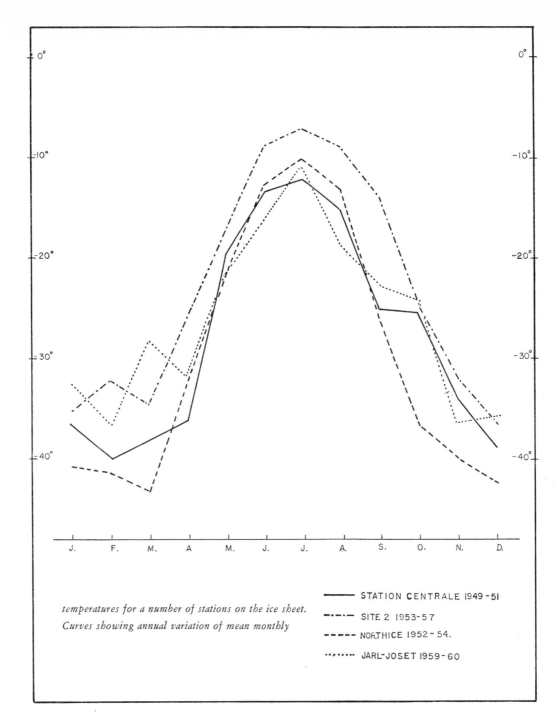

temperatures for a number of stations on the ice sheet.
Curves showing annual variation of mean monthly

——————— STATION CENTRALE 1949-51

—·—·— SITE 2 1953-57

— — — NORTHICE 1952-54.

·········· JARL-JOSET 1959-60

there can be no doubt that the northern part of the ice sheet is in a way the coldest region of the
northern hemisphere, for the temperature here does not rise above melting point even in summer.
Over the whole of the ice sheet July is the warmest month, with an average temperature at Station

219

Centrale of —12.2° (10.1° F), at Northice of —10.2° (13.6° F), and at Site II of —7.2° (19.1° F). The temperature will not be able to rise much above 0° (32°F), for the heat would then be absorbed by the melting of the snow, but nevertheless at the stations of Mint Julep 6.7° (44° F) has been measured, and at Hiran 26, 6.1° (42.4° F), while at Station Centrale and at Northice no temperatures have been recorded that are much above 0° (32° F). It seems therefore natural to regard the very high maximum temperatures recorded as the result of difficulties in recording the temperature properly.

It does seem to be evident from the pits that have been dug (and this is also in agreement with the theoretical temperatures calculated from the maximum temperatures at the coast) that exceptionally anywhere on the ice sheet melting may occur in the summer, and in north Greenland Benson has demonstrated that even at a height of 1,700 m (5,480 ft) above sea level there is a considerable melting each summer. Experience at Camp Century has also shown that the odd days of summer warmth that occur are one of the difficulties there. In the deep pit at Station Jarl-Joset two ice layers were encountered proving that even there the snow had melted in certain summers. As far as the whole of the southern part of the dome is concerned, melting seems to take place every summer, and this is also supported by the findings of the British Trans-Greenland Expeditions and by the observations of R. Ragel.

The snow surface has a very high reflectivity (0.45—0.95) and at the same time the radiative ability of snow cover amounts to 0.99 of a black body. This means that the surface of the snow, unlike the rest of the earth's surface, has a negative annual radiation balance and is a powerful source of cooling. The snow surface, therefore, has very low temperatures, and the absolute minimum temperature of the snow surface that was measured (according to P. A. Shumskiy et al.) at Vostok Station in Antartica is not far from the minimum for the free atmosphere: —97° (—142.6° F) over Halley Bay in the Antarctic.

Because of radiation and reflection from the surface of the snow there will normally be a considerable temperature inversion over the ice sheet, i. e. the temperature of the air will be lowest near the surface of the snow, and will then increase upwards instead of decreasing as normal. Under the high Arctic conditions that exist all over north Greenland, the temperature inversion can be traced up to a height of 2 km (1¼ miles) above the surface, and above this layer of inversion an isothermal layer will often be found.

Because of this inversion the air masses over the ice sheet are very stable. The most pronounced inversion is found in the lowest 500 m (1,640 ft), and quite frequently the inversion extends no higher. Because of the domed formation of the ice sheet, the cold air will nearly constantly flow outwards towards the lower parts at the periphery, and nearly all travellers on the ice sheet have

American helicopters on the ice sheet.

The American Dye stations were built on the ice sheet in 1960.

The foundations of the Dye stations started 35 feet below the surface of the snow.

Terminal moraines of the ice sheet near Camp Tuto.

Eqip sermia is one of the most investigated of the outlet-glaciers that descend from the ice sheet.

The front of a glacier in Peary Land.

Free-dropping of fuel.

A Danish sledge expedition pausing before the final ascent onto the ice sheet.

Glacier spurs from the ice sheet descend between the mountains.

In the evenings of spring and autumn, when the sun arrives and departs, the ice sheet's white surface will be coloured red or lilac by Alpenglühen.

had the experience that the wind was against them as they travelled inland until they reached the summit ridge. Usually it was not a very strong wind, but very constant. From the summit ridge out to the coast, however, they had a following wind, and several expeditions found it possible to fit a sail onto their sledge to assist their progress even if they could not travel by wind power alone.

If wandering depressions invade the layer of inversion, very great temperature fluctuations in a very short time may occur. In four days in March 1950 the temperature at Station Centrale rose from —62° (—79.6° F) to —15° (5° F), i. e. a rise of 47° (84.6° F), and 22—23 February 1950 there was a variation in temperature from —64.8° (—86.6° F) to —36° (—32.8° F) or a rise of 29° (53.8° F) in twenty-four hours. Similar, even if not quite so violent, rises in temperature have been known at other stations. The sudden cooling of the air and the resulting inversion

229

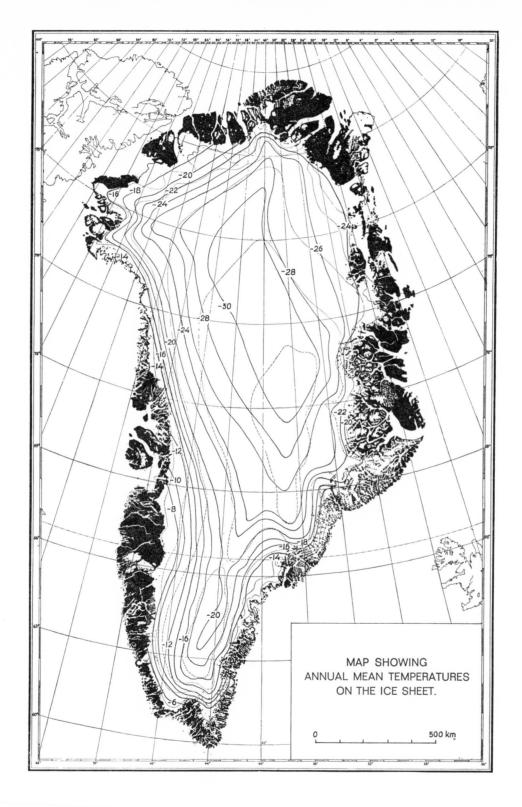

MAP SHOWING
ANNUAL MEAN TEMPERATURES
ON THE ICE SHEET.

0   500 km

*This map is based on work
done by
Carl S. Benson,
R. W. Gerdel,
H. Bader,
C. Langway,
and others.*

230

are of great importance for the local climate of the ice sheet. But because of the stable weather conditions over the ice sheet, the cold is not able to influence the air in the higher layers, and there is therefore no question of a general glacial anticyclone such as Hobbs had imagined.

It has often been said popularly that the weather of northern Europe has been brewed up first on the Greenland ice sheet, so that conditions on the ice sheet should be decisive for the weather conditions of northern Europe. The intense cold over the ice sheet is, however, only a local phenomenon that can have a great influence on the strength and direction of wandering depressions, etc., but the weather of north-west Europe is first and foremost conditioned by the general air exchanges between the cold Arctic air masses and the subtropical warm air masses brought about by the difference in pressure between the high pressure area of the Azores and the low pressure area of Iceland.

Gales on the Ice Sheet

Reports of older expeditions frequently mentioned very great gale-force winds that were encountered on the ice sheet, but the direct measurements that are now available do not confirm this. Very high wind velocities have, it is true, been recorded at the periphery of the ice, up to 70 m/sec (155 m. p. h.) for instance at Inglefield Bredning by workers at the Danish glaciological station which investigated conditions on Hurlbut Gletscher during the International Geophysical Year, and wind velocities of over 60 m/sec. (134 m. p. h.) have been recorded at P-mountain near the Thule Air Base just in front of the ice wall. Great wind velocities have also been recorded at Søndre Strømfjord and Narssarssuaq, and during the greatly feared *pieteraq* in the Angmagssalik district. This last is really a katabatic wind from the inland ice in connexion with local cyclones. At winter stations in the interior such winds have not been recorded however, and at Station Centrale 70 % of the wind velocities recorded were between 6 and 20 knots, and for North-ice the corresponding figure is 79 % within the same range. The katabatic winds are so sustained that neither at Station Centrale nor at Northice has even 1 % of the entries recorded complete calm, whereas at Hiran 26, which lies almost on the summit ridge, 32 % of the entries recorded no wind.

Measurements of precipitation on the ice sheet are very problematical, for at the moment there is no type of precipitation gauge that can measure snow precipitation with any accuracy. The problem with all snow gauges is not only in collecting the fallen snow, but also in distinguishing between the snow that is whipped up and re-distributed during a snow storm from that which belongs to a fresh snowfall. Measuring snowfall against markers bored down into the ground yields a more-or-less reliable figure for the accumulated snow, as also do stratigraphic studies of

231

accumulation over several years. Such figures may present the true annual snowfall, but it is also possible that the katabatic winds cause a constant wind transport of snow from the centre towards the edge of the ice sheet. At any rate, the map of snow accumulation shows that the central parts of the ice sheet have relatively small quantities of snow.

All precipitation of any consequence on the ice sheet falls in the form of snow; only in the marginal zone is there any chance of rain in the summer. The snow accumulation varies greatly with the geographical latitude of the ice sheet and distance from the coast. The greatest precipitation is recorded in southern and south-eastern Greenland, and the smallest snow accumulation has been recorded in the central and northern parts of the ice sheet. On average snow accumulation decreases by 2.5 cm (1 in.) of water for every degree of latitude further north until about 80° N. There is no direct relationship between the course of the summit ridge of the ice and the distribution of precipitation.

Climatic Change

Throughout this century, and particularly in the period from 1920 to 1940, a considerable rise in temperature has taken place in large areas of the earth. This warming-up of the climate applies in particular to Greenland and Spitsbergen, and the effect of it is greater the further north one goes. It is especially the winter that has become warmer, so that the difference between summer and winter temperatures has narrowed, and in Greenland, for instance, temperature conditions today in the Upernavik area are much as they were in Jakobshavn fifty years ago. This rise in temperature seems to some degree to have culminated about 1940, and at many stations lower January temperatures are now being recorded than ever before during this century, although the mild spell seems still to apply to autumn and spring. The average temperatures for January are still, however, above those at the end of the last century.

The present climatic change seems also to apply to the ice sheet. Diamond's investigations of the amount of precipitation at Site II have demonstrated that the annual accumulation of snow on the ice in north Greenland was particularly low in the period 1885—1890; after that it increased again until about 1899, then decreased until 1914 when it rose once more. Since 1934 there has been a steady decrease. Bull (1957) has proved, however, that there has been an increase in precipitation at Northice from 7 cm (2.73 in.) of water in 1940 til 11 cm (4.3 in.) in 1950. It is not possible to decide whether this variation in snow accumulation points to a change in precipitation conditions or just to a change in wind conditions.

Since 1920 the summers have been warmer, for in deep drillings at Site II no ice lenses (which are the sign of summer melting) have been found in layers older than 1920. During the winter

232

Drifting snow on the ice sheet.

spent at Station Centrale an annual mean temperature was recorded about one degree warmer than that recorded by the Germans at Eismitte. Several writers have taken this as a sign that the climate is becoming warmer, but it is really only to be regarded as a result of the slightly different sites of Station Centrale and Eismitte. Station Centrale lay slightly lower so that the temperature variation is merely the result of altitude difference.

The International Glaciological Expedition had drilled down in the ice to a depth of 20—30 m at different sites, and on the basis of these drillings the Danish professor W. Dansgaard has been able to show from oxygen isotope analyses that the temperetature had been rising up to the middle of the 1940s, after which a fall occurred which for the different sites varied between 0.6° C and 3.0° C. The temperature fall since 1950 has, with respect to the ice sheet, been as large as the total temperature rise for the whole of the first half of this century.

Whether this drop in temperature which has been established in the past few years is a temporary change on an otherwise rising temperature curve or is really a fall which will continue in the

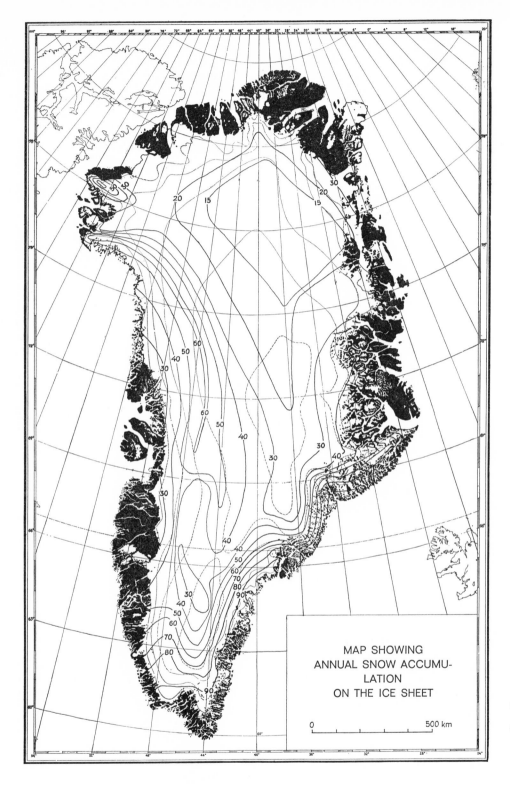

MAP SHOWING
ANNUAL SNOW ACCUMU-
LATION
ON THE ICE SHEET

0   500 km

*This map is based on work by
Carl S. Benson, R. W. Gerdel,
H. Bader, C. Langway, and
others, and the curves give the
accumulation in cm of water
equivalent to the accumulated
snow.*

The chaotic crevasse zone in Qarajaq glacier presents an impenetrable barrier.

coming years cannot yet be decided. There can be no doubt that, especially in Greenland where the economy is based on the cod catch, special attention will be paid to the climatic developments in the coming years.

The Temperature at the Bottom of the Ice

The temperature in the deeper parts of the ice is governed by the surface temperature and the altitude above sea level. As the ice sinks to lower altitudes, part of the energy is transformed into heat; thus, for each metre that the ice descends, a heat emission of 2.34×10^{-3} gcal. takes place, which means that there is a rise in temperature of $0.47°$ C for every 100 metres drop in altitude. If this $0.47°$ is regarded as the average temperature rise for a 100 m descent, then the temperature at the bottom of the ice sheet would still be below $0°$ ($32°$ F) over most of Greenland. Only in the most southerly part of the ice sheet would there be temperatures around the melting point.

235

Normally the ice just near the surface will be colder than the atmosphere and will therefore absorb heat from it, so it cannot be assumed that a negative temperature gradient necessarily means that a change in climate has taken place.

At the bottom of the ice sheet there will be emission of geothermal heat from the earth to the ice equivalent to 40 gcal./cm² per annum, and this heat can only be conducted up through the ice if the temperature gradient is greater than 2.5° per 100 m. If the gradient is less than this (and it normally will be) the heat cannot be conducted upward, and therefore melting will take place at the bottom of the ice, which will therefore be wet. But since wet ice cannot conduct heat, only a very thin layer will melt, and even though a somewhat greater heat may be generated by internal friction, it must be assumed that there is only a very thin layer of wet ice.

From the French seismic investigations carried out around Station Centrale it would seem that under the ice there is a layer of permafrost over 200 m (650 ft) thick. Along the periphery of the ice sheet the ice is normally frozen solidly to the substratum, and therefore no real erosion takes place. In the northern part of the ice cap, where the British made their investigations, the temperature at the bottom of the ice sheet seems to be very close to melting point.

The Thickness of the Ice Sheet

The Measurement of Ice Thickness

In nearly all glaciological investigations knowledge of the ice thickness is of the greatest significance, and this is particularly true of all the problems connected with ice caps. There are several ways of determining the thickness of the ice in a glacier. The simplest and most certain method would, of course, be to drill through the ice and measure directly from surface to bedrock, but as has been discussed on page 189 drilling through the ice is technically very difficult, and hitherto no successful drillings right through the ice sheet have been made. At the end of the last century, however, drilling was used on some of the small Alpine glaciers, for at that time there was no other way of finding out how thick the ice was.

Nowadays the methods most frequently used are to make seismic measurements and gravity measurements. Recently, too, experiments have been made using measurements involving radio waves or measurements of the electrical conductivity of the ice. These methods, though, are still at the experimental stage. As far as the Greenland ice sheet is concerned, gravity measurements and seismic measurements only have been of any importance.

The principle involved in the method of measuring ice thickness by gravity measurement is that the difference in gravitational power between a known point and the point in question is determined. It is well known that the force of gravity varies with geographical latitude, it is greatest at the two poles and least at the equator. It is also dependent on the elevation above sea level and the specific gravity of the strata. Gravitational force is thus normally greater in valleys than on mountain peaks. One measurement of gravity is the acceleration it gives to a falling body, and gravity normally is expressed in gals (named after Galileo, who proved that the oscillation time of a pendulum depends solely on the length of the pendulum line and on the gravity at that place). This unit of measurement, a gal, is the force required to give a falling body an acceleration of 1 m per second per second. Very often milligals (i.e. one thousandth part of a gal) are also used. The absolute value of gravity can be determined by pendulum measurements, i. e. by measuring with

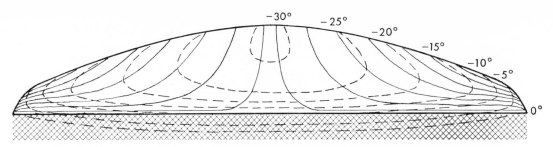

Diagrammatic representation of the theoretical temperature distribution in an ice sheet. Based on G. de Q. Robin. The unbroken lines are flow lines; dotted lines give temperature of ice in centigrade.

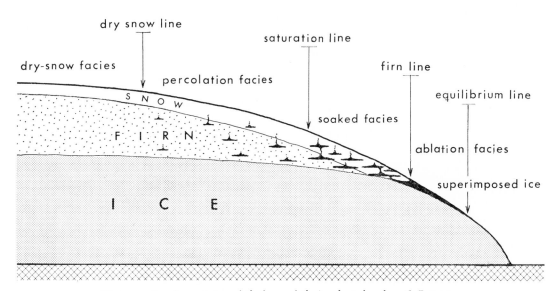

Diagrammatic representation of the faces of the ice sheet; based on C. Benson.

great accuracy the oscillation time of a pendulum of fixed length. In the last century particularly, a large number of such measurements were made all over the earth, but they are extremely difficult to carry out and very time consuming, so that nowadays they are normally only done in observatories and similar establishments.

Even though it is difficult to determine the absolute value of gravity, it is relatively easy to determine the difference in gravity between two measuring stations: this can often be done by using an instrument known as a spring gravimeter, which is much used not only by scientists but also by prospectors and others. The principle of the gravimeter is a spring balance with a small body suspended on an extremely sensitive thread of quartz or metal. The length of the thread will depend on the amount of attraction exerted by the earth upon the suspended body.

Thus, even when the exact value of gravity is not known, the difference can be measured by recording the length of the thread. With modern gravimeters gravity difference can be measured to hundredths of a milligal. With rock of normal density underneath, a change of ice thickness of about 14 m (45 ft) will produce a change of one part per million in gravity, but a mere 3 m (10 ft) change in surface elevation will also produce a change in gravity of one part per million. Variation in altitude between two reading points must, therefore, be measured to an accuracy of less than one metre, and for the same reasons latitude differences must be determined to about one tenth of a mile. Gravimeters are very sensitive to vibration and to fluctuations in temperature, so that while the expedition is at work they must be handled with utmost care, but the setting up and carrying out of the measurements does not take very long, so that measurements can be made at many points. Gravimeters are of various designs, but they are all so sensitive and so easily get out of adjustment, that it is very important to check the measurements by constantly comparing them with a reference point where the gravity value is already known.

To compare gravity measurements made with various instruments, it is necessary to reduce all the figures in terms of one particular point, and by international agreement it has been decided to compare all measurements with Helmer Tower in Potsdam. The absolute value of gravity is not required in determining the thickness of the ice sheet, but the gravitational anomaly, i. e. the difference between the theoretical gravity and the actual gravity of the site.

In order to calculate the theoretical gravity it is necessary to fix the exact position of the site and to determine its altitude above sea level: correction must be made both for the centrifugal force of the earth and for the flattening of the earth at the poles (as it is well-known the surface of the earth is closer to the centre of the earth at the poles than at the equator). Correction must also be made for height above sea level, and in making this correction the instrument is regarded as being in the open air at that altitude. The difference between the theoretically calculated gravity and the value actually measured is known as the free air anomaly, and it is this value that is of interest in determining the thickness of the ice. It will be seen that this value depends on the attraction, and therefore of the mass, of the formations lying between sea level and the point of measurement. If a number of calculations of gravity anomaly are made at different places on the ice, the variations will depend much more on the thickness of the ice than on the varying constituency of the bedrock, for the difference between the specific gravity of ice (0.9) and the specific gravity of the various types of rock (varying around 2.6) is much greater than the differences between the var-

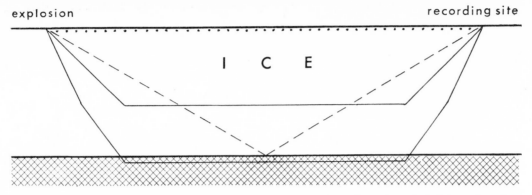

The reproduction of seismic waves. Dotted line, the direct wave along the surface; dashed line, the reflected waves; unbroken line, reproduction of refracted waves.

ious types of rock themselves, for this is seldom more than 0.7. At a single point it is not possible to determine how much of the gravity anomaly is due to the changing of the rock below and how much is due to variations in the thickness of the ice.

However, if several points are taken at which the thickness of the ice has already been determined by seismic measurements or other means, and these are continually compared, it is possible to gain considerable information about the ice thickness there, for as more or less constant geological conditions can be assumed, most of the variations in gravity can be ascribed to differences in the thickness of the ice.

The most exact method of determining the thickness of the ice is by seismic measurements, i. e. by measuring the propagation of an artificial earthquake. The tremors from an explosion in the ice propagate in wave form partly along the surface of the ice and partly through the ice. As long as the specific gravity and elasticity of the ice remain the same, the waves are propagated at a definite velocity, but if there are changes in the physical properties of the ice, then the waves are refracted, and if there are sudden changes in structure, such as a transition from ice to bedrock, they may be reflected. As in the propagation from a normal earthquake, the tremors from a seismic explosion propagate as shock waves.

The surface waves spread only along the surface and do not penetrate the lower levels of firn and ice. The waves which are propagated down through the ice are of a different type, and we differentiate between the rapid longitudinal waves which are propagated by oscillations in the direction of scatter, and the transverse waves at right angles to the direction of propagation. By placing seismographs at various distances from the site of the explosion, it is possible to record the propagation of the various waves and thereby to determine the thickness of the ice.

Explosives must be drilled into a number of bore holes at different depths in the ice and a large

A melt water stream in the margin of the ice sheet where the stone and gravel covering protects against melting.

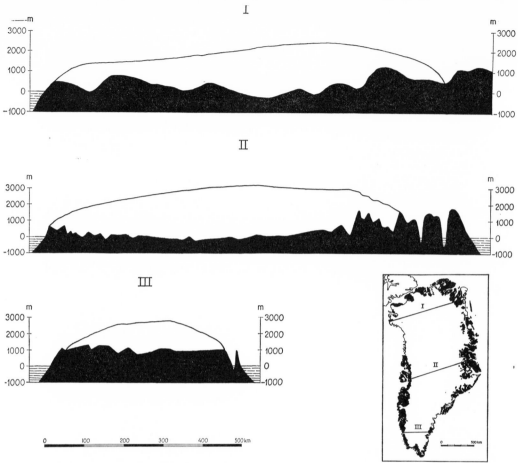

Three sections through the ice sheet. These are based on measurements made by Jean-Jacques Holtzscherer. I. Section from Thule Air Base to Kap Georg Cohn. II. Section from Disko Bugt to Cecilia Nunatak. III. Section from J. A. D. Jensens Nunatakker to Skjoldungen. Vertical exaggeration approx 1:40.

number of geophones with their cables must be fitted up to receive the seismic shock waves. These measurements are therefore extremely time consuming, and it can also be very difficult to analyse the individual wave motions.

In seismic determinations both refraction and reflection measurements are used. The simplest method is reflection measurement, which works on the same principle as echo sounding by recording the time taken for a wave to travel through the ice and be bounced back by the bedrock. Unlike normal echo sounding, however, there can be no question of placing the measuring apparatus immediately above the site being measured: the blast from the explosion makes it necessary to place the recording apparatus some distance away. So it can be difficult to differentiate between the reflected waves and other seismic waves, and if the contact zone between the ice and the bedrock is not horizontal but inclined, the waves may be reflected in various directions and

242

be difficult to pick up. Not only this, but no information can be obtained in advance about the velocity at which the reflection waves will propagate in the ice, for this is highly dependent on the specific gravity of the firn and the ice.

The rate of propagation will be directly proportional to the specific gravity, and increases therefore with greater depth, until in layers of pure ice with no bubbles it is constant. As it cannot be known in advance how thick the firn layer is, nor how rapidly the layers of actual ice are reached, it is impossible to calculate the thickness of the ice purely on the basis of the time it takes for the reflected waves to travel from the site of the explosion down to the bedrock and back to the measuring site.

It is necessary first to determine the rate of propagation in the ice by a series of refraction measurements at various distances from the site of the explosion. When this condition has once been established, it is possible to commence the actual reflection measurements which can give the thickness of the ice with great exactness.

In addition to these two methods, the thickness of the ice can also be determined by using radio echo soundings, once again making use of the echo sounding principle, but in this case using electromagnetic waves instead of sound waves. On the American Antarctic expeditions it had been noticed that radio aerials functioned just as well whether they were raised up above the snow or lay buried in the ice. When the first air flights were made in Antarctica after the Second World War, there were a number of problems with using radio altimeters, for reflections were received not only from the surface of the snow, but also from lower layers of ice. The problems was particularly great if a plane was flying at a low altitude over the ice. In 1948 and 1949, therefore, the possibility had already been considered of using radio altimeters for measuring the thickness of the ice in glaciers, and a number of experiments were commenced in America.

However, it was not until the International Geophysical Year that experiments were made in Antarctica and later in Greenland. On these tests an American altimeter of type SCR 718 was used which is fitted in many American aircraft. From specially constructed aerials a high frequency impulse of 440 megahertz with an output of 7 watts was sent out and most of this was absorbed by the ice. At first the tests were a failure, but in a series of measurements near Wilkes Station reflections were received, and as it was assumed on the basis of laboratory experiments that the radio waves had a rate of propagation in ice about 1.8 times their velocity in air, the thickness of the ice at the station could therefore be determined to be about 160 metres, and later seismic measurements in the same area have given a similar figure.

The tests were continued on the ice sheet near Camp Tuto, partly by building an instrument into a Weasel, and partly by taking measurements from a low-flying aircraft. The tests were encoura-

243

ging, but also proved that it was not possible to use this method for measuring ice thickness much above 900 m (3,000 ft), for at great depths the echo could not be received above the noise level. Experiments have also been made in Britain with radio measurements, and such measurements were also one of the main topics of discussion at the last conference on the results of Antarctic ice research that was held in Austria in 1962. In April 1963, on American initiative, the various electrical and radio methods for measuring the thickness of the ice were tried and compared at Camp Tuto, and it was confirmed that better results were achieved with the radio measuring apparatus in April than in summer, presumably because the energy loss is less in the cold winter snow than in the wet snow and ice of the summer.

In the summer of 1964 Dr G. de Q. Robin and Dr. S. Evans of the Scott Polar Research Institute of Cambridge and Dr. Amory H. Waite of the US Army Electronics Research Laboratory collaborated in making radio echo soundings on the Greenland ice sheet near Thule Air Base. Under the direction of Dr. J. Rinker of the US Army Research Support Group a journey was made of 130 miles from Camp Tuto to Camp Century and then to points 40 miles south and 50 miles north west of Camp Century and then back to Camp Tuto.

Along the whole route a nearly continuous profile of the form of the bottom surface of the ice was obtained by transmitting radio waves at a frequency of 35 Mc/s and having the recorded echoes displayed on an intensity modulated cathode ray tube and photographed by a continuously moving photographic film. This continuous profile will be of the greatest value in mapping and studying the bottom relief, and at the same time it will contribute to a better understanding of the factors governing the surface form and the flow of ice sheets.

It is of particular importance for the method that the ice and firn should be cold, for loss of signal strength by dielectric absorption of the radio wave in the ice is highly temperature dependent. At a point 150 miles east of Camp Century Dr. A. Waite in 1964 measured 6,500 ft of ice, which is the deepest radio echo sounding that has ever been made. It is likely that this method will be used to establish a detailed map of the depth of the ice sheet over extensive areas of Greenland and Antarctica.

The trials of measuring the thickness of the ice by using radio waves continued in 1965. Experiments have been made with the frequencies of 440, 110 and 30 Mc/s, and the best results were obtained with 30 Mc/s. With improved aeriels, more powerful transmitting equipment and another registration method the technique has now been so thoroughly tested that it is applicable to many arctic glaciers. One advantage is that the dielectric properties of the ice deflect the radio waves so that they reflect from a very small area more accurately than the seismic waves. The radio wave method of measuring the thickness of ice has given results that are in good accordance

244

On the way down from taking measurements on Hurlbut Gletscher. In the background the ice-floes on Inglefield Bredningen.

with seismic control measurements, though the figures registered by radio lie a little below the others. This might be due to the fact that the dielectric constants of the ice at greater depths are not known, i. e. in old ice under pressure. It is therefore intended to register the electric conductivity of ice of different ages from the core samples taken at Camp Century.

Measurements were made during the summer of 1965 along the route from Camp Tuto to Camp Century and further on. It proved that the bedrock under the ice is quite even, as soon as we are outside the marginal zone. The same instruments have been tested in the Antarctic during the Antarctic summer season 1965—66, and a set has been lent to an American archaeological expedition, which has worked in Turkey and among other things studied the glacier on the top of Ararat. All the experiments have been made from sledge trains, but naturally the method might become of special importance if aeroplanes or helicopters could be used. It should be practicable as it is possible to distinguish between the reflection from the snow surface and that from the ice bottom by means of different frequencies, and trials to this effect are actually planned. Thus, a flight from Thule Air Base across the ice cap to Mesters Vig and from there to Søndre Strømfjord should have been carried out in the summer of 1965 for the purpose of measuring the thickness of the ice during the flight. The route was laid out so that the areas flown over would include those in which the French E. P. F. expeditions and the International Glaciological Expedition had previously been working with measurements of the ice thickness. Unfortunately, this flight across the ice sheet had to be abandoned, however, because no plane suitable for the purpose could be obtained. But the flight will be carried out in 1966.

The Thickness of the Greenland Ice Sheet.

The French, British, and American measurements of the thickness of the Greenland ice sheet indicate that there is a considerable difference between the topography of the bedrock beneath the southern ice dome and that beneath the northern ice dome. The southern part of the ice sheet is resting on a mountainous base which for the most part is about 1000 m (3,300 ft) above sea level, and here the ice forms a close-fitting cap with a maximum thickness of 850 m (2,700 ft); the profile of the ice is steeper here than in the northern part of the ice sheet, and this may suggest that the ice sheet is more dynamically active than it is further north.

The ice reaches its greatest thickness in the central and northern parts of the ice sheet, i. e. 3,200 —3,400 m (10,500—11,100 ft), and here the bedrock is for large areas at sea level or up to 400 m (1,300 ft) below. From the nunatak zone of the east coast the mountain range continues in under the ice, and the seismic measurements here suggest a very steep and rugged subglacial relief. In the central and western areas the topography of the bedrock is more even. If the ice were to melt away, there would here be a landscape with low-lying rounded rock faces, which would doubtless resemble in many ways the landscape now found around Hudson Bay in Canada. There is no direct relationship between the topography of the bedrock and the crest of the ice sheet. The average thickness of the ice sheet is 1,500 m (5,000 ft).

Because of the many crevasses, it has not been possible to make seismic measurements in the actual marginal zone around Disko Bugt. However, measurements made further in on the ice sheet show that there are large areas where the bedrock at present lies below sea level by as much as 300 m (1,000 ft), but that these low lying areas do not form a continuous basin, but are interrupted by higher areas. Along the whole of the eastern margin of the ice sheet, the altitude of the bedrock beneath the ice is between 500 m (1,650 ft) and 1000 m (3,300 ft), while the bedrock inland of Søndre Strømfjord and the peninsula of Nugssuaq is at a height of 250—500 m (825—1,650

246

ft) above sea level. Nothing is known of the depth of the ice under Jakobshavn Isbræ since the dangerous crevasse area obstructs measurements.

In the area between Lat. 75° and Lat. 78° N precise information about the thickness of the ice is lacking, but American investigations seem to suggest that the most northerly part of the ice sheet rests on an elevated bedrock, and that the thickness of the ice there is less than in the central parts of the ice sheet. By and large in central and northern parts of the ice sheet Greenland can be regarded as a huge bowl filled with ice up to the brim — i. e. the coastal mountains.

There is much to suggest that the edge of the bowl is serrated on the west side, and that valleys, such as that occupied by Jakobshavn Isbræ, continue far in under the ice to join up with the low-lying central parts below sea level. Holtzscherer (1954) has attempted on the basis of existing measurements to draw a map of the topography of the bedrock, and this shows that inland of Disko Bugt there are two or three valleys with floors well below sea level. These valleys could possibly be traced right to the coast, where they would be found to be occupied by the most active of the calving glaciers. Similar deep valleys are not known in the ice sheet in east Greenland; all the investigations that have been made in the east suggest that the ice is cut off from the coast by high mountain chains. Neither is there any sign that Greenland consists of several islands joined into one by the mass of ice. Antarctica has been proved to be a series of land masses and islands fused together by the ice mass into one continent, but the same is not true of Greenland. Even if the ice were to melt away, Greenland would still remain one island.

Many attempts have been made to explain the topography of the ice sheet with its two domes and its assymetrical summit ridge. As we have pointed out on page 224, there is nothing in present precipitation conditions to explain the position of the height axis, but the fact cannot be ignored that it is over the depression between Disko Bugt and the Angmagssalik area that there is relatively little precipitation. Nor is there any subglacial ridge or other similar topographical feature to determine that the crest of the ice sheet should follow the particular course that it does. Attempts have therefore, been made to explain it as the result of earlier climatic conditions (L. R. Wager), assuming that it represented the zone of greatest precipitation during earlier periods, or as being where the ice is thickest (Sorge). But seismic investigations have shown that the greatest ice thicknesses are encountered further west, where the bedrock is lower.

As has been particularly emphasized by Holtzscherer, the high bedrock to the east will prevent any strong subglacial ablation to the east, while the low-lying areas (and probably also the occurrence of subglacial valley systems as a continuation of the Disko Bugt fjord systems) will encourage drainage to the west. But the assumption underlying this idea is still that an ice movement takes place in the lower parts of the ice sheet and not in the upper layers, where it would not be influenced by the topography of the bedrocks. However, investigations that have been made by B. Brockamp indicate that even far in on the ice sheet where there is a considerable thickness of ice surface formations can be observed that have a relationship to the form of the bedrock. Normally glacier crevasses are only found in the marginal zone of the ice sheet but single crevasses have been found as far as 145 km (90 miles) inland where the ice was more than 1,000 m (3,300 ft) thick. In this connexion it may be worth mentioning that the assymetrical position of the summit ridge is particularly pronounced in central Greenland and less marked in northern Greenland where it lies closer to the centre.

Compared with the Antarctic ice sheet that of Greenland is thin, for in Antarctica a maximum thickness of 4,300 m (14,100 ft) and an average ice thickness of 2,500 m (7,750 ft) have been found.

The Movements of the Ice

Measuring the Movement of the Ice

There can never have been men who lived in closer contact with or who were more dependent on great glaciers than the old Icelandic farmers. The first descriptions of glaciers and the first confirmation of ice movements can be traced back to the works of the Icelandic chroniclers. They have been preserved by Saxo Grammaticus in his famous work *Gesta Danorum,* which was written about 1200 A. D. We have also already drawn attention to *Speculum Regale* (see page 32) as giving a good insight into the natural conditions of Greenland in its description of the ice sheet itself and of the ice floes along the coast. Saxo himself never visited either Greenland or Iceland, but his very detailed descriptions of the ice masses in Iceland and Greenland contain such a wealth of information that they must be based on reports from an Icelander who had first-hand knowledge.

The old inhabitants of Scandinavia, therefore, had a clear understanding of the nature of glaciers, and it would seem that they also made long journeys of exploration in Iceland and Greenland. While the learned men of Europe were busy with their sterile scholastic disputations, Norsemen at great risk to their lives were venturing forth onto the glaciers and ice streams of Iceland in order to explore them. Even in the early Middle Ages the people of Greenland and Iceland realized that the glacier ice was in motion and that the glaciers could alter in extent with the course of time — it was not until several centuries later that the inhabitants of the central European Alps reached the same conclusions about their glaciers.

The first direct measurements of ice movement were made in the Alps. In 1760 a row of stones was placed on Grindelwald Gletscher, and by using tape measures it was possible to demonstrate that there was a movement of the ice and to determine the speed at which the stones, and therefore the ice, moved in relation to fixed points at the sides of the glacier. In six years the stones moved sixty paces downwards, and the rate of movement was greater in the centre than at the edge of the glacier. Another story that is well known in older glaciological literature is that of

Hugi aus Soluthorn, who in 1827 built himself a hut on the ice on the medial moraine of the Unteraar Gletscher, and in the course of three years the house moved 110 m (120 yd) downward on the ice.

There was a great interest in the study of glaciers in the mid-nineteenth century, and it was at that time that the first systematic measurements were made on the glaciers of the Alps. In 1840—41 Louis Agassiz began to measure the movement of the ice in Unteraar Gletscher, and in 1842 J. D. Forbes made similar measurements on Mer de Glace on Mont Blanc. All the first measurements that were made were of valley glaciers of various sizes, and it was a long time before any interest was shown in the glaciers and ice sheet of Greenland.

In Greenland. H. Rink had discovered which of the glaciers descending into Disko Bugt and Umanak Bugt and calving there, were the most active, and he had also attempted to estimate their production of icebergs. In 1875 the Norwegian geologist, Amund Helland, travelled to Greenland, where he visited the area between Egedesminde and Umanak with the idea of determining the rate of ice movement by making direct surveyings. Using a theodolite, he established the positions of stones and particularly noticeable points of ice on the ice sheet. By repeating his measurements some days later, he was able to determine how far they had moved. Helland found that Jakobshavn Isbræ moved 15—20 m (50—65 ft) a day, and this was a much greater distance than any other glacier was known to move. At Torssukátaq he found a movement of 4—10 m (13—33 ft) a day. In later years numerous measurements have been made on the ice sheet of Greenland, both on the local glaciers outside the ice sheet and on the glacier spurs from the ice sheet itself, but exact measurements are still lacking for the central areas of Greenland.

In these early investigations on the glaciers it was customary to measure only the movements of stones or easily recognized peaks on the ice. But in more detailed investigations it was necessary to use bamboo stakes drilled down into the ice or aluminium tubes frozen fast into the ice and so

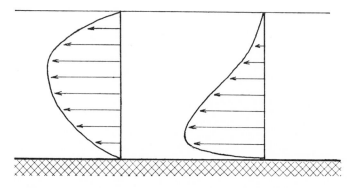

Diagram to show to the left plastic flow, to the right extrusion flow.

250

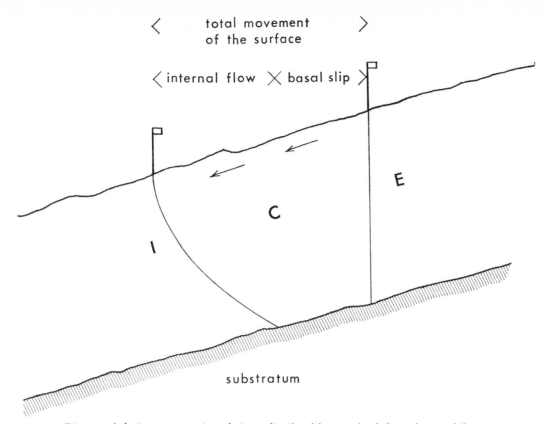

total movement
of the surface

< internal flow ✕ basal slip >

E

C

I

substratum

Diagram of the ice movement in a glacier as distributed between basal slip and internal flow.

moving with it. It can be difficult to establish such measuring points in heavily crevassed terrain, and not many measurements have been carried out in the crevasse zone of the ice sheet. The position of the stakes can be determined with great precision so long as it is possible to set up the theodolite on firm ground off the ice sheet itself. When the measuring points are so far in on the ice sheet that it is only possible to fix their position by triangulation from point to point, then the degree of exactitude is considerably less.

As a rule bamboo stakes or aluminium tubes are used as markers and protrude some feet above the ice. In the melting zone it can be difficult to keep them in position for some length of time, for they gradually melt loose and fall down onto the ice. In the area of accumulation there is yet another difficulty, for the poles are gradually covered by the accumulating snow, and it is difficult to locate them again. To get round this problem, the French glaciologist, Louis Lliboutry, tried using iron tubes about 2 m (6½ ft) in length, which he drove down vertically into the glacier. He allowed them to get covered with newly fallen snow, then by using a magnetometer, he was

251

able to locate them again even when they were covered by as much as 10 m (33 ft) of snow. This method has been used with great success on Mont Blanc, where there is a heavy annual snowfall, but it has never as yet been used in Greenland, where it would seem to have considerably advantages. The Americans have attempted to relocate metal plates and wire mesh by using radar measurements, but no data about these experiments are available.

When measurements are made with a theodolite, it is possible to determine the amount of ice movement at only a few points, and it takes a considerable time to carry out the measurements. In high mountains and under Arctic conditions in difficult terrain it can be very exacting work for those who have to make the measurements. In ordinary surveying work it has long been practice to use photogrammetry. In this, the actual plotting out of the map is done on the basis of stereo photographs taken from ground level, or, more frequently, by aerial photography. At the end of the 1920s experiments were made in Germany using photogrammetry in glaciological investigations, and as early as 1897 S. Finsterwalder had published an excellent map of Vernagtferner Gletscher purely on the basis of photogrammetry. It was now thought that it might be possible to use this method for determining the movement of glaciers. By taking two series of stereoscopic photographs at an interval of several days it should be possible to plot the movement of stones and ice peaks in the same way as had been done with theodolite measurements. But a much more detailed and exact picture would be obtained by this method. For in the laboratory the movement of a large number of points could be plotted out, whereas in the field using a theodolite only a few points could be plotted. The photogrammetrical method was used for the first time by R. Finsterwalder on the Nanga Parbat expedition to Karakoram in 1928, and it has been used since by many other major expeditions.

Finsterwalder's method was to take photographs from two or more stations outside the edge of the ice, and this method has been used on many glaciers; it was used for instance, by W. Pillewizer in Spitsbergen in 1938.

As part of the programme of the International Glaciological Expedition to the ice sheet, the possibility was also examined of determining on the basis of aero-photogrammetry alone the ice flow in the active glaciers which descend from the ice sheet into Disko Bugt and Umanak Bugt, so that it would not be necessary to transport men to the various glaciers; it would merely be a matter of making a number of flights at various intervals of time. The German photogrammetrician, W. Hofmann, and the French geodesist, M. Baussart, succeeded in finding a method by which it was possible to determine the movement of the ice on the basis of two series of aerial photographs, and a calculation of the flow of a large number of west Greenland glaciers is at present being worked out.

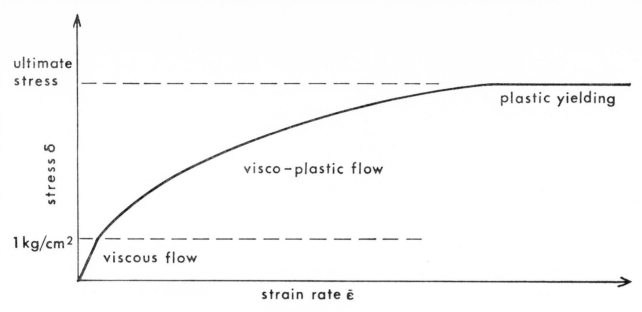

ultimate stress

plastic yielding

stress δ

visco-plastic flow

1 kg/cm²

viscous flow

strain rate ē

Diagram to show the relation between stress and strain rate in ice.

Besides using theodolites and photogrammetry to measure the rate of movement, it is also possible if conditions are just right to make an automatic recording of the movement of the ice by means of "glacier clocks" or cryocinographs. By this method, the movement of stakes stuck into the ice is transferred by way of taut invar wires to a recording instrument placed on a rock or stone outside the edge of the ice. As the wires are kept at a constant tension over a drum, their length can be registered on a recording cylinder driven by a clockwork. By this method it is possible to study the flow in detail, and also to confirm whether there are any diurnal rhythms or other variations. The method has been used in Greenland by R. P. Goldthwait in studying the flow of the edge of the ice at Red Rock on the peninsula of Nunatarssuaq near to Thule Air Base. R. P. Goldthwait (1960) found here that the movement of the ice varied between 6.8 and 18 millimetres (½—¾ in) per diem, the higher rate being reached during the day when the temperature was highest, and the smaller rate of movement occurring at night.

For recording very small movements of the ice, such as occur in the ice tunnels in Greenland, the American glaciologist, René O. Ramseier, has used X-ray film upon which a strontium 90 beta source frozen firmly into the glacier wall marks out a path.

The Rate of Movement

To give some idea of the rate of movement in glaciers in general, some figures may be given. The amount of movement in the glaciers of the Alps, for instance, varies between 4 in. and 20 in. a day. The Rhône Glacier moves 2 ft in a day, and the Glacier des Bossons 3 ft. The Austrian glaciers Vernagtferner and Hintereisferner move 1—4 in. in a day. The Blue Glacier in Washington State moves 10 in. in a day, and Salmon Glacier in British Columbia 1—8 in. in a day and Taku Glacier in Alaska 2 ft in a day. The Scandinavian glaciers are small, and the movement in them is consequently less. In the case of the Swedish Isfallglaciär at Kebnekaise and other glaciers in the area the rate of movement is only 20—40 m (65—130 ft) a year or 5—10 cm (2—4 in.) a day. In Spitsbergen photogrammetrical measurements have given varied figures ranging from a few centimetres to over one metre per day.

In Greenland the rate of ice flow varies greatly with the individual glaciers. The most rapid movement is found in the largest of the outlet glaciers that descend from the ice sheet itself; in these it is possible to find rates of flow up to 20—30 m (65—100 ft) a day, or 7—12 km (5—8 miles) a year. These figures also apply to Jakobshavn Isbræ as well as to Rink Gletscher, and probably also to some of the largest and most active of the glaciers in north-east Greenland. The glacier at Qarajaqs Isfjord has a maximum movement of about 18 m (60 ft) a day, and a similar rate has been found for Upernavik Isstrøm.

In the smaller glaciers that descend to the sea and calve there the rate of movement is not quite so rapid, thus Torssukátaq has a movement of 4—10 m (13—32 ft) a day, and Eqip sermia and Kangerdluarssuaq move as little as 3—5 m (10—16 ft) a day. However, in comparison with most other glaciers in the world this is very rapid, and this is doubtless due to the fact that the glaciers of Greenland calve into the sea, and also to the fact that they have a very large high-altitude catchment area. The rate of movement of the glaciers which do not reach the sea is generally slower, and at the very edge of the ice sheet itself it can be very small indeed — Store Land-gletscher for instance in the Thule area moves only 2—5 m (6—16 ft) in a year. H. Lister showed that Britannia Gletscher in east Greenland moved up to 150 m (500 ft) per annum.

The glaciers outside the ice sheet vary greatly in their rates of flow, but in general they approximate more closely what is found in glaciers in other parts of the world. A yearly rate of movement of the order of 20—30 m (65—100 ft) seems to be very common.

Many glaciers, both in Greenland and elsewhere, have proved to have seasonal fluctuations in their rate of movement; in some there are diurnal rhythms, and on several glaciers what appear to be completely irregular variations occur. The most important variations, however, are those that take place with a change in season. These are now well documented, and they have been studied on a large number of glaciers in the Alps and elsewhere, but in Greenland they have not, as yet, been thoroughly investigated. Few figures are available for winter conditions on the glaciers of

254

The glaciers in north Greenland often have a vertical ice front. The man in the middle of the photograph gives an impression of the size.

Greenland because of the great difficulty in travelling there during that season of the year. In the case of the glacier at Qarajaqs Isfjord Drygalski found no difference in the rate of movement between summer and winter.

In the Alps, on the other hand, very detailed investigations in the area of Hintereisferner and the Rhône Glacier have shown that the movement of the ice in the firn area is most rapid in winter and early spring when the snow cover is at its maximum, whereas the rate of movement in the lower part of the glacier is greatest in summer when the temperature of the ice is highest. Corresponding variations within the seasons could doubtless be demonstrated for the glaciers of Greenland, at least in southern Greenland, and possibly also for some of the outlet glaciers from the ice sheet.

In addition to these seasonal fluctuations, many glaciers also have daily variations, so that the ice flow is more rapid during the day and slows down at night. In northern Greenland, where the daily temperature fluctuations are very slight, these daily rhythms do not occur, but a clear connexion can be proved between the rate of flow and the amount of cloud cover. This means that there must be a connexion between the movement of the ice and the amount of radiation, and this has also been shown to be the case in Spitsbergen. R. Goldthwait's investigation of the movement of the ice at Red Rock also shows a variation of between 6.9 and 18 mm ($\frac{1}{4}$—$\frac{3}{4}$ in) a day, the most rapid rate of movement coinciding with the highest temperatures. In cases where the daily temperature fluctuations are large, as for instance on South Crillon Glacier in Alaska, the rate of movement of the ice can be about four times as great during the day as it is at night.

In Greenland very rapid flow occurs in the glaciers that descend from the ice sheet itself. Further in on the ice sheet there is a drastic reduction in the rate of movement. In the area behind Eqip sermia A. Bauer (1955) found a movement of only 3 m (10 ft) a day. At present no reliable data exist for the ice movement in the central parts of the ice sheet, although measurements have been made. While the French expedition was wintering on the ice at Station Centrale they fixed the position of the station astronomically; in 1950 they established their position as being 70° 54' 50" N and 40° 37' 20" W; re-measurement in 1951 gave the position as 70° 54' 44 " N and 40° 38' 00" W. When Carl S. Benson and his Jello expedition revisited the station in 1955, C. Wallerstein fixed the position again, this time as 70° 54' 25" N and 40° 37' 57" W.

Thus during the period from 1950 to 1955 the station seemed to have moved 774 m (approx. $\frac{1}{2}$ mile) due south. When the stakes that the French had set up were re-measured, a similar shift of position was recorded which varied between 0.6 and 7.1 km ($^3/_8$ and $4^3/_8$ miles) — at a point near Camp Milcent, for instance, there appeared to have been a westerly movement of 611 m (2,000 ft). Such rapid movement of the ice seemed extremely unlikely, so much the more as the winter station itself bore no signs of major lateral movement, and the deep drill hole that had been made by the one-ton drilling rig on Victor's expedition was still very well preserved with little movement of the walls to be seen. It seemed therefore likely that there had been an error, either in the measurements made by the French or in those made by the Americans.

As part of the HIRAN project the station was visited again the following year (Hiran station 26 is situated practically at the entrance to Station Centrale) and a new determination of position was made. This time the position was fixed as 74° 54' 45" N and 40° 37' 21" W. At the same time work was started in France to check the figures of the expedition and the calculations based on them, and the result of this check was published in 1959 by A. Bauer and L. Tshaen. The new calculations — as far as the positions of the stakes were concerned — gave figures that were so close to those of the Americans that nothing could be deduced from them as to the movement of the ice. As far as Station Centrale itself was concerned, however, Bauer assumed that a movement really

256

A French Alouette at the front of the ice sheet at Søndre Strømfjord during reconnaissance for the International Glaciological Expedition.

had taken place: that the station had moved in a south-westerly direction at a rate of 170 m (550 ft) per annum, i. e. an amazingly rapid rate for central Greenland, equal in fact to the most rapid rate of movement found anywhere in the Alps.

The position of Station Centrale was once again fixed on the International Glaciological Expedition which visited the site in July 1959. By astronomical means, J. Commiot determined the position as 70° 54' 42" N and 40° 38' 10.5" W, whereas on the basis of geodetic measurements W. Hofmann from Germany arrived at 70° 54' 41" N and 40° 37' 21" W. It is at present impossible to decide which of these two is the more correct. However, both of them are so close to the original French figures, and in view of the fact that the French were in the area for some length of time and therefore had time to make careful observations, it must be assumed that the error is to be found in the positions worked out by Wallerstein. As the first and last of the positions are so

257

close to each other, it can also be assumed that the movement of Station Centrale was only very slight, in fact within the margin of error of the instruments. This means it is at present impossible to decide whether there has indeed been any real movement of the station at all. A more exact knowledge of the movement of the ice on the ice sheet beyond the marginal zone will not be obtained until the markers that were set up by the International Glaciological Expedition in 1959 have been re-measured. There is also another series of stakes set up by the Americans in 1961 from the coast at Melville Bugt inland as far as Camp Century and then on to Academy Gletscher at the head of Inglefield Bredning. It has been planned that the position of the markers set up by the International Expedition should be re-determined in 1967 as the stakes were revisited in 1964 and re-lengthened to prevent them from disappearing.

Older Theories about Ice Movement

Measurements of the movement of stakes yield information about the surface movement of the ice, but tell us nothing about the movement in the lower layers of the ice, nor about how the movement takes place. There are many theories about the mechanics of ice movements, but there are still many unsolved problems. What makes research on ice so difficult is that it is impossible to measure and study the interior of the glaciers directly.

To understand the movement of the ice sheet it is necessary to have some general idea of how movement in many glaciers takes place. Glaciers originate when the annual accumulation of snow is greater than the amount that melts away; the snow is then transformed into firn and then gradually into glacier ice itself. When the pressure of the accumulating masses of snow and firn becomes sufficiently great, the glacier ice begins to "flow", and sends down spurs to the lower areas of land. By definition it is characteristic of glaciers (in contrast, for instance, to permanent snow drifts and snow fields) that the ice is moving from the upper part of the glacier towards the front of the glacier snout, or at least that the ice has been in motion at some earlier period. In this latter case the name "dead ice" is given to it. The ice descends into areas where melting is greater than the annual accumulation, and thus the amount of ice diminishes, but any deficiency is made good by ice moving down from the upper part of the glacier. If the glacier front is in a state of balance, the year's snow accumulation will offset the amount of ablation. If a change in climate causes a greater amount of ablation, the glacier front will retreat; if ablation diminishes or precipitation increases, then the glacier front may advance.

If the glacier ice is exposed to pressure, it becomes plastic and flows, yet at the same time it reacts to blows in a brittle manner and shatters like glass.

258

In reality glacier flow can be considered as the result of two different kinds of movement — basal sliding of the ice over the glacier bed, and differential movement within the ice (see page 251). The proportion of basal slip to differential movement depends on the rheological conditions of the glacier, i. e. the shape and size of the glacier, the topography of the substratum, the temperature of the ice and the impurities it contains. Valley glaciers are usually steep, and it can often be assumed in their case that half of the surface movement is due to sliding of the ice over the substratum and that half is due to plastic deformation. In the case of an ice sheet such as that in Greenland which is normally resting on a more-or-less horizontal bed, sliding will be of less significance, and plastic deformation is thus a correspondingly more important factor.

The first attempts to explain the movement of the ice in a glacier were based on what was known as the *dilation theory*. This assumed that in summer the ice of the glacier was filled by melt water which forced its way into all the cracks and fissures in the ice. When this water froze, it expanded and forced the ice sideways, so that the glacier continually advanced.

There were many supporters of this theory, and there can be no doubt that this process does take place, but it cannot account for the ice movement in the Antarctica ice sheet and in the inner parts of Greenland, for no ice melting takes place there. Back in the mid-eighteenth century, J. G. Altmann had attempted to explain the movement of the glacier by saying that the force of gravity caused the whole glacier to slide over the substratum in one coherent mass. He further thought that melting of the ice would take place at the bottom of the glacier because of the effect of warmth from the earth, and that a thin film of water would act as a lubricant to cut down the frictional resistance.

This theory, too, had its supporters, and there can likewise be no doubt that this process does actually take place, but it cannot by itself explain the movement of a glacier. It does not, for instance, explain the fact that the rate of flow varies in different parts of the glacier, nor the fact that seasonal variations are different for the firn area and the glacier tongue.

As the amount of data about the glacier movement in the Alps grew, it became possible to establish certain principles for the ice movement in valley glaciers. Both measurements using lines of stones and theodolite measurements of stakes bored into the ice showed that the rate of ice flow normally increased from the upper edge of the glacier down towards the firn line, but then decreased again from the firn to the glacier front. It had long been known by guides and others who moved about on the ice that things buried in the firn high up on the glacier would re-appear far down on the glacier snout, whereas things buried further down toward the firn line would melt their way out not so far down. In the years 1888-1895 very careful measurements were made on the small glacier Vernagterferner in the Ötzthaler Alps in Austria, and in 1897 S. Finsterwalder, the German glaciologist, established his theory of flow lines for the movement of glaciers on the basis of these measurements.

Finsterwalder assumed that the movement of the ice took place constantly and regularly, and that the rate of flow in the different parts of the glacier increased and decreased continually, so that there were no sudden fluctuations. This being the case, a particle of snow that fell on the firn area was obliged to move in a certain pre-determined path from the time it was transformed into ice in the upper part of the glacier until it melted away on the lower part of the glacier snout. Thus the glacier snout can be regarded as a kind of reproduction of the conditions further up in the firn area.

Observations of Hintereisferner and the Rhône Glacier were continued, and they confirmed Finsterwalder's theory. Even very careful measurements carried out by H. Kinzl and O. Lütschg on several Alpine glaciers did not indicate that there were sudden changes in the rate of flow. According to this theory the movement of the ice could be regarded as a current in a highly viscous fluid. Finsterwalder's theory was, however, attacked by several authorities, including H. Phillipp, who on the basis of a series of measurements he had carried out claimed that the movement of the ice could be explained by regarding the glaciers as consisting of a varying number of ice blocks which slid and moved in relation to one another, and that this movement occurred along special shear planes which can be observed in places where there are sudden variations in the height of the ice surface on the two sides of a fissure or crevasse in the ice.

Drygalski's measurements of the ice movement in the 6—8 km (3¼—5 mile) wide glacier of Qarajaqs Isfjord had demonstrated that the rate of movement of the ice increased very rapidly from a narrow, scarcely moving zone along the side of the glacier until throughout the whole of the central part it was almost constant. By photogrammetrical methods R. Finsterwalder in the case of Rakhiot Glacier on Nanga Parbat has demonstrated, that the rate of ice movement only 5 m (16 ft) from the edge of the glacier was 142 m (465 ft) per annum, and that the maximum rate was 147 m (482 ft) per annum. Thus across most of its width Rakhiot Glacier must move forward at a uniform rate as one massive block of ice, and this movement was quite dissimilar from the movement his father, S. Finsterwalder, had envisaged in his flow line theory. A similar *block floe* movement had been shown to apply to several other glaciers, particularly in Arctic regions: for instance, Kongsbreen in Spitsbergen, such glaciers in Greenland as Jakobshavn Isbræ and the glacier at Qarajaqs Isfjord, Umiamako, Rink Gletscher, and presumably also some of the more active of the glaciers of north-east Greenland.

The valley glaciers which follow the flow line theory have an ice movement which may be compared to the currents in a viscous fluid. Using the formulae that apply to movement in a fluid, the

260

Ice breaking off the glacier front of the ice sheet
and sailing away as ice-bergs.

Italian glaciologist, C. Somigliano, in 1921 propounded a formula for calculating the movement in the lower parts of a glacier if the surface movement were known. His theories were carried further by M. Lagally (1930), who determined the viscosity of glacier ice by studying the increase in movement from the edge of the glacier toward the centre. Basing his calculations on the assumption that ice is a liquid with a high, but constant, Newtonian viscosity, and using normal

261

hydraulic principles, he produced a formula for calulating the thickness of the ice when the rate of movement at the surface, the extent of the glacier, its surface gradient, and gravitational acceleration were known. If it is assumed that there is no movement at the bottom of the glacier (and this seems to be the case with many of the smaller Alpine glaciers) then the formula is very simple, and it has been used to calculate the thickness of many glaciers. Mathematically, Lagally's formula can be expressed thus:

$$b = \sqrt{\frac{2\ L\ V_0}{\varrho\ g\ \sin \alpha}}$$

in which b stands for the thickness of the ice at the centre of the glacier, V_0 is the rate of movement of the ice at the surface, L is the width of the glacier, e is the specific gravity of the ice, g is the gravitational acceleration, and d is the gradient of the surface. To check his theory, Lagally calculated the thickness of the Austrian Pasterze Gletscher, in which the ice movement had previously been closely studied, and for which the ice thickness had been determined by seismic measurements by the German geophysicist, B. Brockamp, assisted by J. Mothes, in 1928. It was on this glacier that they had tried out the technique that was later to be used by Wegener's expedition for determining the thickness of the ice sheet. A remarkable degree of agreement was found between the figures calculated according to the formula and those actually measured. Lagally's formula only applied to glaciers with a temperature around 0° (32° F) and only to valley glaciers; it thus applied neither to the ice sheet itself, nor to the cold glaciers of north Greenland. Lagally's formula is worked out on the basis that the movement of ice is laminar, and that the rate of flow decreases from the surface towards the bottom of the glacier. Geomorphologically, it is impossible by this theory to explain how glaciers are able to erode the great U-shaped valleys or form the great glacial cirques that cut into the steep mountain walls and which are such a typical feature of all glacial landscapes that were eroded at an earlier period.

On the Michigan University Expedition to Greenland during the 1930s, Max Demorest, a young American geologist, carried out research on the geomorphological conditions in the heavily glacially eroded landscape on the peninsula of Nugssuaq near Upernavik. In order to account for the occurrence of roches moutonnées and other eroded formations, Demorest assumed that the ice movement had, on the contrary, increased with depth, and he explained this as being the result of increasing plasticity with increasing hydrostatic pressure.

Demorest assumed that the greatest amount of erosion occurred where the ice was at its thickest. By his theory, the viscosity of the ice should increase as hydrostatic pressure increased, and he dif-

262

ferentiated between two types of glacier movement: a simple sliding due to gravity when the gradient was sufficient to overcome frictional resistance of the substratum, and extrusion of the lower layers when the gradient was insufficient to overcome bottom friction. It was, however, possible that both forms of movement might occur simultaneously, but in an ice sheet resting on a horizontal substratum extrusion would be the more important factor, and Demorest assumed that even at a pressure of 4 kg per cm² (28½ lb/sq. in), i. e. at an ice thickness of 45 m (131 ft) there would be a possibility of extrusion of the lower layers of ice.

Demorest had support for his theory from a thesis that was published about the same time by the Austrian-born Swiss geographer and glaciologist, Rudolf Streiff-Becker, who since 1916 had been making comprehensive studies of the small Swiss glacier Claridenfirn. By very careful measurements he had determined the mean annual snow accumulation as being 3.167 m (10.84 ft), and since he had also confirmed that in the period 1916—1937 there had been no change in the altitude of the firn surface, this meant that throughout that period the amount of ice that had melted away had exactly corresponded to the amount of snow that had accumulated.

By various means he was able to work out a cross-section of the glacier tongue, and it was possible for him to determine how rapid the rate of ice movement must be for a sufficient quantity of ice to flow through this cross section to keep the firn basin constant. His calculation seemed to suggest that if the firn level was to remain constant the average rate of ice movement through the cross-section would have to be three times as great as the rate of movement recorded at the surface.

By this, Streiff-Becker explained that the movement of the ice in the lower parts of the glacier must be greater than at the surface, in other words that the lower layers of the ice were extruded. A further support for the theory of extrusion was the observed fact that the movement of the ice was greater in winter and slower in summer - in round figures the proportion was 11:3 - and this could be accounted for by the greater amount of extrusion resulting from the increased pressure caused by the winter snow lying on top of the ice.

Similar investigations of the state of balance of Grosse Aletsch Gletscher have also been worked out by R. Haefeli and P. Kasser. In this case very careful measurements of snow accumulation set against the rate of ice movement seemed to suggest that there was a greater rate of flow in the deeper parts of the glacier than at the surface. An attempt to prove by direct observations that the ice in the lower layers was extruded was made by Perutz and A. Roch in 1949 by the depth drilling method that has been mentioned on page 191. Measurements made with a clinometer in the drill hole showed that while the upper edge of the hole had moved 38 m (125 ft) in the course of one year, the lower part of the hole had moved only 14 m (46 ft), and there could therefore be no question of the lower layers being extruded in the place where the drill hole had been bored. Similarly, it has not been possible to point to any evidence of extrusion in the lower part of the 305 m (1,000 ft) deep drill hole bored in 1951 on Malaspina Glacier by Robert Sharp.

There was a lively discussion in the specialist literature of the thirties about the various theories of ice movement, but no satisfactory explanation of the problem was arrived at, and none of the theories that had been propounded could account for the observations and measurements that had been made on recent glaciers while at the same time explaining the results of investigations on the forms of glacially eroded landscape dating from earlier ages.

Sufficient experimental measurements of the physical properties of ice were lacking. Lagally had assumed that ice flow was laminar, and Demorest, without making any experiments, had assumed that the plasticity of ice increased as hydrostatic pressure increased. Observations in the field were too sporadic and had been made on such a variety of glaciers under such differing conditions, and laboratory experiments on ice had not, as yet, been carried out. Such investigations were not made until the Second World War, and then they were carried out in Cambridge.

The Plan for an Aircraft Carrier Constructed of Ice.

In the autumn of 1942, when the submarine war had entered one of its critical phases and the British were doing badly in North Africa, it became plain to the British military authorities that in the event of an allied invasion of Europe from a base in Africa, one of the handicaps would be the long distances that British bombers would have to fly to reach the front line. It would be a great advantage if, instead of taking off from British bases, they could take off from an aircraft carrier close to the theatre of war.

But all existing carriers had proved extremely vulnerable to enemy air attack and to submarine attack. In October 1942 a suggestion was put forward that a natural or artifical ice floe might be used as a base for heavy bombers. It could be towed southwards through the Atlantic. In December of the same year Churchill approved of the plan and tried to push it forward in every way. Aerial reconnaissance had shown, however, that it was not possible to find a natural ice floe that was suitable: all were either too thin, so that they would be broken up by the waves of the Atlantic, or too small, for the planes would require a runway 600 m (2,000 ft) long and 60 m (200 ft) wide.

If the plan was to be realized, it would be necessary to build a ship of ice shaped like a gigantic barge. Such a vessel would be unsinkable, and if the aircraft and crew could be brought under cover in the interior of the craft, they would be protected. So that the vessel would have a reasonable life, it was worked out that it should have a freeboard of 15 m (50 ft) above the water. It

Autumn in the large glacier-filled valleys of east Greenland. The large sheets of sand in front of the face are deposits from the melt water streams.

was no easy task that the British naval engineers were faced with. They soon found, however, that there was not enough information available in existing literature for them to design the vessel. It would be necessary first to make experiments in the laboratory to determine the reaction of ice to pressure and to loads of various kinds. These experiments were made in the Admiralty laboratories using both natural and artificial ice. At an early stage the researchers discovered that addition of 10—15 % of wood pulp would be a considerable advantage. By 1943 the experiments had proceeded so far that it was possible to commence designing the ship, but the technical difficulties in the construction of the 884 m (2,900 ft) long ship were many.

It would involve 1.7 million tons of ice and wood pulp, and preparations were made for the casting, which would have to be done in a cold climate, to be carried out in Newfoundland. But in 1944 the strategic situation had altered; modern aircraft now had a greater range, and they also needed longer runways, so that the vessel that had been envisaged would not be long enough. The whole project was therefore called off, but before this happened so many experiments and direct investigations on the ice had been carried out that this project was of the greatest significance for future scientific research, and above all, the value of laboratory research in glaciology was realized.

The Present Conception of Ice Movement.

Glacier ice is a polycrystalline mass which at low temperatures can be studied in the same way as any other crystalline material. The experiments in Britain proved that at a temperature around freezing point ice has most properties in common with other polycrystalline materials, such as metals, when they are close to their melting points. If a block of ice is loaded with a weight of some kind, momentary deformation will occur, but if the load continues, there will, as with metal under stress, be a slow change of shape or creeping of the ice, and the speed at which this takes place will gradually settle down to be constant. In 1949 E. Orowan showed that the rate of deformation of ice under pressure was proportional to the square of the pressure. This is not in accord with the law for liquids, where the alteration is directly proportional to the pressure. In contrast to the earlier theories in which the movement of the ice had been seen as analogous to the currents in a viscous fluid, the ice movement was now to be regarded as a plastic deformation. Thus, over a certain period of time even a small increase in load would give rise to greatly increased deformation. In the case of ice, this is in close agreement with the observations that have been made in the field, and it is now possible to explain why, as has been observed at Claridenfirn, even a slight increase in the winter snow cover can sometimes unleash a very great increase in the rate of ice movement. (See page 253).

Orowan's studies were continued by the British physicist, J. W. Glen, at the Cavendish Laboratory. While previous experiments had been carried out on blocks of ice without close control of the temperature, Glen now continued his experiments under the most careful control, using only single ice crystals. Glen determined the relationship between the rate of strain and stress and the deformation of the ice and expressed it in a simple power law which has been fundamental for the whole understanding of ice flow. Over the stress range 1—10 kg/cm² it can be expressed by the equation:

$$\varepsilon = k \, \sigma^{n}$$

in which ε is the strain rate per unit of lenght per year, σ is the stress expressed in bars, and k is a constant dependent on the crystal structure of the ice and its temperature etc., n is an exponent

266

that will normally be constant for a limited range of stress but actually is stress-dependent and in the case of glacier ice varies between 2.8 and 4.2 according to investigations of the closure of cylindrical tunnels and boreholes in glaciers. Investigations by S. Steinemann indicate, however, that for ice deformed along the plane of easiest glide n may fall as low as 1.5 for ice under low stresses.

It may be asked whether laboratory experiments on artificial ice really can be applied to glaciers in nature, but since the ice in the large continental ice sheets is usually very pure laboratory results can be normally applied to natural conditions. G. de Q. Robin has thus demonstrated that solid material trapped or dissolved in the Antarctic ice constitutes only a few parts per million of the total masses, and he therefore found that the variation with temperature of the velocoity of compressional elastic waves in ice as measured in the laboratory shows close agreement with extensive field observations made in Antarctica between 1956 and 1963.

Glen's experimental method was to place loads of various sizes and types on thin rods of ice consisting of a single ice crystal. His results cannot be applied directly to the conditions in a glacier, where hydrostatic pressure is also a factor — any point in the ice would be affected not only by the pressure of the firn and ice mass above it, but also by pressure from the ice around it.

Independently of Glen the Swiss glaciologist, S. Steinemann, arrived at the same formula to express the relationship between deformation and pressure while making comprehensive glaciological experiments both at Weissfluhjoch laboratory and with Professor P. Nigglis at the Institute of Mineralogy and Petrology at Zürich. As we have mentioned Glen's law of flow does not apply to small loads, for which H. H. G. Jellinek and R. Brill, and T. R. Butkovich and J. K. Landauer have demonstrated from measurements made in ice tunnels at Camp Tuto that the deformation of the ice is directly proportional to the load, i. e. that n = 1, as is the case with liquids.

If the results of Glen's and Steinemann's experiments are applied to conditions in the Greenland ice sheet, it will be seen that the stress to which the ice at any point is subjected can be defined as a combination of the downward hydrostatic pressure and the upward shear stress. The hydrostatic pressure, even at the bottom of the Greenland ice sheet, will not rise above 300 atmospheres (i. e. the weight of a 3,000 m (10,000 ft) column of ice) and in other glaciers it will be correspondingly less.

The results of experiments with other polycrystalline materials show that the plasticity of these materials decreases as the hydrostatic pressure to which they are subjected increases. As experiments have shown that ice in nearly all other respects behaves like other polycrystalline materials, both Glen and Orowan were agreed in rejecting the theory, first put forward by Max Demorest, that the ice was extruded in the lower layers. However, they were not universally supported in this: the Swiss glaciologist, R. Haefeli, for instance, emphasised that even if laboratory experiments had shown that ice behaved as other polycrystalline materials, this did not necessarily mean that ice would behave in the same way at the bottom of an ice sheet or glacier, for heat from the earth or from friction might cause melting to take place. Even if only a minute amount of water were present, it was nevertheless possible that this could alter the plasticity of the ice, which might therefore be greater at the bottom of the glacier than at the surface.

On the basis of Glen's results, J. F. Nye in 1952 calculated the relationship of ice flow to the thickness of the glacier, assuming that a purely plastic deformation took place. Nye first calculated the conditions of a typical valley glacier with a semi-circular or semi-elliptical cross section and laminar flow. He completed calculations for a number of Alpine glaciers, for which the thickness of the ice was already known from seismic measurements. He was on this basis able to calculate the shear stress of the ice at the bottom of these glaciers, and he found the values for this to vary between 0.49 bars for Unteraar Gletscher, and 1.51 bars for Grenz Gletscher.

If the rate of surface movement and the cross-section of the glacier were known, the law of purely plastic deformation made it possible to calculate the movement of the ice at the bottom of the glacier.

Thus Nye found that the rate of flow at the bottom of the Rhône Glacier must be 79 m (255 ft) per annum, but at the bottom of Arolla Gletscher only 4 m (13 ft) per annum. Nye's conclusions on velocity distribution in a glacier have been confirmed by the studies made on the Athabasca Glacier in Canada, where W. S. B. Paterson and J. C. Savage have taken very careful measurements of the surface movements and deformation of eight bore holes, in order to get information about the movement in the deeper part of the glacier. The results were a confirmation of Nye's theory with an exponent $n = 4.2$ for the stress-strain rate relation.

From valley glaciers Nye now turned his attention to the movement of an ice sheet resting on a horizontal base, i. e. approximately the condition of the Greenland ice sheet. Once again using Glen's law of flow, and the principles of plastic deformation, Nye was able to put forward a formula for the relationship of ice thickness to the surface gradient of the ice, gravity acceleration, and shear stress at the bottom of the ice. Under the simplified conditions of laminar flow, where all shear stress is parallel to the top and bottom surfaces of the glacier, we find that shear stress on the bed, which must be even for flow to occur, is given by

$$h = \frac{k}{\varrho \; g \sin a}$$

in which h is the thickness of the ice, ϱ is the specific gravity, g is the gravity acceleration, and a is the inclination of the surface.

268

Using the Danish maps of Greenland, Nye now attempted to calculate the thickness of the ice, assuming that the shear stress at the bottom of the ice sheet would be of the same order as that found in the Alpine glaciers, i. e. varying between 0.5 and 1.5 bars. In order to simplify the calculations, it was assumed that the shear stress was constant for the whole of the ice cap.

By assigning to it a value of 0.88 bars, Nye found an extraordinary close agreement as far as the southern dome was concerned between the theoretical calculations and the actually occuring ice thickness that had been measured by the French under Victor. However, as far as the northern part of the ice sheet was concerned the theoretical calculations seemed to indicate that the bottom of the ice must lie far below sea level. Using the figure of 0.88 bars for the shear stress meant that the bottom of the ice sheet would lie some 1200 m (3,900 ft) below sea level, which seemed unlikely in the light of the data that was available. And indeed it was later proved to be incorrect. Nye was first inclined to ascribe this lack of agreement between his theoretical calculations and the actual conditions to a mistake in the contours shown on the Danish maps, for this would alter the ice surface gradient. More recent investigations, however, have proved that even though it is possible to find odd contours that are misplaced slightly to either east or west, this would not alter the overall distribution of altitude. Nye's calculation was based, however, exclusively on the plastic deformation of the ice, and had not taken into account the fact that a sliding of the whole ice sheet across the substratum also takes place.

In 1959 Nye therefore made a fresh attempt to calculate the thickness of the ice sheet on the basis that surface movement was due to both differential movement within the ice itself and to sliding of the whole mass across the substratum. In such a theoretical calculation it is immaterial whether the sliding takes place directly in the zone of contact with the bedrock below, or whether it occurs in the lower part of a basic layer of permafrost. To find how much of the movement was due to sliding and how much was due to plastic deformation, the conditions of one particular point in the northern part of the ice sheet were examined in detail. For this purpose Nye selected a point, Station A 125, at 78° N and 53° W, for which the ice thickness had been determined by Bull on the British North Greenland Expedition.

The ice thickness was 2,300 m (7,500 ft) and the annual precipitation here amounted to 21 cm (8¼ in) of water equivalent, and the temperature at the surface was —23° (—9° F). In working out the theoretical distribution of temperature down through the ice, Nye came to the conclusion that the temperature at the bottom of the ice sheet must be about —4° (25° F), which would be considerably below the melting point of ice at the hydrostatic pressure that would obtain there. On the basis of his calculation, however, Nye assumed that the temperature rose fairly rapidly near to the bottom of the ice because of friction and heat from the earth. The higher the temperature of ice is, the greater is its rate of deformation. The shear stress at the surface was 0.7 bars, and at the bottom it could not be much above a maximum of 0.833 bars, with a minimum of 0.537 bars. Nye therefore assumed that the movement of the ice would mainly occur in the lowest part of the ice and that the differential movement of the ice could to all intents and purposes be regarded as purely plastic movement.

On this assumption it can be shown that the plastic movement amounts to twice the annual precipitation. As the movement at the surface is considerably greater (at the point in question it was fixed as being about 11 m [36 ft] per annum), Nye took this as proof that most of the surface movement can be ascribed to the sliding of the whole ice sheet over the substratum. Nye is of the opinion that this also applies in general to the ice sheets of both Greenland and Antarctica. On the basis of this reasoning he compiled a new balance profile for a two-dimensional ice sheet with a sliding base that can be mathematically expressed thus:

$$\left(\frac{H}{h}\right)^{2+\frac{1}{m}} + \left(\frac{x}{L}\right)^{1+\frac{1}{m}} = 1$$

in which h is the altitude of the ice surface at the distance x from the centre of the ice, H is the altitude of the ice surface in the middle of the ice, L is the distance from the middle of the cross-section to the edge of the ice, and m is a constant with values between 2 and 2.5. It will thus be seen that the cross-section of the ice is only to small degree dependent on the size of the snow accumulation. It is also characteristic that both the Greenland and the Antarctic ice sheets seem to approximate to the same balance profile in spite of the fact that the dimensions and annual snow accumulation of each are extremely different.

The assumption behind Demorest's theory of extrusion was that the rate of flow of ice would increase as hydrostatic pressure increased, but this was a postulate that was never proved. As Glen and Orowan have emphasised, it would seem most unlikely for ice to be the only polycrystalline material which behaved in this way. Attempts to determine directly the relationship between pressure and the rate of deformation were made in 1954—55 by the American glaciologist, George P. Rigsby, who was working for SIPRE. By exposing ice crystals to a pressure of up to 350 atmospheres, corresponding to the pressure at the bottom of the ice sheet, he succeeded in showing that for a single ice crystal the rate of deformation depends only on the solar stress and is independent of hydrostatic pressure provided that the difference between the ice temperature and the pressure melting point remains constant. Thus ice at —1° at a pressure of 1 atmosphere deforms at the same rate as, say, ice at —2.8° at a pressure of 300 atmospheres subject to the same shear stress.

270

Camp on the sea ice in front of Marie Sophie Gletscher in Peary Land.

At approximately the same time as Nye was setting forward his new theory, R. Haefeli (1960) also published a calculation of the profile of the ice sheet. In the 1950s he had made a series of investigations on a small ice cap at Jungfraujoch. Because of its great altitude above sea level, the ice temperatures were below 0° (32° F), and Haefeli regarded it as a kind of small-scale model of the conditions on a polar ice sheet. On the basis of Rigsby's experiments Haefeli assumed that Glen's law of flow applied regardless of the hydrostatic pressure. From the French investigations (which are thought to have confirmed the existence of permafrost at the bottom of the ice sheet) he assumed that all ice movement took place relatively high up, and that at the bottom of the central part of the ice sheet there was no movement at all. On the basis of these theoretical observations, a series of parameters was compiled for calculating the surface form and thickness of the ice. The calculations were only valid for the firn area, and only if a state of equilibrium was assumed for the ice sheet. A consequence of the rapid increase in the flow rate of ice with applied

271

stress is that the profiles of glaciers and ice sheets on approximately horizontal beds vary relatively little from one glacier to another. Nye had demonstrated that the ice thickness of an ice sheet would be proportional to the sixth root of the rate of accumulation, and there would, therefore, be only a slight difference between two ice sheets that were similar in form, even though one of them had double the precipitation of the other.

The Antarctic ice sheet is even less dependent on variations in precipitation; there, even a tenfold increase in snow accumulation would increase the ice thickness by only 25 %. A check of these calculations on the Greenland ice sheet was carried out by comparing the theoretically calculated profile of the ice sheet with the profile that Holtzscherer had actually plotted seismically from the coast to Station Centrale. The divergences were slight, and did not exceed 1 % of the ice thickness measured.

Whereas in their calculation Nye and Haefeli had assumed that the movement was evenly distributed, A. Bauer in 1960 attempted to calculate the ice movement on the assumption that the movement took place mainly in the ice streams. Rink had already pointed out that the ice movement is especially rapid in certain parts of the ice sheet, and on the basis of observations made on flights and from aerial photographs Paul-Émile Victor had subjected Rink's designation, ice streams, to renewed analysis.

From the movement of Jakobshavn Isbræ Bauer assumed that its annual production of icebergs was 20 km³ (4.8 cub. miles) of ice. By comparing this quantity of ice with the average snow accumulation in the high land in the vicinity, he reached the conclusion that if Jakobshavn Isbræ were in a state of material balance, it must drain an area of 73,429 km² (28,400 sq. miles). If this drainage area is regarded as a segment of a circle with an angle at the centre of 90°, the radius will be 306 km (190 miles). On this basis Bauer calculated the movement of the ice at various distances from the glacier front, and found that at a point some 90 km (56 miles) in on the ice there was a theoretical movement of 118 m (387 ft) per annum, and 200 km (124 miles) in on the ice there was a theoretical movement of 24 m (79 ft) per annum.

The average rate of movement for the whole drainage area would thus be about 170 m (560 ft) per annum, and it would also, therefore, be possible to calculate how long a particle of snow which fell at the edge of the drainage area would take to reach the front of the ice: for snow which fell some 300 km (185 miles) in on the ice, the length of time would be about 1800 years.

The Age of the Ice in the Ice Sheet

Hitherto, the method used in measuring movement within the ice sheet had been to record, over various periods of time, the movement of particular points on the surface — a method only feasible in the marginal zone. However, if the age of the ice appearing at the ice fronts could be determined, and if it could also prove possible to ascertain where this ice had originated, then the average rate of movement could be calculated.

In 1958 the American Arctic Institute sent an expedition to west Greenland under the leadership of C. Nutt and P. F. Scholander. Its object was to study the air content of the glacier ice with a view to determining the age of the ice. Professor Willy Dansgaard of the Biophysical Laboratory of the University of Copenhagen joined this expedition to investigate the oxygen isotopes of the ice. The expedition arrived in Greenland on board the Norwegian sealer *Rundøy* which was equipped with a laboratory for air analysis in which it would be possible to extract the carbon dioxide from the specimens of ice that were collected. Ice samples were gathered from eleven glaciers ranging from Bredefjorden in the south to Melville Bugt in the north. As the samples had to be from actively calving glaciers, and since it was difficult and dangerous to sail right in under the glacier fronts, the samples were taken from newly calved icebergs near the glacier fronts.

Glacier ice normally contains some quantity of air bubbles; these can vary in size from fractions of a millimetre to about 4 mm in length. The bubbles give the ice a greyish or milky white appearance. The air in them was originally trapped between the snow crystals when the ice fell as snow. When further snow continued to accumulate above the old snow, the air was first confined in the firn and then later took the form of actual bubbles in glacier ice. The air in the bubbles is, therefore, under considerable pressure: in the ice from the 300 metre (975 ft) drill hole near Site II a pressure of thirty atmospheres has been measured. In ordinary glacier ice the air content is about 4—9 % of the volume, and the chemical composition of the air in the bubbles is very nearly the same as that of the atmosphere — it is, though, richer in carbon dioxide, and this has not been explained.

As it is well known, it is possible to determine the age of a specimen from carbon - 14 tests, and so, if sufficient quantities of carbon can be obtained for analysis, the age of the air in the bubbles can be determined. For each test it was necessary to collect about 100 tons of ice; the ice was then chopped clean, so that only samples were left which had not been in contact with sea water or melt water. By expelling the carbon dioxide from the ice under a vacuum, it was possible to obtain sufficient quantities of carbon -14 for H. de Fries in his laboratory in Holland to be able to determine the age.

According to C. Nutt and P. F. Scholander (1961) an analysis proved that in only two cases they were dealing with ice that was more than a thousand years old, and in two cases the ice was less than one hundred years old. The oldest sample was taken from Upernavik Isfjord, and the age of the ice was reckoned to be 3,100 years (plus or minus 150 years). This was a much lower figure than had been anticipated, but it was in close agreement with the figures that Albert Bauer had arrived at from his calculation of the movement in the ice streams. (see page 272).

Dansgaard made an analysis of the oxygen isotope composition of the air in the ice. The air in the atmosphere contains a certain quantity of water vapour, and at the lower temperatures obtaining in Greenland the air will normally be close to saturation. In addition to the normal water molecules, consisting of oxygen of atomic weight 16 and hydrogen of atomic weight one, there would be a certain quite small quantity of oxygen with an atomic weight of 18 instead of the normal 16, and hydrogen (or deuterium) with an atomic weight of 2. If air is forced to rise and is then cooled, thereby forming ice from its water vapour, the heavy molecules will be discharged first, so that the air that remains will be poor in heavy isotopes. The ratio between oxygen[18] and oxygen[16] in natural precipitation therefore depends on both how rapidly and at what altitude condensation took place. On an average the air at the higher latitudes will be relatively poor in heavy isotopes and in 1960 Dansgaard proved that there was a linear correlation between the O^{16}/O^{18} content in the precipitation and the annual mean air temperature at a large number of coastal stations all over the world.

In 1958 the American physicist, S. Epstein, demonstrated that the ratio between the two isotopes was different in winter than in summer. This made it possible to differentiate between the annual layers of snow accumulation in those parts of the ice where ordinary stratigraphic analysis was no longer possible because of the advanced degree of deformation. By studying the ratio of oxygen isotopes that had been gathered on the American expedition, Dansgaard proved, just as Epstein had done, that there was a clear relationship between the O^{16}/O^{18} ratio of the snow (or rather ice) and the geographical latitude and the altitude above sea level. By analysing samples of snow from many years, Dansgaard could prove a relationship between the O^{16}/O^{18} ratio of the

Melt water river on a west Greenland glacier.

ice and the mean temperature of the spot where the snow had fallen. By comparing the analysis results with a mean temperature map of the ice sheet, it was possible to determine the shortest path between the ice front and the areas where the mean temperature corresponded to that recorded for the ice sample.

This proved that before the ice in the glacier fronts reached the stage of calving it must have covered a distance ranging from 60 km (38 miles) to 460 km (280 miles). Only in the case of one of the samples, that from Upernavik Isstrøm, had the ice covered more than 400 km (250 miles). Two of them had originated some hundreds of kilometres in on the ice sheet, but four of the samples had not covered as much as 100 km (60 miles) before calving. If the distance travelled is correlated with the age of the ice, it will be found that the rate of movement has varied between 110 ± 30 m and 270 ± 140 m with an average annual rate of 154 ± 15 m per annum (i. e. of the same order as the rate of movement in the Alpine glaciers).

The low age of the ice also proves that it cannot have passed through the deep layers of the ice sheet; the ice that calves from the ice front can only be ice from the ice streams that move in the surface of the ice sheet in the form of rapidly flowing ice masses. This supports the assumption that the deeper parts of the ice sheet are composed of inactive ice of very great antiquity: that it must be old is clear from the thickness of the ice alone, for this is equivalent to the snow accumulation of 10,000 years. But it is still an open question whether movement of the ice does occur in this zone, as Nye has suggested, or whether it is a surface movement only, as Haefeli claims.

It will be clear from the above that the problem of movement in the ice sheet has been studied from various aspects, partly by direct determination of the movement of points on the surface; partly by analysing the age and origin of the ice in the calving ice fronts; and partly on the basis of purely mathematical analyses, but none of these methods has been able to give a final result which can be recognized by all.

In spite of the great technical and scientific advances of recent years, glaciology may be regarded as having reached the same stage of development as oceanography before it obtained water-samplers and other instruments for examining the deeper parts of the ocean. At present the surface of the ice is known, and the thickness of the ice can be measured by seismic methods and by radio echo soundings, but little is known about the chemical and crystallographic differences between the ice on the surface and at the bottom, or about the nature of the contact zone with the bedrock below. One of the most important tasks of future research on the ice sheets of Greenland and Antarctica will not only be to compile material balance sheets, but to drill right down through the ice to the bedrock.

The Regimen of the Ice Sheet

Climatic Change and Glacier Oscillations

In the introduction it was mentioned that the size and distribution of glaciers are dependent on the climate, so that glaciers might be regarded as recorders of climatic changes. Studies of glaciers have, in fact, been used to obtain information about climatic changes for which sufficient long-term regular measurements do not exist — it is in fact only for western Europe and Russia and parts of northern America that sufficient series of measurements do exist for studies of climatic changes to be made solely on the basis of meteorological data. For all other areas information about climatic changes can be obtained only by indirect means.

Glaciology can contribute to the study of climatic changes in many ways. Preserved in the detailed stratigraphy of the great polar ice sheet is evidence of the climatic conditions of the past, especially of precipitation, but also of temperature. In the valley glaciers and the small upland glaciers variations in the rates of accumulation and ablation as a result of climatic changes have been propagated downwards by kinematic waves, and therefore we find that the lower parts of the glaciers are unstable, and the snouts and ice fronts of the glaciers are extremely sensitive to such influences.

Glacier fluctuations may thus be due to alterations in one or several factors, and in fact they are almost always found to be the result of complex climatic variations. The material balance of the glaciers may be altered by temperature changes, by variations in the length of the summer melting season, or by changes in precipitation, especially changes in the amount of falling snow, sleet, or cold rain, or an alteration in wind climate, which may mean that a larger amount of snow is either blown off the glaciers or deposited on them. For the glaciers that calve directly into the sea, a change in currents or tidal conditions will mean a change in the amount of ice bergs produced.

From investigations made by Professor Han W:son Ahlmann of Sweden it appears that in the northern hemisphere a general diminution of glaciers took place about the turn of the century after a general advance during the eighteenth and nineteenth centuries. This is evident from a long series of investigations in Iceland and elsewhere where farmers were living so close to the glaciers that every change in their size directly affected the habitable areas. From the region of Breidamerkurjökull there are examples of several of the large and important farms dating from the saga age having been inundated by ice and disappearing; several of them were in ruins until about 1700 when they were completely covered by ice.

Similar examples might be cited from the Alps and from Norway, and it would appear that during the last 200 years the glaciers have in general been at their most extensive since the ice age. In Alaska, too, there was a considerable increase in glacier size from 1750 until 1850, and here the term "the little ice age" is often given to this period.

A diminution in the glacier area of the earth has occurred particularly in this century; in many areas, too, the snow cover is also thinner and of shorter duration than previously. Russian investigations have shown that the sea ice of the Arctic Ocean is thinner than it used to be (in some areas this diminution amounts to as much as 10 %). As far as the Alpine glaciers are concerned, P. L. Mercanton has detected a 25 % reduction in glacier area during the period 1902—1944, which means that the total volume of ice during that period has been reduced by 10 %. It is reported from Russia that the glacier ice in Franz Josefs Land has diminished by about 8 %.

In Greenland, too, there has been a recession of the smaller glaciers outside the ice sheet, and this has been particularly marked in this century, especially in the period 1920—1940. Recession has not only been detected in the local glaciers outside the continental ice sheet, but also in the marginal zone of the ice sheet itself and in the outlet glaciers that descend from it to the fjords where they calve. The literature about this is so extensive that it will not be possible to mention all the works, but we may mention, for instance, that the recession has been particularly strong on Jakobshavn Isbræ, where the variations have been investigated by J. Meldgaard and J. Georgi; on Upernavik Isstrøm, studied by A. Weidick; on Harald Molkte Bræ studied by J. W. Wright and Kiilerick; on Academy Gletscher and Marie Sophie Gletscher, studied by B. Fristrup; and on a number of glaciers in east Greenland which have been investigated by, among others, R. Foster Flint on Miss Louise A. Boyd's expeditions in 1933 and 1937—1938.

We have already mentioned that the glaciers are very sensitive to changes in climate, but the manner in which they react is very complicated, for it is a result of an involved internal inter-action. The individual glaciers react to external changes with varying periods of inertia and adaption. Frontal variations may follow climatic changes with a delay that for small glaciers may only be a few years, but which for larger and the very largest glaciers can be as much as 100 years or even more. For instance, Fritz Müller has demonstrated in Ellesmere Island how the front of the comparatively small White Glacier has shown an annual retreat over the past five years of about 5 m (16 ft) as a result of the present increase in ablation, whereas the nearby Crusoe Glacier and Thompson Glacier are still advancing at a steady rate of some 20 m (65 ft) a year in accord with earlier climatic conditions.

In connexion with climatic changes, alterations in bottom friction stress may also occur, and cold glaciers are also affected by changes in ice temperature. A sudden release of bottom friction caused by temperature changes can also alter the water lubrication at the bottom, and result in catastrophic advances of large glacier snouts. Such sudden outbursts of glacier ice have been known to occur in many places. In Iceland, for instance, Bruarjökull, a northern outlet glacier from Vatnajökull, began to advance suddenly in this way in 1963.

The front here had been constantly retreating for a very long time apart from a sudden advance of some 10 km (6 miles) in 1890. Since then the glacier had been thinning and retreating until in October 1963 it suddenly began to move forward, and by March 1964 it had advanced about 9 km (5½ miles) from its 1956 position. It has now stopped advancing, and has not quite reached the advanced position of the front of the time before the recession started. Similar sudden advances of the 25 km² (10 sp. mile) Medvezhii Glacier, which descends from the western slopes of the highest mountain chain of the Pamir, have been observed by Russian geographers, who report that on 22 April 1962 the glacier suddenly began to advance so that at one stroke its rate of movement rose to as much as 100 m (325 ft) a day, which was more than 200 times its normal rate of movement. Such sudden advances of glaciers in periods in which the general trend was toward decline have also been observed in other parts of the world, e. g. in Alaska.

Glacier variations are, therefore, climatically determined, and glacier changes take place more rapidly and become evident earlier in moist maritime climates, whereas in dry continental climates the glaciers react more slowly. According to P. A. Shumskiy this is a result of the higher total rate of mass exchange in the glaciers of moist maritime regions and also to the longer melting season. These factors mean that the same change in mean air temperature leads to a larger change in positive temperature total and consequently to a more rapid rate of ablation. This has also been shown by the present author to be true of Greenland, where glacier retreat began first and was most rapid in south Greenland, whereas it did not start in north Greenland until much later. In addition to secular variations, which seem to be general over large parts of the earth (and may, in fact, be global in character) we also find smaller local variations, which may make the glacier fronts in certain areas advance or retreat asynchronously, and which are due to purely local meteorological conditions.

It would seem, however, that the general decline in glaciers that has been typical of the first half of this century is now easing. British expeditions, for instance, discovered that the glaciers on Jan Mayen advanced considerably in the period 1949—1961 and similar results have been obtained by a Polish IGY expedition in Spitsbergen. Here it was established that the glaciers are building up a surplus accumulation in their firn area over quite a long time while their snouts are still receding, which will finally cause the glacier fronts to surge forward again. In the Alps and in central Asia a thickening of glacier accumulation areas has been detected. In Alaska, too, it has been confirmed that thickening and advance of glaciers have also been taking place since the end of the 1940s or the beginning of the 1950s, and it is probable that this area of glacier growth is gradually spreading towards the north-west.

However, as has been emphasised by the author, it would seem that a decline of the glaciers took place later in northern Greenland than in southern Greenland, and this is in close agreement with the fact that the ice in these glaciers is cold, being below —$10°$ ($14°$ F) and is therefore less sensitive to rises in temperature. M. Diamond has shown that the annual snow accumulation in the ice sheet of north Greenland has been declining sharply since 1934.

Unfortunately, it has not yet proved possible to analyse the drill cores from the deep drillings made at Site II in order to examine the evidence they might yield about long-term climatic fluctuations.

The investigations there already mentioned have been particularly concerned with recording glacier fluctuations within the past 50 or 100 years. The study of more long-term glacier fluctuations is more uncertain. The Danish geologist Anker Weideck has been making a close investigation of glacier fluctuations and changes in the extent of the ice sheet that have taken place in the Julianehåb district throughout the whole of the post-glacial age, basing his studies on the dating of moraines and elevated marine beach ridges, and also on the position of ruins of Eskimo and Norse dwellings. These investigations prove that in historical times the ice sheet had its greatest extent around 1750 during what is termed the "little ice age", but the ice front once more advanced nearly as far in the period 1890—1900. During the present century the glaciers in the district and the ice sheet itself have been on the decline, as they have in other parts of Greenland. The investigations also show that two prehistoric stages in the extent of the ice can be traced: the older of these is what is known as the Tunugdliarfik stage, which dates back to before the post-glacial warmth maximum, and the more recent stage is the Narssarssuaq stage, which is pre-Norse at any rate, for ruins of Norse dwellings have been found on moraines dating from this stage.

A comparison of the dimensions of the ice cover in the area of Tunugdliarfik and Narssarssuaq stages with the present extent of the ice sheet seems to show that the inner parts of the ice sheet have been at an almost constant altitude. This agrees with the theoretical view previously put for-

280

Aerial photograph of the crevasse system of a glacier.

ward by Nye and Haefeli and also with a calculation of the stability of the ice during the ice ages published by Weertman (see below).

A general retreat of the outlet glaciers from the ice sheet seems thus to have been typical. For the Julianehåb, Frederikshåb, and Godthåb districts Weidick concludes that the edge of the ice is receding with a thinning of the ice by as much as 100 m (325 ft) below an altitude of 600 m (2,000 ft), and that this decline becomes less with greater altitude. Above the firn line there is practically no decline in the thickness of the ice, and Weidick therefore thinks that the regime of the ice is in deficit .

The Balance of the Greenland Ice Sheet.

There can thus be no doubt that since the Pleistocene glaciation various climatically determined variations in the extensiveness of the ice sheet have occurred. The question, however, is whether the present extent and thickness of the ice sheet is in equilibrium under present climatic conditions, and this question is of great importance not only purely theoretically but also practically in places where people live close to the ice fronts.

In all theoretical observations, of course, it has been assumed that the ice is in a state of equilibrium, and this is a necessary pre-condition for applying the mathematical formulae, but in fact little is known about whether this is indeed so. We do not know for certain whether its mass budget is in balance under present precipitation and temperature conditions, nor whether its dynamics are acting in accord with the present geographical distribution of accumulation and ablation.

Nye, in calculating a stable profile for a continental ice sheet, assumed that the line of equilibrium was situated at a certain distance from the mid-line of the ice sheet, but J. Weertman, in making a similar calculation of the theoretical profile of a continental ice sheet, assumed that the borderline between an excess of accumulation and excess of ablation followed a certain altitude above sea level. He succeeded in showing that under certain circumstances even a slight variation in precipitation or ablation would cause the ice sheet to increase to an unlimited extent or to melt away.

At the same time it can be shown that as soon as a small ice sheet begins to grow into a large ice sheet it may suddenly begin to decline again without any changes in general weather conditions than those produced by the ice sheet itself. As the ice sheet increases, the precipitation over it declines, partly because the altitude increases, and partly because the cooling effect of the ice reduces the moisture content of the air above it. The diminishing process is thus started up once more as a sort of autocatalysis. Thus it is probable that a large ice sheet cannot ever be in a real state of balance with the existing meteorological conditions; it must either be increasing or decreasing, as a result of climatic changes brought about by its own previous increase or decrease.

In the deeper parts of the central ice sheet there must be layers of really great antiquity, possibly even remnants of the Pleistocene ice as an inactive bottom layer. There can, therefore, be no doubt that large parts of the present ice sheet were formed under climatic conditions that differed from those of the present time. The present rheological state of the ice sheet can therefore only be understood if it is realized that it is the result of a very lengthy historical development. But the question is whether the ice sheet is a survival from some earlier cold period and would not re-form under present conditions. If it is a survival, it will be in process of breaking down, so that its area and volume will be steadily shrinking.

From the study of glaciers in many parts of the earth it is known that smaller glaciers sometimes take up to 20—25 years or more to react to a change in climate. The reaction time seems to be partly dependent on the nature of the climatic change, and partly on the ratio between the glacier's areas of intake and outflow. If the firn area is relatively small in proportion to the size of the glacier, the glacier will be very sensitive to rises in temperature and the resulting increases in melting on the lower part of the glacier.

As far the ice sheet is concerned, the ablation zone is very small in proportion to the large central area of accumulation, and it is therefore not known how long the reaction time of a mass of ice the size of the Greenland ice sheet might be. Furthermore, the cold Arctic glaciers seem to react more slowly to rises in temperature than the temperate glaciers in which the ice has a temperature in summer of 0° (32° F) and is therefore very sensitive to a rise in temperature.

It is not possible on the basis of theoretical observations alone to determine whether the ice sheet is in equilibrium or not. It would only be possible to determine this if one could compile a balance sheet giving an overall picture of the accumulated snow masses compared with the amounts that melt away, evaporate, or break off as icebergs. But in spite of all the measurements and research of recent years, we can still not be certain about such a calculation, which is extremely important for the solution of many glaciological problems.

On the basis of measurements made in 1912, A. De Quervain came to the conclusion that the ice sheet had a credit balance and so could not be regarded as a survival from the Pleistocene ice age or from any other later cold period, but that on the contrary it was formed under present climatic conditions.

The first real attempt to calculate a balance sheet for the whole of the ice sheet was made by F. Loewe in 1936. To compile such a material balance sheet it is necessary to know the quantity of snow accumulation, for practically all precipitation in the interior of Greenland falls as snow. The ice sheet loses ice partly by ablation (i. e. melting away or evaporation) and partly by the calving of icebergs from the glacier fronts. From Danish maps of Greenland Loewe was able to determine the total area of the ice sheet as 1,650,000 km² (640,000 sq. miles), of which he considered that 1,380,000 km² (535,000 sq. miles) lay above the firn line and had an excess of snow accumulation, while over an area of 270,000 km² (105,000 sq. miles) the ablation exceeded the accumulation.

From the results of the studies made at Eismitte and from the other available literature Loewe assumed that the average annual snow accumulation above the firn line came to 31 cm (12 in) of water equivalent, and that the average net ablation in the ablation zone was 110 cm (43 in) of water. The annual production of icebergs had never been measured, but from some figures from older Danish research Loewe estimated the annual prodution to be something on the order of

Moraine systems in front of a small valley glacier descending to the sea.

150 km³ (36 cubic miles) of water. With these figures it was now possible to compile a balance sheet for the whole of the ice cap:

annual snow accumulation		425 km³ water
annual ablation	295 km³ water	
annual iceberg production	150 km³	
total annual wastage	445 km³ water	445 km³ water
annual deficit		20 km³ water
		(4.8 cubic miles)

According to this calculation the ice sheet should have a small deficit, but in view of the uncertainty of the individual factors Loewe concluded that it might equally well be assumed from this balance sheet that the ice sheet was in equilibrium.

284

The French glaciologist, Albert Bauer, who had carried out investigations at Eqip sermia, compiled a new calculation of the budget of the ice sheet in 1955. Working from American air charts to a scale of 1:1,000,000, Bauer found the average altitude of the snow line on each of the fourteen charts which together cover the ice sheet. From this he determined the average altitude of the snow line for the whole of the ice sheet as 1,390 m (4,550 ft), and from the hypsometrical curve of the ice sheet he found that 83.5 % of the ice sheet, 1,439,800 km² (556,000 sq. miles) lay above the snow line, and that 16.5 %, 286,600 km² (110,000 sq. miles) lay below it. As Loewe had done, Bauer assumed that the snow line was the boundary between a surplus budget and a deficit budget, for he did not take into account the formation of superimposed ice, which is such an important factor under Arctic conditions. In order to ascertain the amount of wastage due to iceberg production, he calculated the width of the calving glaciers from topographic maps, and then from the not very numerous sea charts of the area he tried to determine the thickness of the ice from the depth conditions at the glacier front.

Assuming that the largest of the glaciers had a *daily* movement of 20—30 m (65—100 ft) and that the smaller glaciers moved 3—10 m (10—32 ft) *daily,* and that the stationary glaciers had an *annual* movement of 30 m (100 ft), it was thus possible to calculate the annual production of icebergs. Bauer arrived at a figure of 240 km³ (57½ cubic miles) of ice, half coming from east Greenland, west Greenland having an annual volume of iceberg production of 90 km³ (21 cubic miles), the glaciers descending into Melville Bugt producing 20 km³ (4.8 cubic miles) a year, and the whole of north Greenland only 10 km³ (2.4 cubic miles). If this quantity of ice is transferred into terms of water, there is an annual production of 215 km³ (51½ cubic miles), which gives the following balance sheet for the ice sheet:

annual snow accumulation		446 km³ water
annual ablation	315 km³ water	
annual iceberg production	215 km³ water	
total annual wastage	530 km³ water	530 km³ water
annual deficit		84 km³ water
		(20 cubic miles)

Bauer therefore felt convinced that the balance sheet was in deficit and that there was an annual diminution of the ice sheet corresponding to some 100 km³ (24 cubic miles) of ice.

If this process was thought of as being a permanency, then in 30,000 years' time the whole of the ice sheet would have melted away, thus (not taking into account any possible isostatic movements) raising the level of the ocean all over the earth by about 6.5 m (21 ft). Bauer had assumed that the snow limit formed a line of balance between a profit and loss budget, but this has been found not to be the case if sufficient attention is paid to the significance of superimposed ice. Also Carl S. Benson's careful studies of north Greenland have proved that Bauer's firn line is too high, which means that the area of the ablation zone that he gives is too great while the area of accumulation is too small.

From stratigraphic studies made particularly in the northern and central parts of the ice sheet Benson succeeded in 1959 and 1960 in establishing the annual snow accumulation over the ice sheet with considerably greater accuracy. Benson found the annual snow accumulation to be on an average 34 cm (13½ in). As he himself had not studied the ablation problem closely, he used the same figure of 110 cm (43 in) for ablation as Loewe and Bauer had done, but since his figure for snow accumulation was now greater, the total average melting in the ablation zone would be considerably smaller, i. e. 107 cm (42 in) of water. For want of better figures, he assumed Bauer's figures for iceberg production to be correct but corrected his figures for the glacier areas from his own determination of the firn line in north Greenland.

He then compiled the following budget:

annual accumulation		500 km³ water
annual ablation	272 km³ water	
annual iceberg production	215 km³ water	
total annual wastage	487 km³ water	487 km³ water
annual surplus		13 km³ water
		(3.1 cubic miles)

Unlike Bauer, Benson reached the conclusion that there was a small surplus, but like F. Loewe he considered that when the uncertainty of some of the figures was taken into account, the ice sheet might well be found to be in equilibrium.

American investigations have been centred particularly on north Greenland, and even though the annual snow accumulation in that area is relatively small compared with the southern and south-eastern parts of Greenland, it is sufficient for all depots and buildings to be rapidly buried by the snow.

On the other hand there is an almost complete lack of melt water streams here, and both in Melville Bugt and in Thule district there are few glaciers flowing into the sea that have any major production of icebergs. It is thus difficult to see where the ice from the ice sheet can go. The

The front of a small outlet-glacier in Kangerdlugssuaq.

The Mitluagqat outlet glacier in Angmagssalik district in 1933.

The same outlet-glacier as shown in previous plate in 1958. There has been further retreat since the photograph was taken.

Crevasse zone of the margin of the ice sheet.

Investigation of crystal structure with a Universal Stage.

Before a snow storm on the ice sheet.

previous leader of the American snow research, H. Bader, has therefore long been of the opinion that the ice sheet in north Greenland is on the increase. Bader also estimates that even though signs have been found in the marginal zone as well as many other places in Greenland that the ice is on the decline, this does not necessary mean that the ice sheet as a whole is on the decline; the central parts may, in fact, be piling up, and at some time in the future they may begin to flow down towards the periphery of the ice. In 1961 Bader published a new calculation of the budget of the ice sheet.

On the basis of a map of snow accumulation that SIPRE had drawn up from the results of their investigations Bader determined the annual snow accumulation of the ice sheet as between 21 and 84 cm (8 and 33 in) of water with an average annual accumulation of 36.7 cm (14½ in). These were considerably higher values than had been used in earlier calculations, and this is because R. Ragle's measurements in south Greenland have given a much clearer picture of conditions there: snowfall has proved to be greater than had been assumed, and the annual accumulation south of 63° varies between 80 cm (31½ in) and 100 cm (40 in) of water. It has in fact been proved that the whole area south of the Arctic Circle has a much higher snowfall than had been assumed, and even though this makes up only $^1/_8$ of the total area of the ice sheet, it nevertheless receives about ¼ of the precipitation total. More than this, Bader has made a serious attempt to include the formation of superimposed ice in his reckoning, so that the actual ablation figure comes out considerably less. Bader thus produces the following calculation:

annual accumulation		630 km³ water
annual iceberg production	215 km³ water	
annual ablation	120—270 km³ water	
total annual wastage	335—485 km³ water	485—335 km³ water
annual increase		145—295 km³ water
		(35—71 cubic miles)

Bader considers that this increase will be particularly concentrated in the northern part of the ice sheet, while he considers it still uncertain whether the southern part of the ice sheet is increasing or retreating.

So it is plain that although many calculations of the material balance of the ice sheet have been put forward, there is still no certainty about the problem. It would be tempting in this book to compile a fresh calculation, and there might be justification for doing so, for there is sufficient hitherto unused material in Denmark — I refer to Danish aerial photographs taken for use in mapmaking. An examination of these would doubtless yield much information about the size of the iceberg production from the various glaciers.

The figures for snow accumulation are coming to be based firmly on the many measurements that have been made in drill shafts, so that they can be assumed to be substantially correct, but the figures given for iceberg production are very uncertain, as also are those for ablation.

There have in fact been very few measurements of ablation on the ice sheet: the most important were made in the area around Eqip sermia by Bauer and by the Austrian glaciologist, W. Ambach, and Lister has made some measurements at Britannia Gletscher. There are no figures available for the northern margin of the ice sheet, but the Americans in the Thule area have set in hand a number of very careful measurements there, and the results have been published by, among others, the Swedish glaciologist, Valter Schytt. There are no direct measurements from southern Greenland of the amount of ablation on the actual ice sheet, but Erich Etienne has made observations on the glacial cap of Sukkertoppen. There is therefore still great uncertainty about all the ablation figures given for the whole ice sheet, and also all the previous measurements were only of surface ablation; but it may be that subglacial melting also takes place, and that there is an outflow of melt water into the fjords of Greenland below the ice.

On the International Glaciological Expedition attempts were made to measure any melt water outflow there might be into Umanak Bugt from the glacier at the head of Kangerdlugssuaq fjord. With the German ocean research vessel *Gauss* in support, hydrographic measurements were made in the fjord to determine from measurements of the salinity of the water how much fresh water was mingled with it. These investigations, however, yielded no decisive results; if such an outflow does take place, the production of melt water is not sufficient to be measureable. But even a slight outflow into the fjords would be sufficient to have a considerable influence on the balance sheet for the whole ice sheet.

There is thus no scientific value in compiling any more sets of figures until more material is available and since the ice sheet is so large, it is also probable that the balance is different for the northern and southern parts. So there is really no scientific purpose in discussing the total balance of the ice sheet until some knowledge of the balance sheets of the individual parts has been obtained.

It will be evident that existing measurements and published theoretical views on the question of the equilibrium of the ice sheet present a rather confused picture. The only way of deciding the question will be to discover definite proof of changes in the distribution and the thickness of the ice, not just at the glacier fronts (for there is already a great deal of information about this) but also in the central parts of the ice sheet. The difficulties, however, are very great, and our mea-

292

The large moraines which are common in the Alps are missing from the fronts of many of the glaciers in north-east Greenland. Notice the man in the foreground.

suring techniques are so uncertain that fairly large alterations in the ice thickness have to occur before it is possible to measure them at all accurately.

To have certain knowledge of a possible change in the thickness of the ice would probably demand 20-100 years of comprehensive investigations. It is for this reason that a number of (so far unsuccessful) attempts have been made to determine by indirect methods whether the two great ice masses in the world, the ice sheets of Greenland and Antarctica, are in equilibrium or not. One of the methods is to make exact measurements of changes in the water level of the oceans. If the ice sheet is melting away, there should be a rise in water level in the oceans, although this takes place very slowly.

But it must be realized that a general rise in temperature over the earth would also lead to a higher sea temperature and thus to a higher water level even though the total mass of water were still

293

the same. Even though comprehensive measurements of water level have been made, particularly in connexion with the IGY, our knowledge of the water level oscillations of the oceans is as yet too meagre for us to reach any conclusions about glacier variations by that means. Long-term profile measurements will have to be made, and a profile for this purpose has been established by the International Glaciological Expedition from Disko Bugt via Station Centrale and Station Jarl-Joset to Cecilia Nunatak in eastern Greenland, and another profile has been established by the Americans from the northern part of Melville Bugt via Camp Century to Academy Gletscher at the head of Inglefield Bredning.

Continuing and maintaining these profiles will undoubtedly cost a considerable sum, for modern exploration of the ice sheet is only possible with the aid of large and technically well-equipped expeditions having motor sledges, aeroplanes, and preferably also helicopters, at their disposal. But such measurements are the only possible way of determining whether the earth's two largest ice masses — the ice sheets of Greenland and Antarctica — are each in equilibrium or not. There are thus few problems in glaciology that are more suited for solution by international co-operation than this question of the balance of the ice sheet.

How the Ice Sheet was Formed

At the beginning of the Tertiary period Greenland still had a warm climate with temperature conditions very similar to those nowadays found in the Mediterranean area or in the Everglades of Florida, although possibly with greater precipitation. It is evident from fossilized plant remains in the layer of tufa between the plateau basalts that the land was once wooded with relatively lush species that would need a warm climate.

Large areas of the land were laid down on horizontal plateau basalts, and other areas were peneplains, so we assume that the interior of Greenland was covered by extensive plateaus with some slightly higher mountains along the coast, particularly in the east. The land was intersected by ancient river systems, and as the highest part of the country was on the east, the rivers mainly flowed into Disko Bugt and Umanak Bugt. The southern part of Greenland was relatively highlying, mountainous country of a more Alpine character.

When the climate of the northern hemisphere began to deteriorate, glaciers started to form in Greenland. On the high mountain peaks in southern Greenland small ice caps and highland glaciers formed which gradually joined together to form one large ice cap.

In central and northern Greenland it may be assumed that air masses driven inland from the sea and forced upward by the coastal mountains gradually dropped their precipitation in the form of snow — mainly on the outer side, leaving the inner side with little precipitation. As the climate deteriorated further, the glaciers began to increase in size, spreading down the mountain sides first and then slowly to the hinterland behind the mountain ranges. Where the glaciers were sufficiently large, Piedmont glaciers and floating snouts of ice were formed which united with the newly formed ice shelf along the coast. In the interior, snowfields of various sizes were formed, and then as the mouths of the rivers were blocked up by the coastal glaciers, the interior of the country became marshy. As the temperature fell, permafrost formed which prevented the soil from drying out in summer in the normal way, so that conditions deteriorated still further. The snowfields grew even larger in area and more and more of them merged. At the same time the

295

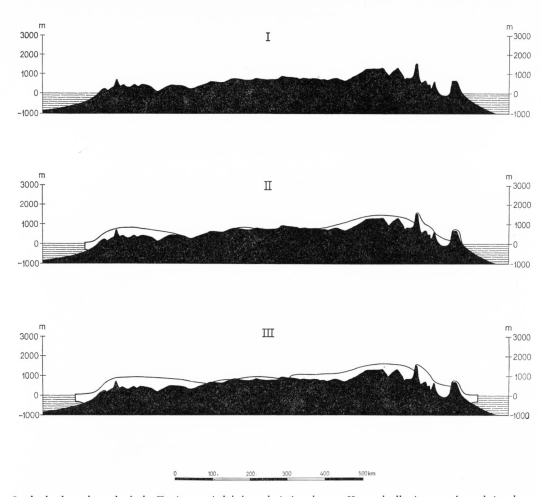

I: the land at the end of the Tertiary period before glaciation began. II: gradually ice-caps formed in the coastal areas of both east and west coast, and shelf-ice began forming off the coast. III: as the climate deteriorated the marginal zone glaciers increased in size and local snow and ice caps of various sizes formed in the interior.

glaciers were still extending seawards where rising saturated winds allowed precipitation to fall, and also inland where the winds were mainly dry katabatic winds. Gradually, the snow drifts and glaciers from the east and west coast united and formed a coherent plateau of snow which continued to grow thicker by autocatalysis until it finally merged with the ice cap of southern Greenland to form one continental ice sheet.

When the ice was at its most extensive, the whole of Greenland including the present lowland was covered, except for Peary Land, which investigations made long ago by Lauge Koch and more

296

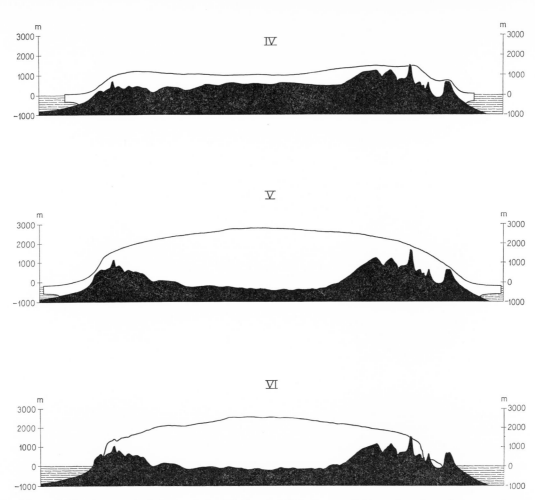

IV: gradually the coastal glaciers united with the central local snow fields and so formed one continuous ice sheet which slowly grew in thickness. V: at the largest extent of the ice, the ice sheet had spread over what is nowadays ice-free coast. At the same time, because of the amount of water that was now ice, the sea level was much lower than it is at present. Because of the weight of the ice the central part of the land mass was depressed and a slight lifting of the mountains in the marginal zone occurred. VI: the present stage. Exaggeration of the vertical scale approximately 40:1.

recently by the Americans prove was not covered. Northern Peary Land had its own local glaciation which was directly connected to the main ice sheet. Investigations of indicator boulders have also shown that Ellesmere Island was probably once glaciated, but it was a local ice cap which only touched the Greenland ice sheet while having independent dynamics and regime.

It must be presumed that when glaciation was at its most extensive the ice sheet spread far beyond the borders of present Greenland, and the great fish banks which lie off the west coast of Greenland are presumably the remains of moraines from this ice sheet. The surface of the sea was 130

297

Over the ice sheet's white surface where nothing breaks the long straight horizontal line are now drawn the tracks of the expedition's tractors and weasels. These tracks will remain for a long time and will often be found again in the years to come.

m (425 ft) lower during this ice age than it is now because of the large proportion of the earth's aqueous vapour that was held in solid form. At present 11 % of the land surface of the earth is covered by ice, but when the extent of the ice was greatest during the Pleistocene glaciation about 30 % of the land surface of the earth was ice covered.

Since it has a total volume of 215 million km³ (51½ million cubic miles) and the total ocean surface of the earth is 361 million km² (140 million square miles) a complete melting of the ice sheet as it is today would (if we do not take into consideration any isostatic changes) cause a rise in sea level of 6.5 m (21 ft). If the Antarctic ice sheet also melted completely there would be a total rise of 75 m (245 ft). The Greenland ice sheet is today the best known in the world, and it is to be hoped that Danish and international scientists will continue to carry out research on the ice itself and on its significance for the climate and the biological conditions of Greenland and the surrounding sea.

298

Index

301

304

Bibliography

Ahlmann, Hans W:son: Glaciological research on the North Atlantic coasts. (Royal Geogr. Soc. Research Ser. 1.). 1948.
— : Glacier variations and climatic fluctuations. (Amer. Geogr. Soc. Bowman Memorial Lect. 3.). 1963.
Ambach, Walther: Untersuchungen zum Energieumsatz in der Ablationszone des grönländischen Inlandeises. (MoG. 174,4.). 1963.
Bader, Henri: Excavations and installations at SIPRE test site, Site II, Greenland. (SIPRE Research Report 20.). 1955.
— : The Greenland ice sheet. (Cold Regions Science and Engineering I–B2.). 1961.
— : The physics and mechanics of snow as a material. (Cold Regions Science and Engineering II–B.). 1962.
Bailey, J. T.: Evans, S. & Robin, G. de Q.: Radio echo sounding of polar ice sheets. (Nature vol. 20). 1964.
Battle, W. R. B.: Contributions to the glaciology of North East Greenland 1948–49 in Tyrolerdal and on Clavering Ø. (MoG. 136,2). 1952.
Bauer, Albert: Contribution à la connaissance de l'inlandsis du Groenland. Synthèse glaciologique. (Expèditions Polaires Françaises, Résultats scientifiques). 1954.
— : The balance of the Greenland ice sheet. (Journ. Glac. II.). 1955.
— : Le glacier de l'Eqe. (Expèditions Polaires Françaises VI. Glaciologie Groenland II.). 1955.
— : Influence de la dynamique des fleuves de glaces sur celle de l'Indlandsis du Groenland. (A. I. H. S. publ. 54. Assamblée Générale de Helsinki.). 1961.
Baussart, M.: Essai de determination par photogrammetrie de la vitesse superficielle d'un glacier du Groenland. (A. I. H. S. publ. 47. Symposium de Chamonix.). 1958.
— : Interpretation des résultats obtenus sur les vitesses des glaciers du Groenland. (Bull. Soc. Franc. Photogrammetrie. 3.). 1961.
Bedel, B.: Les observations météorologiques de la station françaises du Groenland. 1954.
Benson, Carl S.: Physical investigations on the snow and firn of Northwest Greenland, 1952, 1953 and 1954. (SIPRE Research Report 26.). 1959.
— : Stratigraphic studies in the snow and firn of the Greenland ice sheet. (Folia Geogr. Danica IX.). 1961.
— : Stratigraphic studies in the snow and firn of the Greenland ice sheet. (SIPRE Research Report 70.). 1962.
— & *Ragle, R. H.:* Measurements by SIPRE in 1955 on the accumulation markers of Expéditions Polaires Françaises in Central Greenland. (SIPRE Special Report 19.). 1956.
Bouche, M.: Les observations météorologiques de la stations française du Groenland. I–II. 1954.
Bull, C.: Observations in North Greenland relating to the theories of the properties of ice. (Journ. Glac. III.). 1957.
— : Snow accumulation in North Greenland. (Journ. Glac. III.). 1958.
— : Glaciological reconnaissance of the Sukkertoppen Ice Cap. (Inst. Polar Stud. Report 4.). 1962.
Butkowich, T. R.: Some physical properties of the ice from the Tuto tunnel and ramp, Thule, Greenland. (SIPRE Research Report 47.). 1959.
Chapman, F. Spencer: Northern Lights. The official account of the British Arctic Air-Route Expedition 1930–31. 1932.
— : Watkins's Last Expedition. 1934.
Dansgaard, W.: The isotopic composition of natural waters with special reference to the Greenland ice cap. (MoG. 165, 2.). 1961.
— : & *Weidick A.:* Klimaforværring i Grønland, "Grønland" 1965.
Daugherty, Charles Michael: City under the ice. 1963.
Davies, W. E. & Krinsley, D. B.: The recent regimen of the ice cap margin in North Greenland. (A. I. H. S. publ. 58. Symposium of Obergurgl.). 1962.
Demorest, Max: Ice sheet. (Bull. Geol. Soc. Amer. 54.). 1943.
Diamond, Marvin: Precipitation trends in Greenland during the past thirty years. (Journ. Glac. III.). 1958.
— : Air temperature and precipitation on the Greenland ice sheet. (Journ. Glac. III.). 1960.
Drygalski, Erich v.: Grönland Expedition der Gesellschaft für Erdkunde zu Berlin. Band I–II. 1897.
Epstein, S. & Sharp, R. P.: Oxygen isotope studies. (Trans. Amer. Geophys. Union vol. 40.). 1959.
Étienne, Erich: Expeditionsbericht der Grönland-Expedition der Universität Oxford 1938. (Veröff. d. Geophys. Inst. Univ. Leipzig 2 Ser. 13). 1940.
Evans, S.: Dielectric properties of ice and snow – a review. (Journ. Glac. 5.). 1965.
Expéditions Polaires Françaises: Publications Preliminaires –:
  5. Campagne preparatoire au Groenland 1948. 1949.
  10. Campagne au Groenland 1949. 1950.
  15. Campagne au Groenland 1950. 1952.
  16. Campagne au Groenland 1951. 1953.
  17. Hivernage au Groenland 1949–50. 1956.
  19. Ravitaillement aerien des Expéditions Françaises au Groenland 1949–50–51. 1953.
  22. Hivernage au Groenland 1950–51. 1953.
  23. Rapports d'activities. 1956.
  25. Campagne au Groenland 1952 et 1953. 1954
Finsterwalder, R : On the measurements of glacier fluctuations. (I. A. S. H. publ. 54.7.). 1961.
Finsterwalder, S.: Der Vernagtferner. (Zeitschr. d. Deutschen und Österreichischen Alpenvereins. Wiss. Ergänzungshefte.). 1897.
Fitch. F. J. et al.: Glacier re-advance of Jan Mayen. (I. A. H. S. publ. 58. Symposium de Obergurgl.). 1962.
Freuchen, Peter: The First Thule Expedition 1912. General observations to natural conditions in the country traversed by the expedition. (MoG. 51. 9.) .1915.
Fristrup, Børge: Investigations of the Greenland Ice Cap. (Geogr. Tidsskr. 58.). 1959.
— : Studies of four glaciers in Greenland. (Geogr. Tidsskr. 59.). 1960.
— , ed: Physical Geography of Greenland. (Folia Geogr. Danica IX.). 1961.
— : Indlandsisen. 1963.
Garde, T. V.: Beskrivelse af Expeditionen til Sydvestgrønland 1883. (MoG. 16, 1.) 1894.
Georgi, Johannes: Im Eis vergraben. 1933.
— : Mid-Ice. The story of the Wegener

307

Expedition to Greenland. 1934.
— : Im Eis vergraben. Neue Ausgabe. 1957.

Gerdel, R. W.: A climatological study of the Greenland ice sheet. (Folia Geogr. Danica. IX.). 1961.

Glen, J. W.: The creep of polycrystalline ice. (Proc. Roy. Soc. Ser. A. 223.). 1955.

Goldberg, E. D.: Geochronology with lead. 210.
Symposium on radioactive dating. I. A. E. A. Athen. 1962.

Goldthwait, Richard: Regimen of an ice cliff on land in Northwest Greenland. (Folia Geogr. Danica. IX.). 1961.

Griffiths, T. M.: Glaciological investigations in the TUTO area of Greenland. (Folia Geogr. Danica IX.). 1961.

Haefeli, R.: Contribution to the movement and the form of ice sheets in the Arctic and the Antarctic. (Journ. Glac. III.). 1961.
— : Glaziologische Einführung zur Frage des Beseitigung radio-aktive Abfallstoffe in den grossen Eiskappen der Erde. (Schweiz. Zeitschr. f. Hydrolog. 23.). 1962.

Hamilton, R. A. et al.: British Greenland Expedition 1952–54. Scientific Results. (Geogr. Journ. 122.). 1956.

Hamilton, R. A. & Rollit, G.: Climatological tables for the site of the expedition's base at Britannia Sø and the station on the inland-ice "Northice". (MoG. 158,2.). 1957.
— : Meteorological observations at "Northice", Greenland,, (MoG. 158,3.). 1957.

Hammer, R. R. I.: Undersøgelser ved Jakobshavns Isfjord og nærmeste Omegn i Vinteren 1879–80. (MoG. 4,1.). 1883.

Hansen, B. L. & Landauer, J. K.: Some results of ice cap drill hole measurement. (A. I. H. S. publ. 47, Symposium de Chamonix.). 1958.

Hayward, H. O'b.: The Oxford University Greenland Expedition 1935. (Geogr. Journ. 88.). 1936.

Helland, Amund: Om de isfyldte Fjorde og de glaciale Dannelser i Nordgrønland. (Archiv f. Mat. og Naturv. 1.). 1876.

Heuberger, Jean-Charles: Forages sur l'Indlandsis. (Expéditions Polaires Françaises V. Glaciologie Groenland I.). 1954.

Hobbs, William Herbert: The glacial anticyclones. (Univ. Michigan Studies. Scient. Ser. IV.). 1926.
— : The North Pole of the Winds. 1930.
— : Report of the Greenland Expeditions of University of Michigan. I–II. 1941.

Hofmann, Walther: Die geodätische Lagemessung über das grönländische Inlandeis der Internationalen Glaziologischen Grönland Expedition (EGIG) 1959. (MoG. 173,6.). 1964.

Holland, M. F. W.: Glaciological observations around Mount Atter, West Greenland. (Journ. Glac. III.). 1961.

Holleymann, J. B.: Climatological means and extremes on the Greenland ice sheet. (CRREL Research Report 78.). 1961.

Holtzscherer, Jean-Jacques: Contribution à la connaissance de l'inlandsis du Groenland. Mesures Seismiques. (Expédition Polaires Françaises. Resultats scientifiques.). 1954.

Høygaard, Arne & Mehrens: Ajungilak eller Grønland på tværs. 1931.

Jellinek, H. H. G.: Compressive strength properties of snow. (Journ. Glac. III.). 1959.

Jensen, J. A. D.: Indberetning om Expeditionen til Sydgrønland i 1878. (MoG. 1,2.). 1879.

Kasser, F. & Müller, W.: Uber die Gletscheränderungen seit 1900 in den Schweizeralpen mit Hinweisen auf die Bedeutung für die Wasserwirtschaft. (Wasser- und Energiewirtschaft 8–10). 1960.

Kingery, W. D., ed.: Ice and snow-processes, properties and applications. 1962.

Klebelsberg, R.: Handbuch der Gletscherkunde und Glazialgeologie. I–II.1948–49.

Knuth, Eigil: Fire Mand og Solen. 1937.

Koch, J. P.: Gennem den hvide Ørken. 1913.
— : & Wegener, Alfred: Wissenschaftliche Ergebnisse der dänischen Ekspedition nach Dronning Louise Land und quer über das Indlandseis von Nordgrönland 1912–13. (MoG. 75.). 1930.

Knuth, Eigil: Fire mand og solen. 1937.

Koch, Lauge: Report on the Danish Bicentenary Jubilee Expedition North of Greenland 1920–23. (MoG. 70,1.). 1926.
— : Contributions to the glaciology of North Greenland. (MoG. 65,2.). 1928.
— : Nord om Grønland. 1932.

Langway, Chester.: A 400 metre deep ice core in Greenland. (Journ. Glac. III.). 1958.
— : Bubble pressure in Greenland glacier ice. (A. I. H. S. publ. 47. Symposium de Chamonix.). 1958.
— : Accumulation and temperature on the inland ice of North Greenland, 1959. (Journ. Glac. III.). 1961.
— : Some physical and chemical investigations of a 411 metres deep Greenland ice core and their relationship to accumulation. (I. A. S. H. publ. 58. Symposium of Obergurgl.). 1962.

Lindsay, Martin: Those Greenland days. 1932.
— : Sledge. 1935.
— : Three got through. 1946.

Lister, H. & Taylor, P. F.: Heat balance and ablation on an Arctic glacier. (MoG. 158,7.). 1961.

Loewe, F.: Höhenverhältnisse und Massehaushalt des grönländischen Indlandeises. (Gerlands Beitr. z. Geophys. 48). 1936.
— : Das Klima des grönländischen Inlandeises. Köppen und Geiger. Handbuch d. Klimatologie II. 1935.
— : Das grönländische Inlandeis nach neuen Feststellungen. (Erdkunde XVIII, 3.). 1964.

Lorius, C.: L'utilisation des isotopes dans l'etude glaciologique des calotees polaires. TAAF, no. 25. 1963.

Maigaard, Chr.: Beretningen om den af civilingeniør Robert E. Peary ledede Expedition på den grønlandske Indlandsis. (Geogr. Tidsskr. 9.). 1888.

Meir. M. F. & Post, A. S.: Recent variations in mass net budgets of glaciers in Western North America. (I. A. S. H. publ. 58, Symposium de Obergurgl.). 1962.

Mellor, Malcolm: Building on polar ice caps. (Polar Notes III.). 1961
— : Oversnow transport. (Cold Regions Science and Engineering III–A4) 1963.
— : Oversnow travel: flying. (Polar Notes V.). 1963.
— : Snow and ice on the earth's surface. (Cold Regions Science and Engineering II–C1.). 1964.

Mercanton, P.L.: Glacierized area in the Swiss Alps. (Journ. Glac. II). 1964.

Mikkelsen, Ejnar: Lost in the Arctic. 1913.
— : Report on the expedition. Alabama Expeditionen til Grønlands Nordøstkyst 1909–1912 under Ledelse af Ejnar Mikkelsen. (MoG. 52,1).
— : Two against the ice. 1957.

Miller, D. H.: The influence of snow cover on local climate in Greenland. (Journ. Meteorol. 13.). 1956.

Mirrlees, S. T. A.: Meteorological results of the British Arctic Air Route Expedition 1930–31. (Meteo. Office, Geophys. Memoirs 61). 1934.

Mott, P. G.: The Oxford University Greenland Expedition, West Greenland 1936. (Geogr. Journ. 90). 1937.

Müller, Fritz: Glacier Mass-Budget Studies on Axel Heiberg, Island, Canada, Arctic Archipelago. (I. A. S. H. publ. 58, Symposium de Obergurgl.). 1962.

Mälzer, H.: Das Nivellement über das grönländische Inlandeises der Internationalen Glaziologischen Grönland-Expedition 1959. (MoG. 173,7.). 1964.

Nansen, Fridtjof: På ski over Grønland. 1890.

Nevierer, J.: Nivellement geodesique sur l'inlandsis. (Exp. Pol. Franc. Rapports Scientifiques N III, 1.). 1954.

308

Nobles, Laurence H.: Structure of the ice cap margin, Northwestern Greenland. (Folia Geogr. Danica IX.). 1961.

Nutt, D. C. & Scholander, P. E.: Gases in Greenland ice bergs. *(Folia Geogr. Danica. IX.).* 1961.

Nye, J. F.: The flow of glaciers and ice-sheets as a problem in plasticity. (Proceed. Roy. Soc. Ser. A. 207 (109). 1951.

— : The mechanics of glacier flow. (Journ. Glac. II). 1952.

— : The distribution of stress and velocity in glaciers and ice sheets. (Proceed. Roy. Soc. Ser. A. 239 (113). 1957.

— : The response of glaciers and ice-sheets to seasonal and climatic changes. (Proceed. Roy. Soc. Ser. A. 256 (559). 1960.

Patterson, W. S. B.: Altitudes on the inland ice in North Greenland. (MoG. 137,1.). 1958.

Philberth, K.: Ecoulement de la glace groenlandaise. (Revue de Geomorph. Dynamique 13). 1962.

— : Une methode pour mesurer les temperatures a l'interieur d'un Inlandsis. (C. R. S. Acad. Sciences. t. 254). 1962.

Philberth Bernhard: Stockage des dechets atomiques dans les calottes glaciaires de la Terre. (C. R. S. Acad. Sciences t. 248). 1959.

de Quervain, A. & Mercanton, Paul-Louis: Resultats scientifiques de l'expédition suisse au Groenland 1912–13. (MoG. 59.). 1925.

de Quervain, M. F.: On the work carried out by the group »Glaciology Inlandsis« of the International Glaciological Greenland Expedition 1959–60 (EGIG). (Folia Geogr. Danica IX.). 1961.

Ragle, R. H. & Davis, T. C. P.: South Greenland traverses. (Journ. Glac. IV.). 1962.

Rasmussen, Knud: Min Rejsedagbog. 1915.

— : Report of the First Thule Expedition 1912. (MoG. 51,8.). 1915

— : Report of the Second Thule Expedition 1916–19) (MoG. 65,1.). 1927.

Radok, U.: Temperatures in polar ice caps. (Nature 184 (4692)). 1959.

Rausch, Donald O.: Studies of ice excavation. (Quarterly of the Colorado School of Mines 54,2.). 1959.

Rink, H. J.: Om den geografiske Beskaffenhed af de danske Handelsdistrikter i Nordgrønland. (Da. Vidensk. Selsk.

Skr. naturvid.-mat. Afd. V Række Bd. 3.). 1953.

— : Om Grønlands Indland og Muligheden af at berejse samme. 1875.

— : Bemærkningen om de grønlandske Jøklers Bevægelser og Produktion af svømmende Isfjelde. (Oversigt Kgl. Da. Vidensk. Selsk. Forhandl. 1877.). 1877.

— : Resultaterne af de nyeste danske Undersøgelser i Grønland med Hensyn til Indlandet og de svømmende Isbjerges Oprindelse. (Geogr. Tidsskr. 9.). 1889.

— : Nogle bemærkninger om Indlandsisen og Isfjeldenes Oprindelse. (MoG. 8,8.). 1889.

Robin, de Q.: Ice movement and temperature distribution in glaciers and ice sheet. (Journ. Glac. II). 1955.

— : Some factors affecting the temperature distribution in large ice sheets. (I. A. S. H. publ. 39 Assembly Rome). 1954.

Ryder, C. H.: Undersøgelse af Grønlands Vestkyst fra 72⁰ til 74⁰ 35' N. Br. 1886 og 1887. (MoG. 8,7.). 1889.

Schytt, Valter: Glaciological investigations in the Thule Ramp area. (SIPRE Technical Report 28). 1955.

Scott, J. M.: Portrait of an Ice Cap. 1953.

Sharp, R. P.: Glaciers. 1960.

Shumskiy, P. A.: Krenke, A. N.: & Zotikov, I. A.: Ice and its changes. (Research in Geophysics. II). 1964.

Simpson, C. J. W.: North Ice. The Story of British North Greenland Expedition. 1957.

Sorge, Ernest: With Plane, Boat and Camera in Greenland. An account of the Universal Dr. Franck Greenland Expedition. 1935.

Steenstrup, K. J. V.: Bidrag til Kjendskabet om Bræerne og Bræ-Isen i Nordgrønland. (MoG. 4,2.). 1883.

Steinemann, S.: Experimentelle Untersuchungen zur Plastizität von Eis. (Beitr. zur Geologie der Schweiz, Hydrol. 10). 1958.

Sorge, Ernest: Die ersten Dickenmessungen des grönländischen Inlandeises, (Zeitschr. f. Geophys. 6.). 1930.

— : Glaziologische Untersuchungen in Eismitte. (Wiss. Ergebnisse D. Grönlandexp. Alfred Wegener. III). 1935.

Sugden, J. C. & Mott, P. G.: Oxford University Greenland Expedition. 1938. (Geogr. Journ. 95.). 1940.

Tschaen, L. & Bauer, A.: Le mouvement de la partie centrale de l'indlandsis du Groenland. (A. I. H. S. publ. 47. Sym-

posium de Chamonix). 1958.

— : Groenland 1948–1949–1950. Astronomie–Nivellement geodesique sur l' Indlandsis. Nouveau Calcul. (Exp. Pol. Fr. publ. 207.). 1959.

Victor, Paul-Émile: Groenland. Paris 1951.

— : Wringing secrets from Greenland's Ice Cap. (Nat. Geogr. Magazine, 109.). 1956.

Wager, L. R.: The Form and Age of the Greenland Ice Cap (Geol. Mag 20.). 1933.

Wager, W.: Camp Century, City under the Ice. 1962.

Wallerstein, George: Movement observations on the Greenland ice sheet. (Journ. Glac. III.). 1958.

Waterhouse, R. W.: An analysis of density and permeability data from a snow profile. (CRREL Research Report 90.). 1962.

Watkins, H. G.: The British Arctic Air Route Expedition. (Geogr. Journ. LX XIX). 1932.

Weertman, J.: Stability of ice age ice caps. (CRREL Research Report 97.). 1962.

Wegener, Alfred: Mit Motorboot und Schlitten in Grönland. 1930.
Alfred Wegeners sidste Grønlandsfærd. Udg. af Else Wegener. 1933.

— : Else: Alfred Wegener. 1960.

— : Kurt, ed.: Wissenschaftliche Ergebnisse der Deutschen Grönland-Expedition Alfred Wegener 1929 und 1930/ 31. I–VII). 1933–44.

Wegener, K.: Die Temperatur im grönländischen Inlandeis. (Geofisica Pura e Applicata 34.). 1956.

Weidick, A.: Glacial variations in West Greenland in historical time. (MoG. 158,4.). 1959.

— : Frontal variations at Upernavik Isstrøm in the last 100 years. (Medd. Dansk geol. Foren. 14.). 1958.

— : Ice margin features in the Julianehåb district, South Greenland. (MoG. 165,3.). 1963.

White, S. E.: Glaciological Studies of two Outlet Glaciers, Northwest Greenland 1953. (MoG. 137,8.). 1956.

— : Preliminary Studies of Motion of an Ice Cliff. Nunatarssuaq, Northwest Greenland 1955. (A. I. H. S.) Symposium de Chamonix. publ. 47. 1958.

Wilson, L. R.: Minor Surface of the Southwest Greenland Ice Cap. (Mint Julep Reports. A. T. D. I. C.). 1955.

Wright, J. W.: Contribution to the Glaciology of North West Greenland. (MoG. 125,3.). 1955.

Chronology

982   Greenland is discovered by Eric the Red.

985   The first Norse colonization of Greenland.

1576   Greenland is rediscovered by Martin Frobisher.

1585   John Davis visits Greenland.

1721   The second colonization of Greenland commences with Hans Egede's missionary activity.

1728   Claus Enevold Paars attempts to travel across the ice sheet hoping to reach the Eastern Settlement.

1751   Lars Dalager's first journey on the ice sheet.

1806–13   Karl Ludvig Giesecke travels in west Greenland and visits the margin of the ice sheet.

1852   Hinrich Rink's work about the geographical nature of the Danish trading districts in north Greenland is published.

1860   I. I. Hayes penetrates onto the ice sheet at Porte Foulke.
The *Fox* Expedition investigates the possibility of laying a telegraph cable across the ice sheet.

1867   Edward Whymper attempts a sledge journey on the ice sheet near Jakobshavn.

1870   Adolf Erik Nordenskiöld's first journey on the ice sheet.

1874   Amund Helland measures the ice movement in the outlet glaciers from the ice sheet in west Greenland.

1876   The Danish Commission for the Direction of Geological and Geographical Investigations in Greenland is set up and sends out Steenstrup's expedition to Tasermiut Fjord.

1878   J. A. D. Jensen's first journey on the ice sheet.

1879–80   R. R. J. Hammer studies the glaciers and ice fjords of northern west Greenland.

1883   A. E. Nordenskiöld's second great journey on the ice sheet.
Peary's first visit to the ice sheet.

1888   The ice sheet is crossed for the first time by Nansen.

1891   Preliminary expedition prepares for the expedition sent out by the Gesellschaft für Erdkunde. under the leadership of von Drygalski.

1891–92   Robert Peary winters at McCormick Bay and crosses the ice sheet to reach Navy Cliff in 1892.

1892–93   Erich von Drygalski winters at Store Qarajaq Gletscher.

1893   Garde's expedition to the southern part of the ice sheet.

1893–94   Peary's second wintering in Greenland. In the autumn of 1893 and the spring of 1894 there are unsuccessful attempts to cross the ice sheet.

1894   Carl Molkte and A. Jessen study the glaciers at Nordre Sermilik Fjord.

1895   Peary again crosses the ice sheet to Navy Cliff.

1906–08   The *Danmark* Expedition under the leadership of Mylius Erichsen operates in north-east Greenland.

1909–12   The Danish *Alabama* Expedition is sent out to find the cairn reports of the *Danmark* Expedition.

1910   Thule Station is set up by Knud Rasmussen with Peter Freuchen as day-to-day leader.

1912   The first Thule Expedition in search of Ejnar Mikkelsen.

1912–13   The Danish Expedition to Dronning Louise Land carries out the first wintering on the ice and then crosses the ice sheet under the leadership of J. P. Koch.

1912   Alfred de Quervain's journeys across the ice sheet from Eqip sermia to Angmagssalik.

1916–18   The Second Thule Expedition surveys north Greenland.

1920–23   The Danish Bi-Centenary Expedition North of Greenland under Lauge Koch crosses the ice sheet by ascending onto it at Independence Fjord.

1926   The First University of Michigan Expedition under Hobbs.

1927–29   The University of Michigan Expedition makes meteorological measurements throughout two years at Søndre Strømfjord.

1929   Wegener reconnoitres in preparation for the large German expedition.

1930–31   The Fourth University of Michigan Expedition winters in the Upernavik area.
The first wintering in central Greenland is carried out by Georgi, Sorge, and Loewe in Eismitte, and the first measurements of the thickness of the ice sheet are made. A. Wegener perishes on a return journey from Eismitte.
The British Arctic Air Route Expedition is working in east Greenland, and Courtauld winters alone on the ice sheet.

310

1931 Arne Høygaard and Martin Mehren make the first purely sporting crossing of the ice sheet.
Von Gronau's first flight across the ice sheet.
The Three-Year Expedition under Lauge Koch is working in north-east Greenland.

1932–33 The Second International Polar Year.
The University of Michigan in collaboration with Pan American Airways sends an expedition to winter in the Upernavik district, and during that summer of 1933 meteorological measurements are made from Camp Watkins on the ice sheet.

1932 Universal, Dr. Fanck's expedition operates in the Umanak area and on this expedition Dr E. Sorge continues his glacier studies.

1933 Charles Lindbergh flies across the ice sheet.

1934 Martin Lindsay's Expedition crosses the ice sheet.
John Grierson flies across the ice sheet.

1935 The first British Expedition to Sukkertoppen Iskappe.

1936 Expédition Française Transgroënland crosses the ice sheet from Nordenskiöld Gletscher to Sermilik Fjord.

1938 The Oxford expedition to Sukkertoppen Iskappe.

1941 The first American bases are set up in Greenland.

1947 A preparatory expedition for the Danish Pearyland Expedition lands in Jørgen Brønlund Fjord with Eigil Knuth as leader.
During "Snowman" manoeuvres the Americans discover a possible landing area on the ice sheet east of Søndre Strømfjord.

1948 Paul-Émile Victor establishes Expédition Polaires Françaises and reconnoitres for an access route for vehicles onto the ice sheet.

1948–50 The Danish Pearyland Expedition winters in Peary Land.

1949 Victor erects Station Centrale; Weasels are used to bring in supplies.
In U. S. A. the Snow, Ice, and Permafrost Research Establishment is established.

1949–51 The French expedition winter at Station Centrale.

1951 Alain Joset and Jens Jarl perish in a crevasse near Mont Forel.
Simpson does reconnaissance in preparation for the coming British expedition.

1951–52 Thule Air Base is established.

1952–54 The British North Greenland Expedition established Station "Northice".

1952 The first American reconnaissance for access routes onto the ice sheet.

Victor drives across the ice sheet from Thule Air Base to Kap Georg Cohn.

1953 Project Mint Julep is carried out on the ice sheet east of Søndre Strømfjord.
The American five-year plan for studying the nature and trafficability of the ice sheet is instituted and comprehensive transportation tests are carried out on the ice sheet. Roadways on Nunatarssuaq are completed, and the same year the first light "swing" is taken from the ice cap to Thule Take Off.

1954 The American trafficability tests continue on the ice sheet. Camp Tuto established and in August the first heavy swing is successfully carried out to Camp Tuto. The Corps of Engineers construct a dirt and gravel road extending a mile up the ramp at Camp Tuto, and Site II is established as a radar site and base for scientific research.
Party Crystal under Carl S. Benson commences systematic scientific investigations of snow in the area between Camp Tuto and Site II.
The British North Greenland Expedition completes its work by crossing the ice sheet to Thule Air Base.

1955 The American Expedition Jello continues scientific snow investigations, and trafficability tests are also continued.
Expedition Eastwind carries out the first long exploratory tractor expedition on the ice sheet, and Operation Southwind makes the first real, though unsuccessful, expedition by tractor on the ice sheet during the darkness and in the extreme temperatures of the winter months.
The first ice tunnel is constructed at Camp Tuto.

1956 The American investigations and tests continue in the area of Thule Air Base. Reconnaissance is made for access routes onto the ice sheet in all parts of west and south Greenland. The Danish IGY expeditions are being prepared.
In the autumn the French under Dumont erect Station Dumont after arriving at the site by parachute.

1957 1 July the International Geophysical Year commences, and three Danish glaciological stations are set up in Greenland. Camp Fistclench is erected at Site II.
EGIG starts to reconnoitre for an access route onto the ice sheet.
The last year of the American five-year plan; there is no new equipment to be tested, but the swings continue to collect weather and terrain data and to develop operational technique.

1958	Danish glaciological investigations continue with studies in the Angmagssalik area. Operation King Dog continues to find and mark routes in Søndre Strømfjord. The Arctic Institute of North America studies air content and age of the ice in the calving ice fronts.

1958   Danish glaciological investigations continue with studies in the Angmagssalik area. Operation King Dog continues to find and mark routes in Søndre Strømfjord. The Arctic Institute of North America studies air content and age of the ice in the calving ice fronts.

1959   EGIG is working on the ice sheet and erects Station Jarl-Joset, where a party spends the winter.
Operation Lead Dog investigates access routes from the ice sheet to both Nyeboe Land and Peary Land.

1960   Camp Century is completed and manned for winter.

1961   Comprehensive tests are made at Camp Century and plans for a deep drilling are made.

1962   Scientific research at Camp Century continues.

1963   Camp Century is closed for the winter.

1964   The American ice investigations are continued and a depth of 1,500 ft is reached by thermoboring; using radio waves ice thickness up to 10,000 ft is recorded.
EGIG's markers are lengthened.

1965   The scientific work at Camp Century is continued and concluded for the time being. The camp is closed and dismantled.
A Scottish expedition crosses the ice sheet.

1966   The deep drilling is continued.
Finnish sporting expedition crosses the ice sheet.

Acknowledgments for monochrome plates

312